CEMEX Conservation Book Series
with Conservation International and the International League of Conservation Photographers

A Climate For Life

MEETING THE GLOBAL CHALLENGE

Foreword by Harrison Ford and Edward O. Wilson

Russell A. Mittermeier, Michael Totten, Laura Ledwith Pennypacker, Frederick Boltz, Cristina G. Mittermeier, Guy Midgley, Carlos Manuel Rodríguez, Glenn Prickett, Claude Gascon, Peter A. Seligmann, Olivier Langrand

Cristina G. Mittermeier, Series Editor

Imagining a Climate for Life

Photographers are trained to visualize the images they make before they ever release the camera shutter. As I worked on the text and photographs for this book, I too began visualizing how our future might look, and had a hopeful image come into focus. Even before you turn to the first page of the introduction, where you will begin to explore the complex issues that have led us to a climatic "danger zone" and how we might go about addressing them, try to visualize what a "climate for life" looks like. This should not be hard. After all, we have enjoyed a very long period of stable, mostly benign climate conditions since the dawn of civilization. Now imagine what that future might require. Living on a planet capable of supporting life will mean that we will not be able to rely solely on our governments to take action. Although they will clearly play a major role by supporting policies that provide incentives for new ideas and discourage destructive practices, it will be up to each of us to take personal responsibility to bring balance back to our planet.

Very soon the number 400 ppm will become part of our everyday vocabulary. As we get dangerously close to this number, we will all know that this is the threshold level of greenhouse gases in the atmosphere at which we must stabilize and which we must avoid surpassing if we are to maintain the comfortable and productive living conditions we have enjoyed so far. In the future I imagine, we will have adopted the strategies and supported the conservation efforts needed to keep our air, ocean, and freshwater resources healthy and viable. As more and more citizens increasingly derive their energy "services" from solar, wind, and geothermal resources, the prices for those technologies will continue to drop, making them affordable not only for wealthy nations, but for the poor around the world as well.

In the future I imagine, power plants fed by fossil fuels will have become obsolete. Their destructive footprints will be seen as relics of a bygone era. Better yet, those relics will be replaced by a portfolio of innovative, clean, and efficient technologies that will provide all of our energy needs at competitive, affordable prices. I imagine a future in which our cars will have evolved even beyond hybrids to plug-in electrics and super-efficient vehicles. Affordable, clean, mass transportation will also take center stage. Human ingenuity will be praised as our most valuable tool as we continue to develop new strategies.

In the future I imagine for my children, we will have reached a global agreement to keep our remaining natural forests standing. The forests storing carbon around the world will be so valuable that governments and landowners alike will make every effort to protect them. In addition to storing enormous amounts of carbon, conserving these forests will protect precious biodiversity and will support local livelihoods. Clean water and clean air will be first of the ecological benefits we will gain by conserving our forests.

As I visualize the future ahead, I am full of hope that human ingenuity and a global refusal to allow climate change to escalate beyond control will reward us with a balanced environment. I hope that after reading this book, you too will be able to close your eyes and imagine a beautiful planet capable of supporting a "climate for life." — *Cristina G. Mittermeier, Series Editor*

Letter from Cemex

CEMEX is one of the world's leading providers of cement, ready-mix concrete, and cement aggregates. Our products are used in everything from roads and bridges to offices, schools, hospitals, and homes. As society develops, high-quality, sustainable construction materials will play an increasingly important role in meeting the need for more sustainable buildings in the future. We are committed to innovation, to developing materials and undertaking initiatives that help to save energy, prevent flooding, foster clean environments, and reduce carbon dioxide and other emissions.

Each year, as we look back at the enormous achievements of our employees, our customers, and our other important stakeholders with which we engage, the publication of the annual CEMEX Conservation Book is always a celebrated highlight. For more than a decade, we have teamed with the world's leading NGOs to publish a series of conservation books that reaffirm our commitment and passion for the preservation of natural resources, draw the world's attention to this biological wealth, and further advance our shared goal of creating a global culture for a sustainable planet.

This year's book, *A Climate for Life*, comes at a time when climate change is at the forefront of global environmental, social, and political agendas from which calls to action are being issued to all segments of society. Experts believe that the natural cycle of changes occurring to our planet are now being accelerated by human activities at a much faster rate than previously understood, threatening the adaptive capacity of wild species and natural ecosystems, as well as society as a whole.

This new book is published in collaboration with Conservation International, The International League of Conservation Photographers, and other highly respected organizations committed to the global conservation of biodiversity. It focuses on the areas around the world where climate change will most impact biodiversity and the potential solutions and actions that can be taken to safeguard them. As in previous years, thousands of copies of this book will be donated by CEMEX to conservation NGOs around the world in support of their biodiversity conservation activities.

A fundamental goal of the Conservation Book Program is to provide an independent forum for our global NGO partners to publish the knowledge and views of their scientists and experts. This book thoroughly covers important and urgent issues concerning a changing climate and carefully examines potential and practical solutions that lie in our hands. The key message of the book—which we must hear and act on together—is that we as a society must now start living a new way in which natural resources are used more wisely and efficiently.

A sustainable world needs sustainable business. CEMEX operates in an industry that meets the core infrastructure needs of society, which are dependent on certain natural resources. Thus, we have made a commitment to conserve biodiversity, minimize our environmental impact, positively contribute to society, and work with all of our key stakeholders to achieve a sustainable planet that most importantly provides a "climate for life."

A CLIMATE FOR LIFE

The forest floor of Barro Colorado Island in Panama provides a snapshot of the biodiversity of a tropical forest. Each year, roughly 13 million hectares of tropical forest are destroyed, resulting in a serious loss of habitat for threatened plants and animals. CHRISTIAN ZIEGLER

HALF-TITLE:
A kinkajou's face becomes covered in pollen during feeding in Soberania National Park in Panama. Pollinators play an important role in maintaining forest health. MATTIAS KLUM

PAGE 2: Jasmund National Park on the Baltic island of Ruegen is a beautiful beech forest with spectacular chalk cliffs. Forests such as this are at risk because of climate change. CHRISTIAN ZIEGLER

Contents

Lush mosses blanket a temperate rain forest in southeast Alaska. Ecosystems like these store carbon both above and below ground. MICHIO HOSHINO

Foreword

We are pleased and privileged to introduce this book. Although our backgrounds and professions are different, we share the same perception of the issues addressed in *A Climate for Life* and applaud the clarity with which they have been presented.

At the foundation of what the authors have brought together are four great but simple truths established by scientific research. First, the changes occurring in every dimension of the environment are accelerating, like interest on a bad debt. Second, the major trends are due to human activity. Third, the changes are, overall, destructive to humanity and the rest of life and, if left unabated, will soon become disastrous.

Finally, and this is the central message of *A Climate for Life*, the global environment cannot be stabilized and restored piece-by-piece and step-by-step. Its deterioration has to halt on all fronts, through intelligent and concerted action, with linkages to the parts given the same attention as to the parts themselves. As just one example, the rise of petroleum consumption pushes up the cost of energy and biofuel production leaps upward in response. More land and crops are converted to biofuels, raising the cost of food, intensifying hunger and civil strife and the destruction of the remaining fragments of the natural environment.

It is now solidly established that current climate change is largely forced by our unsettling of Earth's carbon balance. That, in turn, threatens the global environment to which we and the rest of life are adapted. To face this threat squarely, as the authors of *A Climate for Life* emphasize, we must understand all of the factors linked to it and set out to adjust them as a whole.

The good news is that this nest of problems is soluble. The science is growing ever stronger. The technology exists or is at least imaginable and in practical terms. The economic benefits of a global turnaround are potentially enormous. What is needed now is the popular will to undertake what will be one of the great turnabouts of history. Fortunately, in spite of so many evidences to the contrary in the past, people are basically rational. When they know the problem, how much it will cost if not solved, the solution, and the cost of the solution, they usually take the measure of it all and act. They will, we believe, certainly do so in this case.

Harrison Ford and Edward O. Wilson

A pair of African elephants and two calves share their habitat with a flock of cattle egrets in Kenya. TIM FITZHARRIS

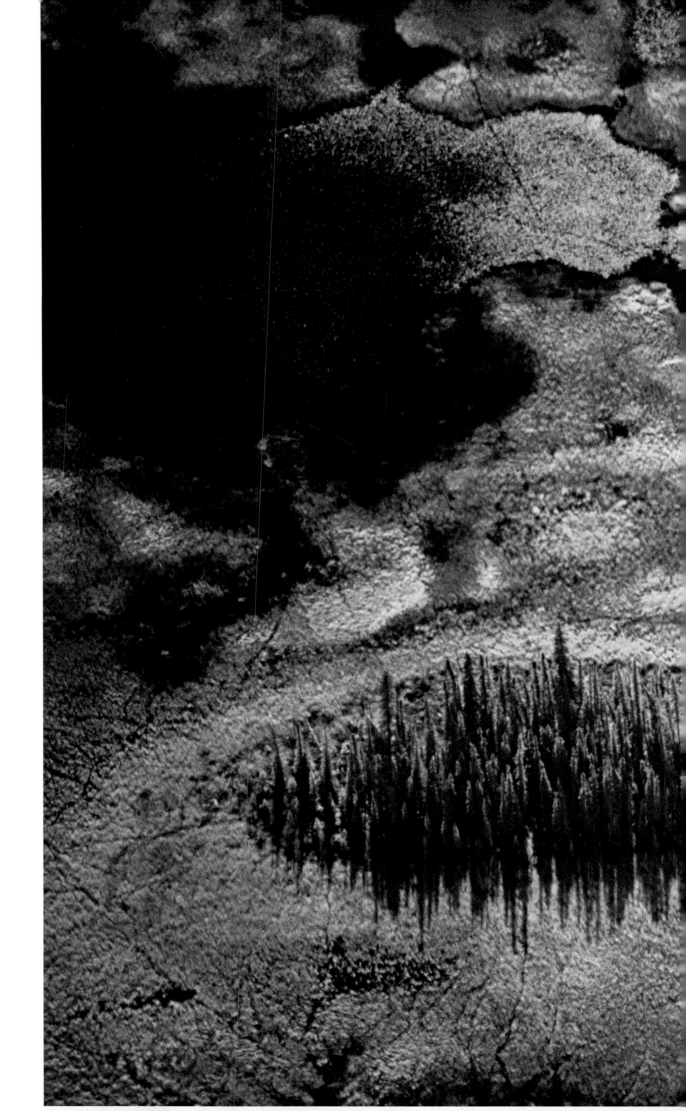

A CLIMATE FOR LIFE

An aerial view reveals the spectrum of color in the wetlands of Wrangell St. Elias National Park, Alaska. Melting of the permafrost in far northern regions poses yet another threat.
FRANS LANTING

A CLIMATE FOR LIFE

Chinstrap penguins break the azure monochrome of an iceberg in Antarctica. Warming polar waters may threaten the migration patterns of many Antarctic species. FRANS LANTING

A CLIMATE FOR LIFE

Above 4,000 meters elevation, ichu grass and huamanpinta dominate the high Andean plateau as heavy weather rolls in to Cotopaxi National Park in Ecuador. Preserving carbon-rich native grasslands is yet another important mitigation strategy.
TUI DE ROY

Introduction

Russell A. Mittermeier, Michael Totten, Laura Ledwith Pennypacker,
Frederick Boltz, Glenn Prickett, Guy Midgley, Cristina G. Mittermeier,
Alistair Graham, Carlos Manuel Rodríguez, Thomas Brooks,
Lee Hannah, Benjamin Vitale, Cyril Kormos, Katrina Brandon,
Timothy Killeen, Toby Janson-Smith, Lisa Handy, Michael Kennedy,
José Maria Cardoso da Silva, Peter A. Seligmann, Claude Gascon,
Olivier Langrand, Lisa Famolare, David Singh, Jorgen Thomsen,
Roberto Cavalcanti, Frank Hawkins, Leon Rajaobelina,
James Mackinnon, Luis Suárez, Jatna Supriatna, Alexander Peal,
Luis Espinel, Vance Martin, Fabio Arjona, Eduardo Forno, Leo Braack,
Mohamed Bakarr, Niels Crone

Boreal forests such as this one in northern Canada, located in Northern Alberta near the town of Grande Prairie, are warming faster than the global average, increasing the incidence of wildfires and carbon release. GARTH LENZ

The world is waking up to climate change. Books and articles on the issue abound, and it is the subject of constant media attention. So why is there a need for a book such as this one? The reason is simple. The search for solutions to human-driven climate change requires an understanding of the natural world, its species, its ecosystems, and its cycles. The emerging perception of climate is a fragmented one, colored by personal belief, political persuasion, education, and economic wealth and aspiration, among other powerful influences. A coherent message from conservationists is needed to place the risk of anthropogenic (human-influenced) climate change in context by clarifying how its causes, impacts, and solutions derive from the intricate, delicate balance between modern society and the natural world. In the following pages and chapters, we examine a wide range of climate issues, with particular emphasis on how natural environments can contribute to and benefit from measures to address climate change.

The most rigorous process of scientific review that has ever dealt with any environmental issue, the Intergovernmental Panel on Climate Change (IPCC), has established the scientific fact of anthropogenic climate change to a high degree of confidence (>90%). This and other synthetic efforts provide a remarkable confluence of scientific findings that have been adopted unevenly across the planet in political declarations, religious calls to action, voluntary commitments from the private sector, and expressions from popular culture. Nevertheless, the uncertainties that surround the potential impacts of this shift and its economic ramifications make this all hotly contested political territory. A deadlock of sorts has arisen in the political arena of the premiere global policy debate on climate, the United Nations Framework Convention on Climate Change (UNFCCC), and its implementation instrument, the Kyoto Protocol. There is now an urgent need to find solutions that will serve the long-term interests of both developed and developing nations and that will avoid a cycle of destruction flowing from expedient self-interest. Perceptions and actions at all levels, from local to international, will play a key role in breaking this deadlock. This book is an attempt to provide a conservation perspective on this issue and hopefully assist in clarifying some of its most critical elements.

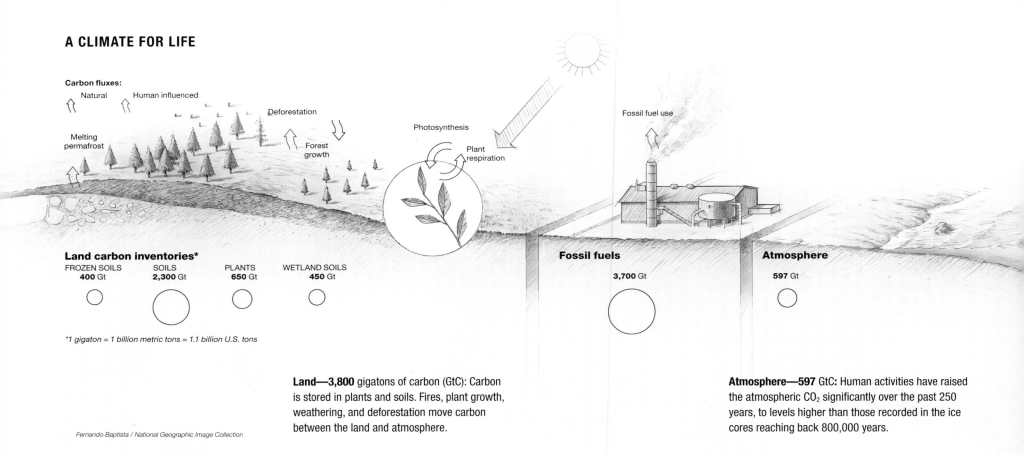

Carbon fluxes:
Natural Human influenced

Deforestation

Melting permafrost

Forest growth

Photosynthesis

Plant respiration

Fossil fuel use

Land carbon inventories*

FROZEN SOILS	SOILS	PLANTS	WETLAND SOILS
400 Gt	**2,300** Gt	**650** Gt	**450** Gt

*1 gigaton = 1 billion metric tons = 1.1 billion U.S. tons

Fossil fuels

3,700 Gt

Atmosphere

597 Gt

Fernando Baptista / National Geographic Image Collection

Land—3,800 gigatons of carbon (GtC): Carbon is stored in plants and soils. Fires, plant growth, weathering, and deforestation move carbon between the land and atmosphere.

Atmosphere—597 GtC: Human activities have raised the atmospheric CO_2 significantly over the past 250 years, to levels higher than those recorded in the ice cores reaching back 800,000 years.

Recognition of the links between human-induced greenhouse gases (GHGs) and climate change is not new. More than 100 years ago, Swedish chemist Svante Arrhenius, future winner of the Nobel Prize, theorized that higher levels of carbon dioxide (CO_2) would increase the atmosphere's natural heat-trapping effect and lead to higher surface temperatures. In the 1950s, Charles Keeling of the Scripps Institute of Oceanography began to track rising CO_2 concentrations in the atmosphere by means of long-term observations at the top of Mauna Loa Volcano in Hawaii. Today, we are more fully aware of the links between natural ecosystems, their biodiversity, and the Earth's carbon cycle and the fact that our stewardship of these ecosystems will play a major role in assuring future climate security (IPCC, 2007).

It is now very difficult to justify a skeptical position on the observed changes in climate and their early impacts. It is almost incontrovertible that changes in weather and the environment are linked to an atmospheric build-up of CO_2 and other heat-trapping GHGs that result from human activity. Winters are becoming shorter, especially at high latitudes. Summers are becoming hotter, especially in the subtropics and tropics. Coastal storms are becoming more intense. Glaciers are retreating worldwide and mountain snowcaps are shrinking, with less freshwater available to downstream communities. Even if GHG emissions could be halted immediately, warming would still continue in the coming decades (IPCC, 2007). Left unchecked, the two leading sources of GHG emissions—fossil fuel combustion and tropical forest destruction—will accelerate, driven by expanding populations and rising living standards in a globalized world.

However, even more worrisome is that the ecology of our planet itself is changing in response to climate change. Some plants and animals are disappearing from certain places, while others are appearing in new ones as growing conditions and microclimates change and habitats shift. These and other as yet minor shifts in local, regional, and global temperatures presage future damage to nature and human society, from wider ranges of insect-borne diseases such as malaria, to lower crop yields in India, many African countries, and elsewhere in the developing world, and to mounting economic losses from storm damage in coastal areas.

The impacts will affect us all, even though we may not feel them to the same extent, at least initially. While the developing world displays a high level of vulnerability to the emerging impacts, due mostly to inadequate wealth and infrastructure to allow appropriate adaptation, the developed world has also suffered. The aftermath of Hurricane Katrina, the impacts of the 2003 European heat wave, and the growing global food crisis provide us with a sober message on the risks of being unprepared for ongoing climate change and even greater climate variability to come, and how vulnerability gives way to societal damages. It is disturbing to realize that the most under-appreciated and economically under-valued service that nature provides—global storage of carbon and sequestration of anthropogenic carbon dioxide from the atmosphere—may be weakening now and may turn into a carbon-emitting source during this century.

Ocean—38,153 GtC: The oceans' deep, cold waters hold huge amounts of carbon, about 50 times as much as the atmosphere. Carbon dioxide moves quickly between the air and upper ocean waters but can take centuries to reach the lowest depths.

Moving Carbon: The atmosphere, land, and oceans hold vast inventories that emit carbon (sources) and absorb it (sinks) in a natural cycle, much as water cycles around the planet. But over the past 200 years, humans have put massive amounts of carbon into the atmosphere through deforestation and fossil fuel use, altering natural rhythms that have prevailed for thousands of years.

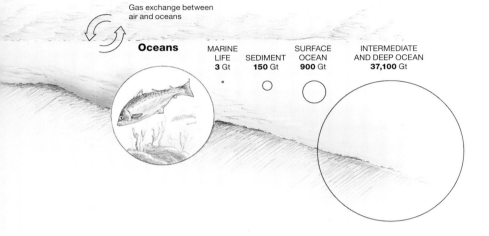

Gas exchange between air and oceans

Oceans

| MARINE LIFE **3** Gt | SEDIMENT **150** Gt | SURFACE OCEAN **900** Gt | INTERMEDIATE AND DEEP OCEAN **37,100** Gt |

What We Know Now about the Problem

CO_2 and other naturally occurring "radiatively active" gases in the atmosphere, including methane, nitrous oxide, and water vapor, function like a heat-trapping blanket by reflecting outgoing solar infrared radiation back to the Earth's surface. This natural greenhouse effect provides the hospitable climate that makes life on Earth possible. Over geological time spans of millions of years, the atmospheric concentration of these gases has fluctuated, sometimes greatly, as a result of volcanic emissions and other natural processes including geological weathering. Earth's climate has been in a cold phase, together with low GHG concentrations, for several millennia, in a time when subtle variations in the orbit of the Earth around the sun have influenced climate cycles and sensitive feedbacks via the global carbon cycle. Our understanding of how these cycles are naturally regulated is incomplete, but it is clear that the climate system may change rapidly and may be sensitive to shifts in solar radiation and atmospheric composition. In recent millennia, however, as complex human societies and civilizations have developed, climate change has been buffered within habitable limits by complex positive and negative feedback systems, especially those based on the biological behavior of terrestrial ecosystems in the short term and the chemical behavior of oceans in the longer term.

The unprecedented scale of anthropogenic emissions released from almost explosive economic growth and development after the Industrial Revolution is altering this natural balance. The concentration of CO_2 and other heat-trapping gases in the atmosphere has increased 30% since 1750, rising from ~280 to ~386 parts per million (ppm). This is a level higher than at any other time in at least the last 650,000 years, which scientists have been able to determine from analysis of ancient air bubbles trapped in ice-core samples. Significant here is *both* the accelerated *rate* at which this growth is occurring *and* the *levels that may be reached*. These are very likely to threaten the adaptive capacity of wild species and natural ecosystems, as well as human societies. The rate of temperature change in the twentieth century is four times greater than the average rate of change over the previous four centuries. Atmospheric CO_2 may reach levels not seen for tens of millions of years—an evolutionary shock to the system that could be unprecedented. There is no evidence that the rate of possible future global change (>7°C by the end of this century at the upper end) has been matched by any comparable global temperature increase over the last 50 million years! In other words, we are really entering into uncharted waters.

The primary sources of CO_2 emissions are combustion of fossil fuels (for electricity, manufacturing industry, and transportation) and changes in land use (primarily the destruction and degradation of tropical forests and peatlands), both of which continue largely unabated. With business as usual, CO_2 levels will double over pre-industrial levels in our children's lifetime and could double again in our grandchildren's lifetime. Indeed, annual anthropogenic CO_2 emissions are now even higher than the highest level considered reasonable by the IPCC in its development scenarios (Raupach et al., 2007). Methane and nitrous oxide emissions have also increased significantly over pre-industrial levels. Atmospheric methane concentrations have more than doubled in a few decades, largely from agriculture (livestock and rice paddies), fossil-fuel production (gas venting and pipeline leaks), and landfills. The recent slowing of methane increase in the atmosphere is cause for some hope, but concern remains because of our limited understanding of what drives this cycle and whether critical temperature levels exist that could trigger accelerated emissions. Nitrous oxide has risen nearly 20%, primarily from agriculture (nitrogenous fertilizer use and livestock urination). Each molecule of methane has a global warming potential about 20 times greater than CO_2, while nitrous oxide has a global warming potential 310 times greater than CO_2 (CO_2 is used as the reference molecule for comparing the so-called "global warming potential" of the different heat-trapping GHGs over a 100-year reference period, allowing the warming characteristics of these various gases to be compared as CO_2-equivalents, or CO_2e).

Added to these naturally occurring GHGs are a number of anthropogenic chemicals, most notably the stratospheric ozone-depleting chloro- and fluoro-carbons (chloro-, per-, hydrofluoro-, and hydrocloro-, or CFCs, PFCs, HFCs, and HCFCs), a new class of chemicals used for refrigeration, air conditioning, propellants, and industrial processes. These and other human-made chemicals are 140 to 23,900 times more potent global warming gases than CO_2. The most potent ozone-depleting of these compounds are being phased out under the 1987 Montreal Protocol. In late 2007, nearly 200 countries signed a UN agreement to accelerate the elimination of HCFCs, the chemicals that most seriously threaten the ozone layer and exacerbate global warming so much more than CO_2. Developed countries have committed to phasing out the production of HCFCs by 2020, and developing states have until 2030 to do the same—ten years earlier than previously agreed.

A variety of other factors influence the greenhouse effect (i.e., they act as forcing factors), especially the amount of water vapor in the atmosphere, which is the most prevalent naturally occurring GHG. Apart from significant infrared absorption by water vapor, the water cycle exerts many indirect controls over the planet's energy balance. One of the most uncertain relates to the reflectivity (albedo) of clouds. Also of particular importance is the albedo of sea and land surfaces (i.e., ice is light and reflective, seawater and vegetation are dark and absorptive), and small airborne particles (or aerosols), which can exert a countervailing cooling effect (notably aerosol and cloud formation associated with anthropogenic and volcanic sulphur dioxide emissions). The net effect of all changing elements is, however, a pronounced and growing warming effect.

The IPCC (2007) estimates that the projected impact of these changes will be a rise in global average surface temperature of 1.8 to 4°C by the end of the 21st century, and notes that temperatures already are ~0.7°C higher than they were a century ago. The last decade has witnessed nearly all of the hottest years on record. In the northern hemisphere, temperatures in the last 50 years were likely higher than any time in the last 1,300 years. The European Union has called for stabilizing total atmospheric CO_2e at a sufficiently low level to provide a high probability of preventing an ultimate global warming of

more than 2°C above pre-industrial levels. A target of 450 ppm of CO_2e was originally chosen, although ongoing research indicates a stabilization target of 350 to 400 ppm may be necessary (Hansen et al., 2008).

What Impacts Are Being Observed and What Could Happen in the Future?

Despite the fairly low level of warming that has occurred to date (~0.7°C increase in the last century), many changes can be attributed to anthropogenic global warming and climate change, both of physical and biological systems (IPCC, 2007). Complex biophysical responses and their feedbacks are already becoming apparent (IPCC, 2007), highlighting how difficult it will be to project the rate and trajectory of change into the future.

Among the more dramatic and observable effects of global warming to date has been the widespread melting of glaciers and snowcaps and reductions in large ice sheets in Greenland and Antarctica. The extent of seasonal sea ice in the Arctic has declined markedly, with declines also recorded in Antarctica, though less marked. From the 1970s through the 1990s, perennial ice in the Arctic declined by about 309,000 square kilometers each decade. Since 2000, that rate of decline has nearly tripled, and Arctic sea ice may be entirely gone during summers *within a decade,* rather than in the latter half of this century as previously thought. The runoff from this melting ice and snow, combined with the expansion of warmer oceans, likely contributed to an observed rise in global sea level of 17 centimeters (cm) over the course of the twentieth century. A *linear* projection of this trend indicates a sea level rise of one meter by 2100 (Rahmstorf, 2007; Hansen, 2007).

Recent research using gravity satellite monitoring confirms that ice-sheet disintegration is increasing. The Antarctic ice sheet has been losing mass at a rate of 150 cubic kilometers each year since 2002. That is enough to account for about 0.04 cm of sea level rise each year, twice as fast as even recent estimates had projected. The potentially disastrous implications of continued melting of Antarctic ice has become a matter of major concern for several reasons. Antarctica covers some 13,209,000 square kilometers (41% larger than the United States, including Alaska), of which 97.3% is covered with inland ice sheets and 2.4% by ice shelves. Its ice sheet averages 2.4 kilometers thick with a volume of 30 million cubic kilometers. It contains 90% of the world's ice and more than 70% of its freshwater, and almost all of it is above ground (in contrast to the Arctic, where the ice is floating and, thus, already displacing 90% of its volume).

Antarctica has been covered with ice since the beginning of the Pliocene, some 5 million years ago. If all the land-ice covering Antarctica were to melt, the seas would rise by more than 60 meters. Fortunately, this is considered very unlikely within the next few centuries. Of greatest concern for this century is the loss of major ice shelves in Antarctica. The shrinking of ice shelves reduces resistance along exit routes for ice from further inland. Warming ocean waters are now thinning some West Antarctic ice shelves by several meters per year.

Seven ice shelves on the Antarctic Peninsula declined by some 13,500 square kilometers between 1974 and 2002 (NASA, 2002). In 2002, the Larsen B ice shelf collapsed, due to a combination of surface melt and ice-shelf thinning from below. A total of about 3,250 square kilometers of shelf area disintegrated in a 35-day period. The Larsen shelf shrunk by 5,700 square kilometers in five years to about 40% the size of its previous minimum stable extent. The fact that West Antarctica is losing mass at a significant rate is evidence that the thinning ice shelves are already beginning to have an effect on ice discharge rates. Increasing summer surface melt in West Antarctica has been detected recently (Nghiem et al., 2007) and raises the danger that feedbacks among these processes could lead to nonlinear acceleration of ice discharge from Antarctica. In early 2008, satellite imagery revealed that the 13,680-square-kilometer Wilkins Ice Shelf on the southwest Antarctic Peninsula had begun to collapse (NSIDC, 2008).

NASA climate scientist James Hansen put forward the following quantitative example of the impact of melting ice sheets on sea-level rise. If "the ice sheet contribution is 1 cm for the decade 2005-15 and it doubles each decade until the West Antarctic ice sheet is largely depleted...that time constant yields a sea level rise of the order of 5 meters this century" (Hansen, 2007).

Analysis of the *non-linear* response, or positive feedback, that ice-sheet disintegration could trigger under business-as-usual scenarios suggests sea levels could rise by several meters this century. Fossil evidence suggests that sea levels were 5 to 6 meters higher than today during the last inter-glacial period 125,000 years ago, when regional temperatures were 3 to 5°C higher at high latitudes, particularly in the northern hemisphere (though the global temperature was probably not markedly higher than today) (IPCC, 2007). Recent paleo-oceanographic research of the Pliocene epoch three million years ago indicates that sea level was 25 meters higher than today, with global warming only 2 to 3°C higher, CO_2 levels estimated as between 360 and 400 ppm, and without any Arctic sea ice in the warm seasons.

Accelerated melting of the Arctic permafrost could further amplify global warming as thawing tundra peatlands oxidize and are exposed to increasing

> **There is no evidence that the rate of possible future global change has been matched by any comparable global temperature increase over the last 50 million years. In other words, we are really entering into uncharted waters.**

risk of devastating fires, while the immense deposits of methane currently frozen as clathrate in these vast tundra regions may increasingly volatilize and be released to the atmosphere. This is not idle speculation (see Chapter 10: Tipping Points).

Declines in mountain glaciers and snow cover will further decrease the amount of freshwater available downstream. The adverse effect on crop yields from reduced river flows and reduced rainfall could be significant, especially in already drought-prone regions such as the Sahel, Southern Africa, South Asia, the Middle East, and Central America.

Warmer ocean surface temperatures are also increasing the intensity of hurricanes, typhoons, cyclones, and tropical storms. Three of the ten strongest hurricanes ever recorded in the North Atlantic occurred in 2005. While no single extreme weather event can be blamed on climate change, the devastation of Hurricane Katrina in the United States demonstrates the risk to many communities that either cannot marshal the means or do not have the foresight to prepare. Weather-triggered catastrophes have already risen three-fold over the last forty years, and the resulting economic losses have increased by a factor of nine. In 2004, the insurance industry had to pay a record sum of $30 billion for losses caused from North Atlantic hurricanes, especially in the United States and the Caribbean. This figure almost tripled in 2005, to $83 billion, by the insured losses from tropical hurricanes in this region. What is more, uninsured economic losses from these catastrophes rival the insured losses.

"The threat of a large sea-level change," Hansen and his NASA colleagues

Sea Levels Rising: The worldwide concentration of population in coastal areas means that even modest sea level rise would likely affect millions, but effects would be greatest in low-lying areas with high populations. In Florida, for example, sea level rise would affect 48 of Florida's 67 counties, which are home to an estimated 16.8 million people—92% of the state's population.

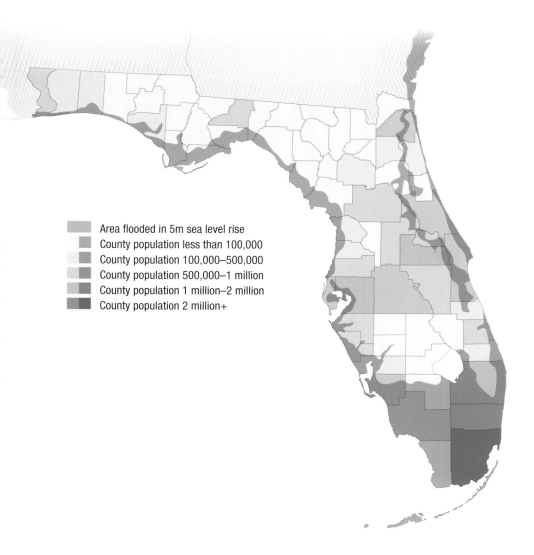

- Area flooded in 5m sea level rise
- County population less than 100,000
- County population 100,000–500,000
- County population 500,000–1 million
- County population 1 million–2 million
- County population 2 million+

warn, "is a principal element in our argument that the global community must aim to keep additional global warming less than 1°C above the 2000 temperature, and even 1°C may be too great. In turn, this implies [setting] a CO_2e limit of about 450 ppm, or less. Such scenarios are dramatically different than business-as-usual, requiring almost immediate changes to get on a fundamentally different energy and GHG emissions path" (Hansen et al., 2006, 2007a, 2007b).

Even a one-meter sea-level rise threatens inundation of low-lying areas that would seriously disrupt many coastal communities and countries worldwide and could create tens of millions of environmental refugees, especially from island nations and densely populated poor countries, such as Bangladesh. It could actually eliminate several low-lying small island nations such as Kiribati and the Maldives. A one-meter sea-level rise would also change the frequency of what are now 100-year floods in metropolitan New York to once every 4 years.

Climate change is more than just "global warming." It is also about weather extremes. The oppressive heat wave that engulfed Europe in August of 2003 is estimated to have killed more than 30,000 people. Scientists who studied the heat wave concluded that given the current emissions trajectory, more than half of European summers will be hotter than 2003 within four decades, and, by the end of the century, "2003 would be classed as an anomalously cold summer relative to the new climate" (Stott, Stone, and Allen, 2004).

From 1998 to 2005, the area burned by wildfires quadrupled in the United States, burning an area equivalent to the state of Pennsylvania. In addition, the frequency of large forest wildfires has tripled and the area burned in these large fires has increased more than five-fold since the 1980s. Wildfires are burning five times longer, and the wildfire season has lengthened by two-thirds. Three-quarters of the area burned in these large forest fires in the western United States coincides with earlier spring snowmelt caused by warmer temperatures (Westerling et al., 2006). The 90,000 fires that burned 2.8 million hectares during the 2000 wildfire season, considered one of the most devastating in half a century, was surpassed in 2005, when 3.4 million hectares were ravaged by fire. This was, in turn, surpassed in 2006 when 3.5 million hectares burned, and this was surpassed yet again in 2007.

More frequent El Niño events, another expected impact of global warming, could increase the frequency of both flooding and droughts and wildfires in different regions. This can be seen in the devastating fires of 1997 and 1998 in Indonesia, a year in which the global growth rate of CO_2 in the atmosphere doubled, reaching the highest on record. In the aftermath of the dry season, during which Indonesian small-scale farmers and large-scale agribusinesses burned forests and drained carbon-rich peatlands, the anticipated monsoon rains failed to occur as a result of an El Niño event. Upwards of 2.8 billion tons of CO_2 was emitted as a result of this devastation of 10 million hectares.

The destruction caused an estimated US\$9 billion in local damages and lost value. Furthermore, haze and smoke spread across southeast Asia, causing health problems affecting some 70 million people, including 20 million who became sick, as well as agricultural losses due to reduced sunlight. The emissions from the destroyed rain forest and peatlands were equivalent to nearly 40% of the fossil fuel emissions that year (Page et al., 2002; Schimel and Baker, 2002).

Continental interiors at mid- and tropical latitudes, especially those that are already arid or semi-arid, will likely see a decrease in rainfall, drying of soils, and an increase in the frequency of droughts, including long-term "mega-droughts" and "mega-fires."

Significant impacts of recent climate change are being felt keenly in the oceans. Coral reefs, home to the greatest diversity of marine life, are most at risk and show many responses, the most famous of which is coral bleaching. Even at the low end of anticipated warming over the next several decades, a combination of coral bleaching (death of coral organisms from increased water temperatures), submersion of corals as sea levels rise, and ocean acidification (an increase in the pH of the oceans as they absorb CO_2 from the atmosphere) could lead to widespread die-off of corals worldwide. These ecosystems are already under severe threat from a variety of causes, including pollution, sedimentation from soil run-off, and destructive fishing practices. The combination of these ongoing assaults places an estimated 60% of coral reefs worldwide at risk of die-off. Climate change will exacerbate these threats even more (Hoegh-Guldberg et al., 2007).

Tropical deforestation and forest degradation, in addition to releasing GHGs and causing biodiversity loss, leads to increased human exposure to insect bites and malaria infection. Research on deforested sites in Peru found that the mosquito biting rate was 278 times higher than the rate determined for areas that were predominantly forested (Vittor et al., 2006). Control measures that reduce the amount of deforestation and forest degradation may be beneficial not only for controlling malaria, but also for reducing GHG emissions, protecting threatened species, and reducing soil erosion.

Other changes in natural ecosystems also put human health at risk. As areas warm and habitats shift, ranges will expand for vector-borne and other

> **Warmer ocean surface temperatures are also increasing the intensity of hurricanes, typhoons, cyclones, and tropical storms....Weather-triggered catastrophes have already risen three-fold over the last forty years, and the resulting economic losses have increased by a factor of nine.**

infectious diseases besides malaria, such as dengue fever, yellow fever, west Nile virus, mosquito- and tick-borne encephalitis, cholera, and lyme disease. Research findings from tropical regions found that a mere half-degree Celsius increase in temperature can translate into a 30–100% increase in mosquito abundance, or what scientists refer to as the "biological amplification" of temperature effects (Pascual et al., 2006; Patz and Olson, 2006).

Floods, droughts, storms, and heat waves all have direct impacts on human health and indirect ones through disruption of food production, increased freshwater scarcity, spread of water-borne diseases, and loss of infrastructure. Floods and droughts, as well as warming of water temperature in ponds and rivers, can promote cholera transmission, depending on the strain and the time scale of variability (Koelle et al., 2005). Freshwater scarcity is a particular health threat for billions of poor people in the developing world, as well as a threat to economic livelihoods for many agricultural regions worldwide.

In 2005, the Amazon region experienced a devastating drought that, in some areas, was the worst since record keeping began a century ago. Whole lagoons and rivers dried up, stranding boats, kindling forest fires, and killing off fish and crops. Scientists suspect the drought is most likely a result of the same rise in water temperatures in the tropical Atlantic Ocean that unleashed Hurricane Katrina. On the Madeira River, a primary trade route for products including soybeans and diesel oil, navigation had to be suspended when water levels fell to less than one-tenth of their rainy-season level. Crops rotted in fields because they could not be shipped to market. The normally free-flowing rivers became stagnant pools, providing ideal breeding conditions for above-normal levels of mosquito populations.

Already, some 40% of the world's people live in water-stressed regions. More than a billion people lack access to clean drinking water, and more than a million children die each year from diarrhea resulting from contaminated water. Climate change will intensify this global crisis.

A recent assessment of the impact of a few degrees Celsius increase in global average temperature, coupled with declining precipitation on global agriculture, indicates crop losses could be as high as 28% for Africa, 24% for Latin America, 30% to 40% for India, and 21% for all developing countries (Cline, 2007). Even industrialized nations like the United States and Australia will suffer losses, including 30% to 35% in the southeast and southwestern plains of the United States.

The very survival of many other species is also threatened by climate change. A large portion of the world's plant and animal species is already at risk of extinction as a result of habitat destruction, over-harvesting, introduction of invasive species, and pollution, with estimates ranging from one in ten species of birds and vascular plants, to nearly a quarter of all mammals, to as much as one in three species of amphibians and freshwater fish. Climate change will further exacerbate these already severe threats, as natural habitats shift and populations in fragmented landscapes are unable to migrate.

The severity of all of these impacts depends on the extent of global warming. Even at the lower end of expected warming, between 1 and 2°C, we can expect to see increased extinction risk for sensitive species, especially those on coral reefs and in montane rain forests, and an increase in droughts and floods, with both wildlife and human populations facing water shortages and devastating damage from more frequent and severe coastal storms.

At higher levels of warming, between 3 and 5°C, catastrophic impacts are anticipated, including significant species extinctions, dramatic declines in food, fiber, feed, and forest yields (even at high latitudes, where crop yields would initially increase as temperatures warm), and significant coastal areas lost to sea-level rise.

The current atmospheric CO_2 concentration stands at ~386 ppm CO_2, and anthropogenic emissions are increasing this concentration at an annual rate of 2 ppm, soon to increase to 3 ppm/yr. With unchecked growth in anthropogenic emissions, the level could even exceed 900 ppm by the end of this century. The deep historical record tells us that similar emissions in the past have been associated with extreme events and mass extinctions. Recent cross-disciplinary research in paleoceanography, biogeochemistry, geology,

and atmospheric modeling indicate many of the ancient mass extinctions occurred in the wake of skyrocketing concentrations of atmospheric CO_2 emissions.

The Permian Extinction 250 million years ago, called the Great Dying, occurred when CO_2 levels were at the highest level in the past 300 million years—3,000 ppm. Ninety percent of ocean-dwelling species and 70% of terrestrial life, including plants, vertebrates, and even insects were wiped out. Other mass extinctions following high CO_2 levels include the Triassic 200 million years ago at about 1,300 ppm; the Toarcian around 180 million years ago at about 2,000 ppm; the Cenomanian/Turonian 100 million years ago at about 1,300 ppm; and the Paleocene thermal 54 million years ago at just below 1,000 ppm (Ward, 2006, 2007). Needless to say, the biodiversity conservation community is greatly concerned about the impacts of climate changes on the many species with which we share our planet (see Chapter 6: Terrestrial Biodiversity and Chapter 7: Freshwater Biodiversity).

What Can Be Done?

Not surprisingly, the economic impact of even a several-degree Celsius temperature increase will lead to profound changes. In 2006, Sir Nicholas Stern, a former chief economist of the World Bank, was asked by Great Britain's then Chancellor of the Exchequer and now Prime Minister, Gordon Brown, to assess the economic impact of climate change. The meticulous and voluminous review concluded that the impact could amount to at least 5% and perhaps as much as 20% loss of global economic output now and into the future (Stern, 2006).

The report also concluded that the benefits of reducing emissions and avoiding these impacts would far outweigh the costs, which he estimated would amount to about 1% of global GDP. These estimates are speculative and have become the subject of vigorous debate (principally over what discount rate to use in calculating future losses, which is as much an ethical question as a quantitative one). Few, however, contest that the consequences of climate change will be anything other than *dangerous* to *catastrophic,* or that the world should take prudent and preventive actions now to mitigate and adapt to those impacts.

Stern (2006) also showed that adapting to the effects of what seem to be unavoidable climate change into the medium term would also provide immediate and medium-term economic benefits. However, it is clear from this analysis that adaptation responses are increasingly ineffective with higher rates and levels of climate change, implying an important interaction between mitigation and adaptation efforts. Conservationists need to explore this trade-off urgently, as their responses will be informed by both the rate and extent of change.

The mitigation challenge is all the greater because it must be addressed in the context of other global priorities. Nearly three billion people today live in poverty on less than $2 per day. Raising their living standards is a moral imperative for the world and a political necessity for governments in developing nations (Pogge, 2008). The success of China, India, and other developing countries over the last several decades in lifting hundreds of millions out of poverty is one of the great achievements of our age. However, as a result of its continued economic growth, the developing world will soon become the largest source of GHG emissions in absolute amounts (but still lower per capita levels than developed nations). The International Energy Agency estimates that China surpassed the United States as the largest single emitter in 2007.

China and India will continue to pursue economic growth and other poor nations will seek to emulate their success, and it is not appropriate that developed nations should seek to frustrate such aspirations in seeking to fix a problem for which they are principally responsible. Therefore, deep cuts in emissions must occur in the context of continued economic growth. Neither developed nor developing economies can be expected to sacrifice the well-being of their citizens today for environmental benefits that will accrue decades from now.

Opportunities to reduce emissions can be grouped into four broad categories:

1) Reducing emissions from deforestation, from degradation of forests and other natural ecosystems, from agriculture, and from other land uses
2) Exploiting the vast pool of energy (and of water and other natural resources) efficiency opportunities to cost-effectively deliver half or more of the world's projected energy and utility services this century
3) Deploying carbon-free or low-carbon (and biodiversity-friendly) energy technologies
4) Making deep cuts in carbon emissions from use of conventional fossil energy sources

Given the magnitude of emissions reductions required in the coming decades—visualize the need to prevent combustion of 25 billion rail cars of coal plus prevent deforestation equivalent to one-third the area of the United

A large portion of the world's plant and animal species is already at risk of extinction as a result of habitat destruction, over-harvesting, introduction of invasive species, and pollution.

States—extraordinary efforts will be needed in all four of these areas.

Reduced Emissions from Deforestation and Degradation (REDD)
Deforestation, forest degradation, agriculture, and other land uses are the second largest source of GHG emissions after fossil fuel consumption (see Chapter 4: Forest Conservation). They are also the most often overlooked opportunity to reduce emissions immediately, often at relatively low cost. This is especially tragic, since deforestation, forest degradation, and the destruction of other natural habitats is also the leading threat to the world's biodiversity. As pointed out in the Stern Report, "Curbing deforestation is a highly cost-effective way of reducing GHG emissions and has the potential to offer significant reductions fairly quickly. It also helps preserve biodiversity and protect soil and water quality" (Stern, 2006). Societies worldwide depend on a wide range of free ecological services that forests, wetlands, mangroves, grasslands, peatlands, and other ecosystems provide, from maintaining a reliable and steady flow of freshwater, to forming a buffer against floods and coastal storms, to housing the insects and other animals that pollinate a large portion of the world's agricultural crops, to regulating local climate and rainfall patterns.

Urgent action to protect and restore these natural ecosystems would not only help to mitigate climate change, it would also preserve biodiversity and enhance human well-being, particularly in the world's poorest regions. According to the mid-range estimate of the IPCC's Special Report on Land Use, Land-Use Change, and Forestry, one-third of a trillion tons of CO_2 could be avoided and/or sequestered (by averting the release of stored carbon, and/or by absorbing CO_2 from the atmosphere and accumulating it in soils and

Wind Power: The total energy contained in wind is 100 times the power used by everyone on the planet. Tapping into just 1 percent of that energy, scientists say, would not produce a major adverse effect on the environment.

doesn't always blow. Storing electricity for later use has traditionally been difficult and expensive. However, with the increase of millions of batteries distributed in plugged-in hybrid vehicles around the country, there would be an ideal energy storage solution that would enable a much higher share of wind or solar power in a nation's power grid. For example, electric vehicles with onboard battery storage and bi-directional power flows could stabilize large-scale wind power (e.g., one-half of the United States' total electricity) with just 3% of the fleet dedicated to regulation for wind, plus 8% to 38% of the fleet providing operating reserves or storage for wind (the percentage depending on advances in battery capacity). In a vehicle-to-grid world, with solar and wind power stored in the mass distribution of plug-in hybrid electric batteries, sixty and thirty times less land area, respectively, would be needed than what would be required for biofuels for the same power output. This would put considerably less pressure on converting both land and water resources for producing substitute vehicle fuels.

Other Renewables. In addition to wind and solar, other promising regionally available renewable energy sources include geothermal, biomass, ocean thermal, and wave technologies. These and other alternative technologies have spurred a wave of private investment. Sensing an opportunity for big returns thanks to societal concerns about climate change and energy security, venture capital firms that pioneered the dot-com boom of the 1990s have turned their attention to clean energy technologies, including both renewable and efficiency technologies.

Recently, a remarkable initiative called "Renewables Cheaper than Coal" was launched by Google Corporation. The Internet search leader and its philanthropic arm, Google.org, have committed hundreds of millions of dollars to researching, developing, and commercializing breakthrough innovations in competitive solar, wind, and geothermal power systems. For example, Google is keen on tapping enormous kinetic energy from the jet stream's constant high winds. The jet stream blows constantly and often at high speeds exceeding 480 kilometers per hour, but its enormous energy remains untapped.

Average power density can be as high as 20 kilowatts per square meter in the jet stream, which is ten to 100 times greater than ground-mounted wind turbines. Google hopes to produce 1,000 MW of power from renewable energy at prices below the rates of electricity generated at coal-burning plants. This is enough power to supply the electricity demands of a city the size of San Francisco. Co-founder Larry Page predicted the goal could be reached in a matter of "years, not decades" (Google, 2007).

So-called "clean technology" investments accounted for an estimated $2.4 billion, or more than 9%, of American venture capital in 2006, and may exceed $19 billion by 2010. Mainstream financial institutions such as Citigroup, Bank of America, and Goldman Sachs are investing as well. Citigroup, for instance, has pledged $50 billion in environmental investments and Bank of America $20 billion.

Reducing GHG Emissions from Conventional Energy Technologies.
This is another immediate priority, since the world is inescapably committed to deriving the bulk of its electricity and transport fuel supplies from conventional sources for at least the next few decades.

Fossil Fuels. The International Energy Agency (IEA) forecasts that by 2030 more than 1,400,000 MW of new coal-fired electric generating plants, more than 2 million MW of natural gas-fired plants, and some 200,000 MW of oil-fired plants will be built under its business-as-usual reference case scenario. Coal plants are likely to operate for sixty years or longer and natural-gas plants for forty years or longer. Once built, these plants are likely to continue emitting at high rates for their entire life unless they can be retrofitted with technologies and systems designed to capture the CO_2 emissions and permanently store them in underground geological structures. If built without the ability to capture carbon, the lifetime carbon emissions released into the atmosphere from this new fossil-burning capacity will be 800 billion tons of CO_2. To put this in context, that is nearly 80% of the total CO_2 emissions from all global energy use over the past 250 years.

Combustion of natural gas releases only half as much CO_2 as coal and

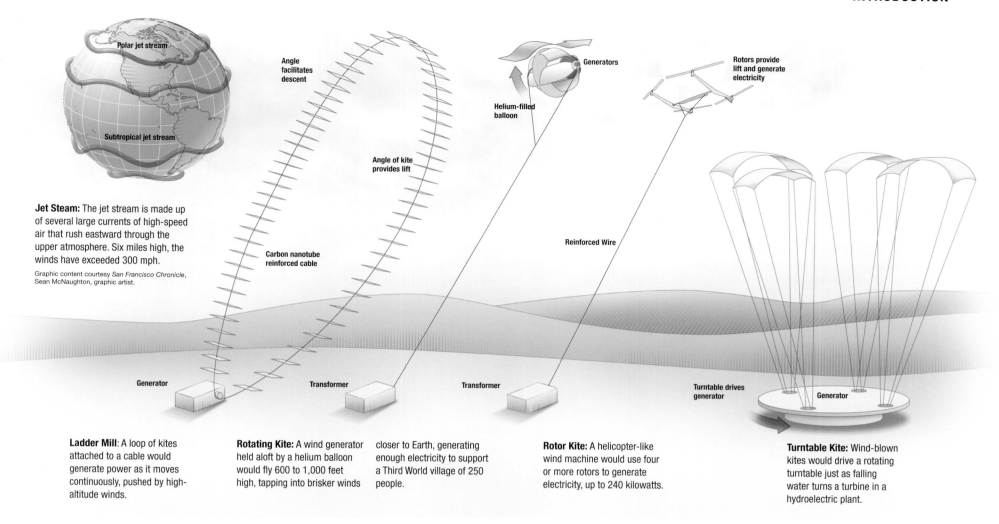

Jet Steam: The jet stream is made up of several large currents of high-speed air that rush eastward through the upper atmosphere. Six miles high, the winds have exceeded 300 mph.

Graphic content courtesy *San Francisco Chronicle*, Sean McNaughton, graphic artist.

Polar jet stream

Subtropical jet stream

Angle facilitates descent

Angle of kite provides lift

Carbon nanotube reinforced cable

Generators

Helium-filled balloon

Reinforced Wire

Rotors provide lift and generate electricity

Generator

Transformer

Transformer

Turntable drives generator

Generator

Ladder Mill: A loop of kites attached to a cable would generate power as it moves continuously, pushed by high-altitude winds.

Rotating Kite: A wind generator held aloft by a helium balloon would fly 600 to 1,000 feet high, tapping into brisker winds closer to Earth, generating enough electricity to support a Third World village of 250 people.

Rotor Kite: A helicopter-like wind machine would use four or more rotors to generate electricity, up to 240 kilowatts.

Turntable Kite: Wind-blown kites would drive a rotating turntable just as falling water turns a turbine in a hydroelectric plant.

just two-thirds as much as oil to produce the same amount of useful energy. This suggests one transitional option for a low-carbon future is to build more natural gas-fired and fewer coal-fired power plants. As detailed in the Rocky Mountain Institute report, *Winning the Oil Endgame,* half of the current use of natural gas in the United States can be saved through efficiency gains at half the current or projected cost of supplying the natural gas. This would free up enough gas to displace some of the expanding demand for coal or oil supplies (Lovins et al., 2004).

More important is getting innovative regulatory policies in place that enable any cost-effective end-use and distributed energy-efficiency opportunities to compete against any new supply option, whether fossil, nuclear, or renewable. This fiscally responsible approach would ensure delivery of energy services at both the least cost *and* the lowest carbon emissions. As noted above, California pioneered such public utility regulations by aligning the financial interests of the utility and customers to capture demand-side efficiency improvements less than or equal to the cost of new supply. (This is explained further in Chapter 1: Energy Efficiency.) As of late 2007, four American states have adopted this innovation for electric utilities, and it is pending in seven more states. Twelve

states have adopted the innovation for natural-gas utilities, and it is pending in twelve other states. California and several other states have also applied the innovation to water utilities.

Given the immense pool of cost-effective efficiency gains, worldwide implementation of this regulatory innovation, coupled with other immensely cost-effective policies such as California's high-performance building standards and national appliance-efficiency standards, could help deliver half or more of the world's projected electric utility services this century while eliminating the need for the equivalent of nearly 14 billion railcars of coal.

Even so, coal will continue to be a dominant fuel source for electricity production. It is a plentiful and inexpensive resource (without CO_2 emissions controls) in the largest electricity-consuming nations, including the United States, China, and India. Low coal costs are also due in large part to policy failure to incorporate into the price the substantial externality costs incurred by society in increased illness, premature mortality, and reduced agricultural and forestry productivity. According to one of the most detailed studies conducted by the European Commission, the price of coal-fired electricity would double if these externality costs were included.

At current business-as-usual rates of growth, China alone is building one to two large coal plants per *week* and will continue to do so over the next twenty years. Aggressive energy-efficiency measures could eliminate the need for half to three quarters of the world's new coal plants. Wind, solar, geothermal, and other renewable energy technologies could displace much of the remainder, though some new coal plants will still be built.

Technologies to increase the efficiency of electricity production from coal must be developed and widely deployed as a matter of urgency. One promising approach, known as an Integrated Gasification/Combined Cycle (IGCC) power plant, uses proven technology to convert coal into gas, which is then used to power an electricity-generating turbine directly and to produce steam to drive the turbine for another cycle. An IGCC plant emits 80% less CO_2 emissions per kilowatt-hour than a conventional pulverized coal combustion boiler, but the IGCC-generated electricity costs 20% more per kilowatt-hour of electricity. Regulation will be needed, therefore, for widespread adoption of IGCC by electric utilities worldwide.

The IGCC coal plant, however, is an essential but insufficient innovation. CO_2 emissions still remain significant (about 800 grams per kilowatt-hour). A complete coal-fueled power plant system must include capturing the CO_2 emissions and permanently storing them away from the atmosphere. Carbon capture and storage systems are still under development and, while the technologies required already exist, it is not common to find power stations close to suitable geological structures, making implementation problematic. No IGCC systems have yet been built at a full scale and with associated carbon capture and storage.

A range of per-ton cost estimates has been put forward for carbon capture and storage. Over the next several decades, costs are anticipated to be at least $40 to $50 per ton of CO_2, but can also range as much as two to six times larger than this estimate in some circumstances. Over the long term, costs are estimated to drop to around $20 per ton. By comparison, the current average cost of energy services from efficiency improvements is −$10 to $0 per ton of CO_2.

Hydropower. While considered a renewable energy source and often claimed to be a carbon-free alternative to fossil fuels, hydropower dams are also large sources of GHG emissions. Many large-scale hydro reservoirs inundate vast areas, especially in low-lying parts of tropical countries, creating significant social, environmental, and even global-warming impacts. Field measurements of these reservoirs have found many to be a large source of methane emissions due to the anaerobic decomposition of submerged vegetation. As already noted above, methane is a GHG about twenty times more potent than CO_2.

Not all hydropower releases GHG emissions, and there are many examples of micro, small, and larger scale hydroelectric systems that have been carefully sited, designed, constructed, and operated. However, hydrologists estimate that hydro dams (not all of which generate electricity) currently account for 8% of *total* global GHG emissions, and this share may increase to as much as 15% given hydro expansion plans in the future. Many hydroelectric stations are also showing limited useful life due to the silting up of their reservoirs, as well as declining utility as a result of severe droughts and lack of replenishing rainfall and snowmelt, conditions that are occurring with increasing frequency and severity.

Nuclear Power. The superficial attraction of nuclear power is the fact that one ton of nuclear fuel can displace 20,000 tons of coal, which is why it is being promoted as an alternative to coal, even with carbon capture and storage. However, recent expert reviews of new nuclear power plants estimate the *delivered* cost of electricity services at 9 to 13 cents per kilowatt-hour. This does not include the many subsidies available to the nuclear power industry, such as federal catastrophe insurance in the United States indemnifying operators against reactor disasters.

Even if nuclear power's cost to reduce CO_2 is less than coal with carbon capture and storage, there are still much cheaper alternatives. Just as in the case of coal with carbon capture and storage, improved energy services from end-use efficiency gains can deliver three to ten times more energy services than nuclear power for a similar investment, as well as at a lower cost per reduced ton of CO_2. Common sense dictates that capturing the full portfolio of low-cost efficiency energy services should be achieved before turning to more expensive options. Hence the importance of regulatory utility reform noted above.

Equally of concern, nuclear power creates a range of seemingly intractable safety and security issues. While a new generation of reactor designs may make another Chernobyl or Three-Mile Island-type accident much less likely, issues of long-term disposal of nuclear waste, the risk of fissile material falling into the hands of terrorists, and the post-9/11 recognition that reactors may be targeted by terrorists have not been fully addressed.

For nuclear power to displace half of projected coal use worldwide by 2100, a

100-MW nuclear reactor would have to be constructed every twenty hours for the entire century. The high nuclear fuel demand would require reprocessing weapons-grade plutonium for use in "breeder" (high-efficiency) reactors in the latter half of this century. This would result in several million kilograms of plutonium—the equivalent of several hundred thousand atomic bombs—annually circulating in global commerce. Even with full compliance with the best inventory-control standards, enough plutonium capable of producing an atomic bomb every forty-eight months could go missing without being noticed. Given these looming problems, some of the most thoughtful nuclear proponents advocate locating reactors underground to shield from attack and prevent radioactive releases in the case of an accident, as well as operating reactors under joint international supervision in order to prevent diversion of weapons-grade fuel.

Bioenergy and Biofuels.

One of the hottest areas of investment is bioenergy, the production of liquid fuels and electricity from plants (see Chapter 3: Biofuels). Liquid biofuels have generated considerable interest since they are economically attractive compared to gasoline at current prices. Ethanol is competitive at $40 per barrel of oil, while biodiesel is competitive at $65 per barrel (but neither is competitive, as noted above, with vehicle-efficiency improvements with an average cost of only $13.50 per barrel). Largely due to substantial government subsidies and policy support, Brazil and the United States are already large producers of fuel ethanol, produced by fermenting starches from crops such as sugar cane and corn. Europe is the largest producer of biodiesel, derived from oilseed crops such as rapeseed (canola), and tropical countries are also accelerating biodiesel production from soybean and oil palm.

While biofuels still make up only a tiny percentage of global energy use, the sector is growing rapidly as a result of public subsidies and government production and use targets. Together, Brazil and the United States account for 90% of world fuel-ethanol production. Each country produces roughly four billion gallons of fuel ethanol, which accounts for 30% of fuel use in Brazil and 3% in the United States. Europe accounts for 85% of world biodiesel production, with 1.5 billion gallons in 2006. The Bush administration has called for American biofuel production to reach 35 billion gallons by 2017, which would replace 15% of domestic gasoline use. The European community plans to meet 10% of its fuel needs from biofuels by 2010.

Policymakers are attracted to biofuels because they can purportedly reduce

To preserve biodiversity and minimize CO_2 emissions from deforestation and forest degradation, policymakers must ensure that the expansion of biofuel crops is carefully planned and regulated, and especially that it does not displace or degrade intact natural systems.

dependence on foreign oil and can revitalize rural economies. In direct response to rising demand for ethanol, corn prices in the United States have doubled and stimulated a boom in the farm belt. Biofuels also have been perceived as offering environmental benefits. In theory, biofuels could be carbon-neutral alternatives to fossil fuels, since the carbon dioxide emitted when biofuels are burned had been taken up earlier by the plant feedstock as it grew.

In practice, however, both the oil-import displacement and the environmental value of biofuels are questionable. Corn requires a large amount of fossil energy to grow, transport, and convert to ethanol, so both the oil-displacement and the net carbon benefits are minimal, and the carbon benefits become negative when produced with coal-fired electricity. While other biofuel feedstocks, such as sugar cane and oil palm, are more efficient sources of bioenergy and yield larger CO_2 reduction benefits when displacing gasoline, the potential for all biofuel crops to destroy natural ecosystems and affect food security is an even greater concern.

Providing 10% of the United States' and European Union's fuel needs from domestic biofuels would require 43% of the United States' and 38% of Europe's farm land. This would have the unintended consequence in the United States of displacing other crops to tropical countries such as Brazil, notably soybeans grown for animal feed. Recent research indicates a knock-on effect of expanding soy production by removing intact ecosystems in Brazil's Amazonia, Cerrado, and Pantanal regions.

What is more, the most energy-efficient biofuel crops, such as sugar cane and oil palm, are tropical crops, well suited to Brazil, Indonesia, Malaysia, and other developing countries. Expanded production of biofuels in these regions will put further direct pressure on tropical forests and grasslands. Already, oil palm production is the leading source of deforestation and forest degradation in southeast Asia. Production of biofuel crops also requires large quantities of freshwater, such that expansion will place further pressure on people and nature in water-scarce regions. Biofuels produced from corn, sugar cane, and other food crops can also create social pressure by increasing the price of food. Global food prices are already rising due to the increased demand for corn and associated land for fuel-ethanol production.

Investors are now targeting new technologies that will allow more cost-effective conversion of cellulose—the non-woody part of plants—into ethanol. Cellulosic ethanol could be produced from a wider range of annual and perennial crops, including native grass and tree species, which would require less energy and water to cultivate and not displace food crops as much. Similarly, perennial oilseed species that theoretically can be grown with modest inputs on marginal lands, such as *Jatropha,* are being promoted for biodiesel production.

However, all these crop species will add pressure to convert natural habitat as their value rises. The potentially larger yields of cellulosic biofuels still fall short in comparison to forest restoration as a CO_2 mitigation strategy or through the system efficiency of connecting efficient, hybrid electric plug-in vehicles to the grid. Unlike other carbon-free energy technologies, biofuels require large amounts of land. If that land were returned to forest instead, it would sequester several times the amount of carbon that biofuels grown on the same amount would keep out of the atmosphere. These figures do not take into account any CO_2 emissions that would result if that land were deforested to make way for biofuel crops.

Biofuels will continue to be sought as a readily substitutable alternative to fossil fuels to promote energy security and rural development, even though they are many times less cost-effective and ecologically sustainable as a climate-mitigation strategy compared to fuel-efficiency gains in vehicles and other options such as wind- and solar-powered plug-in hybrid electric vehicles that are not so readily substitutable. To preserve biodiversity and minimize CO_2 emissions from deforestation and forest degradation, policymakers must ensure that the expansion of biofuel crops is carefully planned and regulated, and *especially that it does not displace or degrade intact natural systems such as forests, peatlands, wetlands, and grasslands.* Special attention must also be given to ensure that biofuel production does not lead to overuse of water.

Collaborative efforts by local communities, the energy and agribusiness industries, governments, and conservation organizations to identify and protect critical habitats and ecosystem functions will be essential.

Adaptation Responses

The world is already seeing and feeling the impacts of climate change. These changes require immediate action. Sea levels are rising faster than scientific models indicated, the Arctic sea ice is melting more rapidly, and sea-surface temperatures are rising more swiftly than anticipated. In some areas, heavier rainfall is causing more flooding, while in other regions and at other times of the year, droughts and wildfires are occurring with greater severity and frequency. Terrestrial, marine, and freshwater ecosystems are changing on all continents, and weather-triggered disasters are affecting more and more communities and economies.

These climate-related changes are causing ripple effects across the globe, from the loss of homes, businesses, and agricultural productivity to contaminated water and infectious diseases, to the loss of irreplaceable biodiversity. These changes will continue to have disproportionate and devastating impacts on the most vulnerable 1.2 billion people living in extreme poverty—those least responsible for climate change—as well as the four billion people who live in developing countries (IFAD, 2001). Efforts to help people and natural systems cope with current and inevitable future climate change—often referred to as "adaptation"—have fallen far short of what is required.

There is no clearer indication of the limited emphasis on adaptation than in the UN Climate Convention's main objective—to stabilize "GHG concentrations in the atmosphere at a level that would prevent dangerous anthropogenic interference with the climate system…." and to achieve this stabilization "… within a time-frame sufficient to allow ecosystems to adapt naturally to climate change, to ensure that food production is not threatened and to enable economic development to proceed in a sustainable manner" (UNFCCC, 2002). In fact, most policy efforts to address adaptation to date have primarily focused on the need to stabilize GHG emissions to avoid the need for adaptation into the future. Taking aggressive action to mitigate climate change will certainly reduce the amount of costly adaptation actions needed later, but the science and empirical evidence indicate a need to pursue adaptation in vulnerable areas now, particularly in developing communities, as negative climactic changes are already upon us (Gilman, Randall, and Schwartz, 2007).

As with mitigation, one major gap in adaptation policies, financing, and actions to date has been the limited pursuit and application of ecosystem-based adaptation solutions. The types of activities pursued under adaptation have been primarily infrastructure-related, often overlooking the health status and resiliency of ecosystems as a possible buffer and tool in helping people and species cope with climate change. Infrastructure adaptation investments are expensive, and, while in some instances they may be the only option, in other instances there may be suitable and more cost-effective alternatives for deploying limited adaptation resources.

Access to clean freshwater will also likely be drastically reduced in many regions due to climate change, despite major planned investments to move water to population centers and agricultural zones. In addition, rainfall patterns that destabilize agricultural productivity and reduce freshwater availability may simultaneously aggravate internal conflicts as well as cross-border conflicts. Since disturbances to extremely large tracts of undisturbed forest strongly influence regional rainfall patterns (e.g., Brazil's Amazon forest impacts rainfall in the agricultural areas of Central America and the United States), there may be common ground between mitigation actions in Brazil and adaptation results in the United States. These intensified domestic challenges, regional security requirements, and cross-border and cross-sector impacts may further complicate climate policy challenges and may also increase the important role that healthy and resilient ecosystems serve in helping people and species cope with climate change.

Ensuring that we not only conserve intact ecosystems for their human services but also make sufficient provisions for the conservation of biological diversity adds yet another dimension to our challenge. The scientific community is increasingly confronting this issue, but the responses advocated so far have been mostly generic and have not been subject to rigorous analysis of effectiveness and cost. Early efforts to "mainstream" climate-change responses in conservation include attempts to increase the size of protected areas in ways that increase their buffering capacity against climate change (e.g., expanding up- and down-slope or along known climatic gradients), which increase the "bioclimatic space" available to species within the protected area. Linking reserves using ecological corridors has also been a popular early response that has been applied in some regions of the world. More extreme interventionist responses, such as translocating species threatened by local extinction due to changing climate, or gene- and seed-banking, have been discussed, but remain largely untested on the scale that may be required under some climate

> **Although some people still believe that … global warming is a result of natural centuries-long climate cycles, mainstream scientific assessments, the scientific community, governments, and overwhelming public opinion now accept the conclusion that human activities are largely responsible.**

scenarios. This is an area of conservation that is in urgent need of serious ecological and socio-economic analysis.

Emerging Political Responses

Since the Kyoto Protocol entered into force in 2006, there has been wider public awareness of the issue and increasing appreciation of what must be done to tackle it. The efforts of former U.S. Vice President Al Gore and others have helped millions to understand that the science of climate change is becoming clearer and more definitive, with Al Gore's film, *An Inconvenient Truth,* making a notable global contribution.

The IPCC's *Fourth Assessment Report* released in 2007 was a watershed. While many uncertainties remain, the world's leading climate scientists for the first time agree that we are now observing the impacts of human-induced climate change. Although some people still believe that the observed global warming is a result of natural centuries-long climate cycles, mainstream scientific assessments, the scientific community, governments, and overwhelming public opinion now accept the conclusion that human activities are largely responsible.

In a befitting decision, the Nobel Peace Prize for 2007 was awarded jointly to the IPCC and Al Gore, "for their efforts to build up and disseminate greater knowledge about man-made climate change and to lay the foundations for the measures that are needed to counteract such change" (Nobel Prize Committee, 2007).

The importance of acting swiftly and not delaying mitigation is a key

> **We need to do more than wake up to climate change; we need to work together as a global community to make sure that it does not undermine the long-term sustainability of our unique living planet—both for ourselves and the many other living creatures that share this planet with us.**

on remaining tropical forests and the trend of growing global deforestation and forest degradation in recent years.

An effective regime for reducing carbon emissions from deforestation and forest degradation should not allow leaks of deforestation and forest degradation to new countries or regions. It should aim to reduce net global emissions by encouraging comprehensive changes in international behavior towards remaining native forests and other natural ecosystems in favor of maintaining the extent and integrity of what native ecosystems we have left. This has led to the proposal of adopting a reference emissions rate indexed to the global deforestation rate for countries or regions with little or no historic deforestation or forest degradation. This would effectively allow HFLD countries to be allocated "preventive annual credits" that these countries would stand to forfeit to an extent dependent on any increase in their extent or rate of deforestation and forest degradation. Income from the sale of such preventive annual credits would provide a significant entry barrier to new forest exploitation or policies that promote or allow deforestation or forest degradation.

HFLD countries would thus receive a significant incentive to maintain low rates and extent of deforestation and forest degradation from any reference emission rate and extent indexed to global averages. At US$10/ton of CO_2, using one-third of the global average deforestation rate as the reference emission rate for HFLD countries, preventive annual credits would be worth US$365 million annually to seven countries. Using one-half of the global average deforestation rate as the reference rate would more than double the qualifying

forest area and would increase credit value to US$630 million annually to ten countries. Using the global average deforestation rate as the reference rate would increase credit value to $1.8 billion annually to 11 countries (Fonseca et al., 2007). It is critically important that these HFLD countries be included in global markets for forest carbon, since they have some of the largest remaining areas of intact forest and are critically important for biodiversity conservation. Their value as intact wilderness areas should also be included, as they serve as important controls and reference points for other more fragmented and heavily impacted forest regions. Failure to include them now would be a mistake of monumental and historic proportions.

The Need for Leadership from the United States

Some argue that a lead must be taken by the United States as an important signal to emerging economies of global cooperation on climate-change responses. As with many of the other major advances in American environmental policy over the last forty years, political leadership on climate change has emerged largely from the grassroots level. Responding to advocacy by citizens groups and environmental organizations, the mayors of 700 U.S. cities representing 75 million citizens have signed the Mayors' Agreement for Climate Protection. This declaration commits their cities to meet or exceed the target that the Kyoto Protocol would have set for the United States, a 7% reduction in CO_2 emissions below 1990 levels by 2012.

Thirty-four out of the seventy-five largest GHG emitters in the world are U.S. states. By itself, state action is vital to national as well as global progress and is laying the groundwork for future federal and state policy development and implementation. By the end of 2007, there were twenty-five states that adopted or were developing climate-action plans. As in previous environmental policy debates, the prospect of a patchwork of state-level regulatory initiatives is one of the key forces behind the gathering political momentum for a national-level regulatory framework to reduce GHG emissions.

The religious community has been a particularly powerful source of grassroots leadership. Religious organizations representing a wide spectrum of faiths and denominations, ranging from the National Council of Churches to the National Association of Evangelicals, have issued calls for their members and their political leaders to take action against climate change. These organizations increasingly see the connections between climate change and the broader social issues of concern to their religious communities, including poverty, human rights, sustainable development, human health, and care for God's creation.

The private sector has been another important source of emerging leadership. For more than a decade, pioneering corporations have anticipated that society would demand action on climate change and have announced voluntary goals to reduce their own GHG emissions. DuPont, for example, succeeded in reducing its emissions more than 60% below 1990 levels. BP and Shell were among other early Fortune 500 companies to set emissions reduction targets, each succeeding in reducing emissions by at least 10%. For its part, CEMEX is committed to energy efficiency leadership. By the end of 2007 it reduced its CO_2 emissions by 12% per ton of cement (as compared to the 1990 baseline) and its goal is to achieve a 25% reduction by 2015.

Other companies, such as ST Microelectronics, have set dates for becoming carbon neutral—making deep reductions in their own emissions, buying renewable energy, offsetting their remaining emissions by funding projects to restore forests, or engaging in other activities that reduce emissions. Recently, companies as diverse as News Corporation and Google announced that they will become carbon neutral as well. In addition to securing important levels of emissions reduction in their own right, these efforts help show policymakers that deep reductions in CO_2 emissions are not only feasible, but also profitable.

Companies are also responding to growing consumer awareness and demand for green and energy-saving products and services. Wal-Mart, in addition to testifying before Congress in support of a mandated cap on CO_2 emissions, set goals to be supplied 100% by renewable energy, to create zero waste, and to sell products that sustain the planet's resources and environment. Wal-Mart launched a nationwide campaign to make the highly efficient compact fluorescent lamp (CFL) America's number-one lamp of choice and sold 150 million in 2007, saving their customers $4 billion on energy bills.

Momentum in the private sector and within governments to address climate change will likely build as people around the world wake up to the reality of the current impacts and future risks of climate change. A recent global poll of 22,000 people in twenty-one countries found that 79% believe that human activity is a significant cause of climate change, 90% believe that action is necessary to address it, and 65% believe that "it is necessary to take major steps starting very soon" (BBC World Service, 2007).

This level of public awareness and concern is a good start, but successful efforts to stem dangerous climate change will depend on translating such concern into changed public behavior. History and experience tell us that this is no easy task. We need to use energy more efficiently. We need to use less of it. We need to accept higher energy prices that allow carbon-free energy technologies to take hold. We need to fund efforts by developing countries to conserve tropical forests and other threatened habitats and ecosystems. We need to demand that our political leaders create the innovative policies and regulations that will bring these changes about in the shortest possible time with the least harm to our economies. We need to do more than wake up to climate change; we need to work together as a global community to make sure that it does not undermine the long-term sustainability of our planet—both for ourselves and the many other creatures that share this planet with us.

The Role of This Book

The following chapters examine a wide variety of issues relating to global climate change, including some that are already receiving a great deal of attention, others that have received far less than they deserve, and still more that have been largely overlooked and yet may be critically important. In particular, the chapters that follow place emphasis on the great importance of avoiding the destruction and degradation of tropical forests and other tropical systems and on the still largely unappreciated issue of melting of the permafrost and other potential tipping points, which we highlight alongside the better-known issues of energy efficiency, renewables, and biofuels. These chapters are divided into two main sections, the first dealing with *mitigation,* including Energy Efficiency, Renewable Energy, Biofuels, Forest Conservation, and Reforestation and Agroforestry, and the second with *adaptation,* including Terrestrial Biodiversity, Freshwater Biodiversity, The Role of Oceans, Human Dimensions, and Tipping Points. Lastly, we provide a conclusion in which we make recommendations as to future directions, including a strong focus on the critical role of nature-based solutions.

As with past books produced by CEMEX, the comprehensive text is complemented by a wide variety of top-quality images produced by the world's leading photographers to give a greater appreciation of the issues to the reader.

We hope that this book, by summarizing and highlighting some of the key elements of this immensely important issue, will make a significant contribution to increasing awareness and achieving lasting solutions, and that it will help us to ensure that future generations continue to have a climate for life on this unique planet.

Poised to burst over an Illinois town, a cumulonimbus cloud may be an ominous sign of things to come. Rising average temperatures put more heat energy and water vapor into the atmosphere, fueling heavier rainfall, more powerful hurricanes, more frequent heat waves, and a greater risk of drought and wildfires. TOM SISTAK

PART I

Mitigating Climate Change

Each succeeding year brings unwelcome record-shattering, extreme weather events triggering devastation and disastrous losses to life and property around the world. U.S. insurers have experienced growth in weather-related catastrophe losses from levels of about $1 billion per year in the 1970s to an average of $17 billion per year over the past decade—far outstripping growth in premiums, populations, and inflation during the same period.

Europe's largest insurer, Allianz, stated that within just a decade, climate change stands to increase insured losses from extreme events in an average year by 37%, while losses in a particularly bad year could top $400 billion (MacDonald-Smith, 2007). This concern of urgency has been echoed by the financial investment sector, as in November 2005, when then-Goldman Sachs Chairman Henry Paulson (and U.S. Treasury Secretary in the G.W. Bush administration) warned, "We don't have a lot more time to deal with climate change" and "voluntary action alone cannot solve the climate change problem" (Mills and Lecomte, 2006).

The growing unease of corporations appears well-justified by the best data and models to date. Studies coupling climate models and insurance loss models conducted by the Association of British Insurers estimated an increase of hurricane and tropical cyclone losses of up to $27 billion in an average year in Europe, Japan, and the United States, corresponding to an estimated 67% increase in premiums. The associated need for increased risk capital would be $76 billion to cover the increased exposure in the United States and Japan. The worst years would bring two to three additional category five Hurricane Andrews in the United States (AIB, 2005; Swiss Re, 2006).

The insurance sector is the world's largest industry, generating about $4 trillion in yearly premium revenue in 2006, plus another trillion or so in investment income. Mitigating and managing risks and controlling losses are central to the insurance business and are evident in the industry's history as founders of fire departments and advocates for building codes. While the primary focus in recent years has been on managing financial risk (through exclusions, price increases, derivatives, and the like), physical risk mitigation and management are receiving renewed attention from insurers.

The sun rises over tabular icebergs on the Antarctic Peninsula.
TUI DE ROY

Energy Efficiency

A combination of smart-energy services; the development of ambitious wind, solar, geothermal, and biowaste solutions; and the dramatic reduction of emissions achieved by preventing tropical deforestation hold our best hope for stabilizing carbon production while sustaining robust global economic growth.

A CLIMATE FOR LIFE

Even modern commerce relies on peasant laborers carrying baskets of coal to ships for transport to the industrial centers below the Three Gorges Dam on the Yangtze River in China.
GEORGE STEINMETZ

PREVIOUS PAGES:
Electrician Randal Brown holds a compact fluorescent lamp (CFL) that over the course of its lifetime will reduce emissions equivalent to burning this 227-kilogram pile of coal.
SARAH LEEN

Energy Efficiency

Michael Totten

Over the past 100 years, the world's industrial production has increased more than fifty-fold. Unfortunately, the cost of this economic growth has been an immense release of carbon dioxide emissions that has already committed the planet to a 1°C increase in global average temperature in the coming years (CDIAC, 2007). This increase will likely force us to cope with more frequent and intense meteorological disasters with potentially catastrophic impacts to all humans, as well as accelerated biodiversity loss. The only good news is that gains in energy efficiency can play a major role in tackling this global challenge and ensuring a more stable environmental and economic future.

Ask any individual where most new energy services have come from in the United States, Europe, and Japan over the past fifty years and the likely answer will be coal, oil or natural gas, or maybe nuclear power. They would all be wrong. The real source has been energy-efficiency gains, or what some now refer to as "smart energy services." This umbrella term refers to the myriad inventive ways to deliver energy services at increasingly lower cost and with less material. Smart energy services often also deliver higher performance and productivity and reduced risk and may also afford unforeseen emerging opportunities.

The long history of technology design reveals rich veins of smart energy service successes. Efficiency emerges from the virtually bottomless well of human creativity and is replenished by ongoing ingenuity that continues to yield new designs, advanced materials, and innovative techniques. Indeed, the evolution of ever-more efficient technologies has been fundamental to sustaining societal development and has been a cornerstone to greater productivity, prosperity, health, and improved well-being (West, 2007; Bettencourt et al., 2007).

Compared to smart energy services, all other energy supply options are plagued with varying degrees of external costs and risks that are not internalized or reflected in their delivered energy price. This makes them appear less costly and risky than they actually are. It is also important to recognize that the economics of all energy options are heavily influenced (and skewed) by government policies, tax provisions, rules and regulations, and

Smokestack emissions pour out from a refinery in Anacortes, Washington. Humans now generate emissions that are the equivalent of a volcanic eruption every 44 hours. AMY GULICK

BedZed, in Beddington, London, is the United Kingdom's largest eco-village, where residents live a sustainable lifestyle with zero carbon emissions. ASHLEY COOPER

enforcement, or lack thereof, at the national, state, and local levels. Common sense dictates that we should try to take advantage of the full portfolio of low-cost smart energy services before turning to more expensive, and potentially dangerous, options.

The economic benefits are obvious. A 2007 assessment by the McKinsey Global Institute concluded that energy efficiency improvements worldwide through 2030 could provide an estimated 75% of projected new energy service demand with a 10% or better return on investment (MGI, 2007). In fact, smart energy services are poised to be one of the prime mitigators of climate change and the accompanying loss of biodiversity. In the United States alone, money-saving efficiency gains have also averted the annual release of more than 1.5 billion tons of carbon dioxide emissions. A combination of smart-energy services; the development of ambitious wind, solar, geothermal, and biowaste solutions; and the dramatic reduction of emissions achieved by preventing tropical deforestation hold our best hope for stabilizing carbon production while sustaining robust global economic growth.

The Historical Record

It is worth remembering that between 1949 and 1973, the energy required to produce the U.S. Gross Domestic Product (E/GDP) declined by 0.4% per year. Then, with the price shocks following the oil crisis of 1973, innumerable efficiency improvements to buildings, vehicles, factories, motors, lights, and appliances accelerated the rate of reduction of Energy/Gross Domestic Product five-fold to 2.1% per year.

Without faster efficiency gains (smarter ways of delivering energy services), energy consumption in the United States would have risen from 79 exajoules in 1973 to 179 exajoules in 2005. Instead, energy consumption in 2005 was only 104 exajoules. The difference (75 exajoules) also avoided $700 billion per year in higher energy bills (Rosenfeld, 2006). How much is 75 exajoules? Envision a freight train annually hauling nearly 18,000,000 railcars of coal, which would wrap around the world seven times. Or imagine 8,800 oil supertanker shipments per year that are then distributed to gas stations by 70,400,000 delivery trucks. There are only two nations that consume more

than 75 exajoules per year: the United States and China.

Even if one-third of these savings are discounted as being due to structural changes in the economy rather than smart efficiency improvements to energy-consuming devices, this still represents more than $460 billion per year in reduced energy bills. By way of comparison, there were only 16 nations out of the world total of 194 whose Gross Domestic Product in 2006 was greater than these energy savings.

Just how impressive these achievements are can best be grasped by comparing these efficiency gains with the conventional energy supply. The 39% drop in Energy/Gross Domestic Product from 1975 to 2000 represented, by 2000, "an effective energy 'source' 1.7 times as big as U.S. oil consumption, three times net oil imports, five times domestic oil output, six times net oil imports from Organization of Petroleum Exporting Countries (OPEC) members, and thirteen times net imports from Persian Gulf countries" (Lovins, 2004).

If the amount of energy consumed to produce one unit of Gross Domestic Product—a measurement known as "energy intensity"—improves or is reduced by only 1% per year, global carbon emissions will still triple by 2100, pushing atmospheric carbon dioxide concentrations and global temperature far into the catastrophic zone (Ward, 2007). Achieving 2% per year in energy intensity improvements will basically maintain the current emission levels throughout the century, raising the global temperature more than 2°C, destroying most of the world's coral reefs and cloud rainforests, and triggering massive, long-term economic dislocations, as well as significant morbidity and mortality impacts from more frequent and severe weather-triggered disasters. If, however, society achieves a 3% per year improvement, emissions will dramatically decrease, stabilizing atmospheric concentration of carbon dioxide at 450 to 550 parts per million.

History tells us that achieving such smart energy service rates is very plausible. Attentive firms are profitably cutting energy per unit of output by about 6–8% per year (Lovins, 2007). The United States cut its energy intensity by 3.4% every year from 1981 to 1986, 2.7% per year from 1997 to 2001, 3.2% per year in 2001 and 2005, and 2.4% per year in 2003 and 2004. California cut its energy intensity about one percentage point faster,

which we utilized energy were highly inefficient (Ford, 1975), a continuous stream of economic-engineering analyses have provided a roadmap for harnessing increasingly smarter energy service opportunities ranging from no cost to highly competitive cost that touch upon virtually every daily action of our lives (Lovins et al., 1982; Goldemberg et al., 1988; Totten, 2007).

Consider several examples. This past century's shift from the candle to the incandescent bulb and now to the compact fluorescent lamp (CFL) has yielded remarkable efficiency gains. One candle consumed about 80 watts of chemical energy to deliver 12 lumens of light for seven and a half hours. This was replaced with the carbon-filament incandescent bulb, which used one-quarter less energy (60 watts), delivered fifteen times as much light (180 lumens), and lasted 133 times as long as the candle (some 1,000 hours). When the tungsten filament replaced the carbon one, the efficiency quadrupled. The tungsten bulb can now match the lifetime output of 8,100 candles, yet the lamp and the electricity cost only about as much as fourteen candles. The compact fluorescent light, however, renders the same lumen output as an incandescent bulb, while consuming 75% less electricity and lasting thirteen times longer, thus eliminating the need for 500,000 candles! (Lovins and Sardinsky, 1988).

Rapid advancements now occurring in solid-state light-emitting diodes (LED) are expected to dramatically eclipse even CFLs in price and performance in the coming decade (DOE, 2007). Lighting experts fully expect that potentially super-efficient LEDs will largely displace incandescent and fluorescent lamps worldwide this century (Schubert and Kim, 2005). Lighting—and the air conditioning required to remove the heat emitted by inefficient lamps—currently consumes 20% of the United States' electricity. This is equivalent to one-third of all coal burned by American utilities. Light-emitting diodes are expected to become twenty to fifty times more efficient than incandescent and fluorescent lamps and eventually eliminate the equivalent of

halving electricity use per capita and achieving 75% less energy use in new homes. China did even better, cutting its energy intensity more than 5% per year for more than twenty years, and 7.9% per year from 1997 to 2001; this then dramatically declined after that country cut efficiency programs and failed to enforce standards (Lovins, 2007). However, in 2006 China adopted one of the world's most aggressive energy efficiency goals (4% per year) in its Eleventh Five-Year Plan, a national economic and social development plan. Although it fell short of this goal for the past two years, it greatly increased funding in July 2007, which should help close the gap.

Smart energy services are without a doubt the best large-scale, least-cost, lowest-risk climate solution available worldwide.

Delivering Efficiency

Energy efficiency is attained by continuously improving the thermodynamic efficiency of delivered energy services. For the past century, this has been narrowly interpreted and artificially constrained to "improving supply options" (e.g., bigger power plants or exploring-extracting-refining larger amounts of fuels derived from concentrated resources that are shipped over longer and longer distances).

However, since 1974, when the American Physical Society's assessment on the thermodynamic efficiency of energy use found that all the ways in

The self-proclaimed "World's Largest Laundromat" in Berwyn, Illinois, operates 145 washing machines and 125 dryers and uses 24 solar collectors to provide 60% of the energy required for heating its water. It is expected to operate for 30 years.
JEFF HAYNES

100 coal-fired power plants, while also reducing consumers' energy bills (Tsao, 2002). Worldwide savings are several times as large.

Computers offer what undoubtedly is one of the most extraordinary tales of dematerialization. ENIAC, the first large-scale general-purpose electronic computer built in the 1940s, was 1,000 times faster than existing mechanical computers or calculators. It occupied a large room filled with 17,400 vacuum tubes and guzzled the output of 180 kilowatts of electricity. Its computer power can now fit on a mini-watt microchip. In fact, there is several thousand times as much computing power in a 5-watt Nintendo 64 game player. If car manufacturing had kept pace with computer innovations and cost reductions over the past fifty years, today we would be able to buy a Rolls Royce for less than a dollar with a fuel efficiency range of several million kilometers per liter.

Environmental Impact of Efficiency

Paradoxically, all the productivity-enhancing efficiency innovations of the past have resulted in more consumption, pollution, and waste in absolute terms than ever before. Today, one-half to three-quarters of the resources consumed annually by industrial economies are returned to the environment as waste within a year (WRI, 2000). This economic activity has been achieved at the cost of an immense release of carbon dioxide emissions. As John Holdren, President of the American Association for the Advancement of Science, said in his 2007 address: "We have already precipitated dangerous climate change. The task now facing us is the avoidance of catastrophic climate change." (Holdren, 2007). The challenge is gargantuan, given that business-as-usual patterns and rates of 2–3% annual economic growth worldwide over a century will result in a roughly ten- to 20-fold increase in economic wealth, and will put us on trajectory to release some 3.6 trillion tons of carbon dioxide into the atmosphere.

The atmospheric concentration of CO_2-equivalent, which is an internationally accepted measure used to express the same global warming potential of the several dozen different greenhouse gases in equivalent units of carbon dioxide, was 386 parts per million (ppm) in 2007 and is increasing 2 ppm per year. Business-as-usual emissions scenarios project in excess of 800 ppm this century, while most atmospheric carbon dioxide stabilization scenarios seek a target of 550 ppm (450 ppm carbon dioxide plus ~100 ppm non-carbon dioxide greenhouse gases). Recent analyses, however, indicate that averting a 2°C increase in the global average temperature this century will require rapid, comprehensive, and continuous emission reductions in order to peak over the next two decades, and then steadily decline thereafter until a concentration level of 350 ppm is achieved (Hanson et al., 2008; Meinshausen, 2005).

Current global energy consumption is about 15 terawatt-years (or 475 exajoules). A terawatt-year is an amount of energy corresponding to a use rate of one trillion watts over the duration of one year and is equal to 31.5 exajoules. An exajoule is equivalent to roughly 34 million metric tons of coal or 28.8 billion liters of gasoline. It would take more than 113 million railcars of coal to generate 15 terawatt-years. Or imagine oil supertanker shipments at the rate of one every ten minutes that are then distributed to gas stations by 437 million delivery trucks per year.

A Tibetan woman heats water with a solar furnace at her home in Gannan Tibetan Autonomous Prefecture. Solar energy is abundant in north and northwest China, and local governments are trying to promote sun energy collectors in residences.
CHINA PHOTOS

The business-as-usual trajectory of cumulative energy consumption worldwide from 2000 to 2100 would be approximately 240 times this amount—around 3,600 terawatt-years or 113,000 exajoules. Fossil fuels will account for three-fourths of this sum, releasing several trillion tons of greenhouse gases. Smart-energy services (i.e., efficiencies) can deliver more than half of these cumulative energy services this century at lower cost and risk, replacing the need for 1,800 terawatt-years or 57,000 exajoules of these more costly energy supplies. Envision eliminating the need for 13.8 billion coal railcars this century. If we also reverse emissions from deforestation and harness the most ecologically sustainable renewable energy options, we will have a viable, affordable strategy for achieving 350 parts per million, which is considered critical for ensuring a high probability of not exceeding a 2°C rise in the global average temperature this century.

The Strongest Alternative

Effectively harnessing smart energy services is an immensely difficult challenge, but no greater than dealing with proposed gigantic carbon capture and storage operations. Undertaking geological sequestration for 60% of U.S. coal plants would involve capturing one billion tons of carbon per year from 600 coal plants with an average size of 1,000 megawatts each and transporting the 50 million barrels per day of supercritical carbon dioxide to acceptable geological

sites for injection and permanent storage. This is a volume equivalent to 20 million barrels of oil per day, the total current U.S. consumption. By contrast, the biggest injection operation in 2007 was 40,000 barrels per day, and the average was merely 3,000 barrels per day.

Carbon capture and storage is projected to cost $40 per ton of carbon dioxide prior for transport, injection, and storage, which then adds an additional cost of $1.50 (low) to $11.50 (high) per ton of carbon dioxide. This puts the cost of electricity generation with carbon capture and storage at 7 cents per kilowatt-hour, not including transmission and distribution costs, which add 2.5+ cents per kilowatt-hour (MIT, 2007). The costs would be twice as high for existing coal plants. In sharp contrast, smart-energy service improvements in the building and industrial sectors are empirically verified to provide the same energy service at zero cost per kilowatt-hour to several cents per kilowatt-hour (MGI, 2007; Nadel et al., 2004; Kats et al., 2003; Krause et al., 2000; Lovins et al., 2002). Simply put, the same level of investment will deliver three to ten times more energy services (kilowatt-hours) through efficiency gains than can coal-fired electricity with carbon capture and storage.

Meanwhile, nuclear advocates argue that reactors are preferable to expensive carbon capture and storage schemes. Constructing new nuclear power plants, however, would result in electricity services delivered at 9 to 13 cents per kilowatt-hour (Keystone Center, 2007), not including the many nuclear subsidies that exist, such as federal catastrophe insurance for reactor disasters (Koplow, 2005). While nuclear power's cost to reduce carbon dioxide is less than carbon capture and storage for coal, it still pales in comparison to smart energy services, which can deliver three to ten times more energy services than nuclear power for a similar investment, as well as at a lower cost per reduced ton of carbon dioxide.

Achieving large-scale, global, century-long efficiency gains through smart

for appliances. Introduction of international best practices in enforcement and monitoring of standard compliances is also critically needed.

Worldwide, an initiative for transforming the motor market would save 2 trillion kilowatt-hours per year, which is equal to one-fourth of all coal plants to be built through 2030, while reducing global energy bills by $240 billion per decade. Chinese motor experts are fully engaged in this process through the Standards for Energy Efficiency of Electric Motor Systems initiative (SEEEM, 2006). Potential motor efficiency savings in China are worth $100 billion per decade by eliminating the need for 63,000 megawatts of coal plants. This initiative would also avoid the shipment of 147 million tons of coal each year in nearly 1.5 million railroad cars, prevent the annual release of 420 million tons of carbon dioxide and 2.3 million tons of sulfur oxide and nitrogen oxide pollutants, and eliminate the need for nearly 600 billion liters of water per year.

Global oil consumption is responsible for 35% of global energy-related carbon dioxide emissions (roughly 10 billion tons of carbon dioxide in 2004). Growing oil demand is projected to increase emissions to 14 billion tons of carbon dioxide by 2030 (IEA, 2007). Rising oil demand is also expected to increase vulnerability to supply disruptions and price volatility. Given the major economic losses and dislocations observed during past episodes, and the concentration of the remaining cheapest oil reserves in conflict-ridden regions, oil security has become a national security issue for many countries. In 2004, a U.S. Department of Defense-sponsored assessment was released—*Winning the Oil Endgame* (Lovins et al., 2004). The densely detailed report concludes that saving half the oil America uses and substituting cheaper alternatives for the other half requires several integrated steps.

The first step is to double the efficiency of using oil. The United States today wrings twice as much work from each barrel of oil as it did in 1975. With the latest proven efficiency technologies, it can double oil efficiency all over again. The investments needed to save each barrel of oil would cost only $12 (as of 2000), one-sixth the current price of oil. The most important enabling technology is ultralight vehicle design. Advanced composite or light-metal materials can nearly double the efficiency of today's popular hybrid-electric cars and light trucks while improving safety and performance. The vehicle's total extra cost is repaid from fuel savings in about three years.

The second step is to apply creative business models and public policies to speed the profitable adoption of super-efficient light vehicles, heavy trucks, and airplanes. Combined with more efficient buildings and factories, these efficient vehicles can cut the official forecast of oil use by 29% in 2025 and another 23% soon thereafter—52% in all. The third step is to use well established, highly profitable efficiency techniques to save half the projected 2025 use of natural gas, making it again abundant and affordable, then substitute part of the saved gas for oil.

The Department of Defense-funded assessment led Wal-Mart, the global corporation with one of the world's largest private truck fleets, to realize it was financially attractive, technically feasible, and environmentally superior to set a target of doubling the fuel efficiency of its Class 8 truck fleet over the next decade (to 5.5 kilometers per liter), and strive for a tripling of fuel efficiency thereafter (8 kilometers per liter).

Wal-Mart's fuel-efficiency targets are instructive of the implications for not

Hydrogen fuel-cell buses share the pavement with gas guzzlers in Hamburg, Germany. Many renewable resources and alternative fuels are highly cost-effective now and will become even more economical in the coming decades. SARAH LEEN

only eliminating oil, but also reducing the need for alternative fuels like biofuel. Wal-Mart's truck fleet consumed 530 million liters of diesel in 2005 (at 2.7 kilometers per liter). Converting 100% to biodiesel would require 120,000 hectares of land if derived from the highest-yielding plant—oil palm—and 7.3 times that area (880,000 hectares) if derived from lower-yielding soy. Tripling the truck fleet efficiency would reduce demand to 178 million liters per year and palm oil plantations to 40,000 hectares (or 293,000 hectares of soy).

What if the entire U.S. Class 8 truck fleet, which consumed 64 billion liters of diesel in 2005, converted 100% to biodiesel at the current 2.7 kilometers per liter? Based on soy, this would require 100 million hectares—roughly the combined area of Texas, Kansas, and Arkansas. Achieving a tripling of fuel efficiency (8 kilometers per liter) would reduce this area to 32 million hectares of soy or about 4.4 million hectares of oil palm. Similarly robust findings apply to America's 220 million cars and vans.

Of greatest interest and economic concern from the perspectives of taxpayers and fuel purchasers is that the cost per barrel saved through the truck (or car and van) efficiency gains would be roughly $13.50 (in 2005 dollars), some five times less than the cost of biodiesel, which needs the price of oil to exceed $65 per barrel to be competitive. In the case of cars and vans, the cost comparison is to ethanol fuel, which requires the price of a barrel of oil to exceed $40 in order to be competitive without subsidies (World Bank, 2005).

High oil prices have driven policy-makers to enact lavish subsidies for investors to develop biofuels. These, however, are not only more expensive than vehicle efficiency gains, but also more expensive than system efficiency gains achievable by connecting plug-in hybrid electric vehicles (PHEVs) to the national electricity grid system. Toyota's impressive commercialization of hybrid electric vehicles, now also offered by most other car companies, has given impetus to the even more exciting plug-in version, the plug-in hybrid electric vehicle. Venture capital firms are investing heavily to accelerate commercialization of this promising technology that would help achieve tremendous system efficiency gains by integrating our nation's one million-megawatt utility grid with the several million megawatts inside the nation's 200+ million vehicles.

Combining the vehicle and electric sectors through connection of plug-in hybrid electric vehicles to an increasingly smarter grid network offers multiple benefits that make it one of the most compelling twenty-first-century technical innovations to be vigorously implemented over the next several decades (Kintner-Meyer, Schneider, and Pratt, 2007). The existing United States electricity infrastructure has sufficient available capacity to power 84% of the nation's cars, pickup trucks, and sports utility vehicles (198 million) each for 53 kilometers, which encompasses the average daily driving cycle for most motorists. This could result in a number of potential benefits. A shift from liquid-fueled vehicles to plug-in vehicles could reduce gasoline consumption by 340 billion liters per year, which is equivalent to 52% of U.S. oil imports (6.5 million barrels per day) and represents more than $350 billion per year in gas-pump savings (at 2008 retail prices). The shift would reduce total U.S. carbon dioxide emissions by 27%, as well as 100% of urban carbon monoxide, 99% of urban volatile organic compounds, 90% of urban nitrogen oxides, 40% of urban particulate matter, and 80% of urban sulfur dioxide. Finally, recent analyses indicate the potential for a percentage of plug-in vehicle owners to receive several thousand dollars per year in payments from utilities in return for allowing the parked plug-in vehicle to be accessed by the grid. Utilities currently incur billions of dollars per year in costs for sustaining and enhancing efficient grid management, and plug-in hybrid electric vehicles are essentially distributed battery storage systems that can be tapped when needed (Wellinghoff, 2007).

Achieving the gamut of smart energy services and system efficiencies discussed above is the single best way of achieving climate stabilization, while also ensuring robust economic growth, promoting human well-being, and protecting the planet's biodiversity wealth. This will require immense changes from the way society evolved technical, policy, regulatory, and market incentives over the past century. Vested interests, risk-averse bureaucracies, and an unmotivated citizenry threaten to prevent this extraordinarily positive outcome. What are needed are new policies and rules that align incentives between suppliers and consumers to ensure there will be a climate for life.

The oilfields of South Belridge, California, stretch out toward the horizon. Oil releases 30% of total U.S. emissions. SARAH LEEN

Renewables: Becoming a Believer

Photographs by Sarah Leen

"FOR ME, IT STARTED WITH an assignment to photograph urban sprawl," said Sarah Leen. "I was impressed with how we've built ourselves into a corner so that where you live is far from where you work, where you shop, or where you go to school. We have become so dependent on fossil fuel, not only for transportation but also for everything from food production to plastics.

"The next assignment was about the end of cheap oil, and it was followed by what comes next—alternative forms of energy—and that completed the trilogy for me."

She admits to having concerns about the environment before, but says, "...the urban sprawl story really got me going." Now she wonders how a society that is so addicted to a way of life can kick the oil habit.

"The change has to be so massive," said Leen. "It's not like you can say 'oh, solar energy is the answer, or wind power.' A little bit of everything has to be involved—solar, wind, biofuels, methane, nuclear. There has to be the kind of thinking that went into the Manhattan Project, or like saying 'how do you put a man on the moon.' The very way we live and work has to change."

"A lot of people living in the suburbs made a conscious choice based on their families. They wanted a more affordable home, decent schools, a safer environment, and you can't blame them. If they had alternatives that were good for the environment they'd probably take them."

Countries making progress in a greener way of life, she observes, are those in which the government mandates change and everyone gets in line. If you want to build a building it has to have a certain amount of alternative energy, if you want to drive a car it must get 35-40 miles per gallon of fuel.

"Here it's all from the bottom up," she says. "A school decides to put in a wind turbine or solar panels, or a city decides to have more green energy. It's very localized here, very small, it percolates up from the bottom instead of coming from the top down. Until we're required to do certain things I don't think we'll see substantial change."

Antique gas pumps in the desert near Barstow, California, portend a future without oil.

LEFT: Urban sprawl is the inevitable result of Las Vegas's status as one of the fastest-growing cities in the United States.

RIGHT: The Foster family of Stow, Ohio, displays their oil-based plastic possessions.

Two brothers play around the family Hummer near Atlanta, Georgia.

Kicking the oil habit is not easy, even for her. Leen bought her first hybrid car in 2000 off the Internet, almost sight unseen. She is now on her second one, and would like to put solar paneling on her home, despite high costs.

"It would be great to get off the electrical grid, but it's expensive to put it in and you don't see payback for 10 years," she said. "The price of fossil fuels has to go high and stay high, until people are screaming for alternatives, instead of just saying 'oh this is just a bump in the road and we'll be back to normal soon.'

"It's not like there's some magic bullet. We have to do a lot of things to wean ourselves off fossil fuels, we have to change our whole infrastructure. Everyone has to get on board."

This turbine in Edgeley is part of North Dakota's largest wind farm. North Dakota has wind resources sufficient to produce most of America's electricity. SARAH LEEN

Renewable Energy

For millennia, renewable energy from the wind, sea, sun, and land provided all of the Earth's energy needs. Today, in response to energy and climate crises, renewables are once again being pursued as one of the key solutions to meet our needs in a sustainable way.

Daggit, California, boasts the world's most technically
advanced solar-power facility. Solar Two focuses the sun's
rays on a tower containing liquid salt, which is pumped into
an insulated tank so that stored heat can drive turbines
and provide electric power twenty-four hours a day.
GEORGE STEINMETZ

PREVIOUS PAGES:
Sunlight illuminates a stand of quaking aspens near
Telluride, Colorado. Solar energy has the potential to provide
many times more than the current annual global energy use.
ANNIE GRIFFITHS BELT

Massive turbines at the Middelgrunden Wind Park dwarf the landscape in Copenhagen, Denmark. Wind power has been growing 30% per year, and has the potential to provide half the world's total energy needs this century. SARAH LEEN

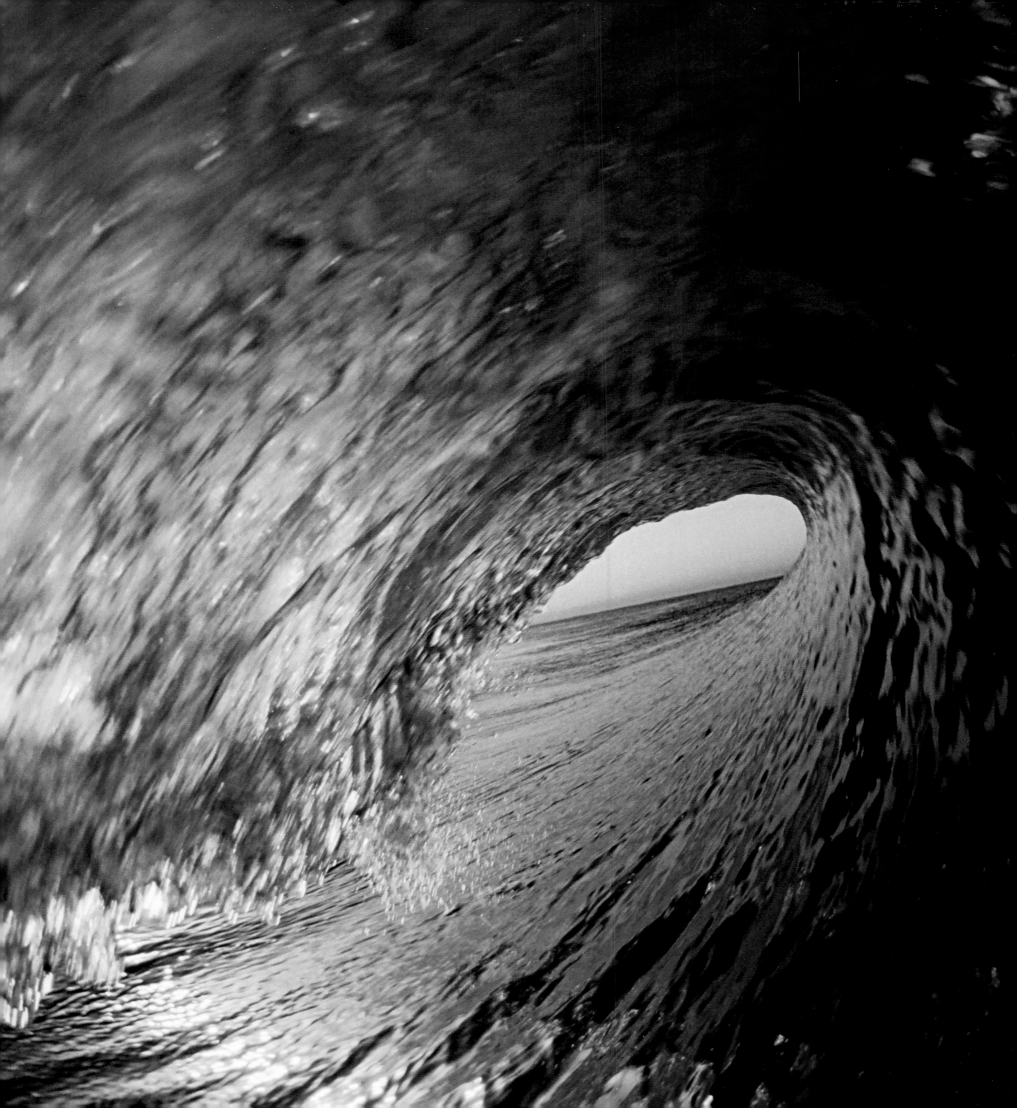

Renewable Energy

Michael Totten

For millennia, renewable energy from the wind, sea, sun, and land provided all of the Earth's energy needs. It was the Industrial Era that drove humanity to use coal, oil, and natural gas fossil fuels (and eventually nuclear energy) to support its nearly insatiable appetite for power. Today we face energy and climate crises that threaten both the survival of the human species as well as biodiversity across the globe. In response, renewables are once again being pursued as one of the key solutions to meet our needs in a sustainable way. This chapter focuses on what they actually are and what they can contribute.

World consumption of fossil fuels has increased exponentially in the past century, and industrialized countries consume the lion's share. In 2005, China consumed as much coal as the United States, Russia, India, and Australia combined. However, the United States, with only 5% of the world's population, consumes one-fourth of the daily global oil supply, whereas China accounts for 6% of consumption with one-fifth of global population. Between 2000 and 2025, oil use is officially forecast to grow by 44% in the United States and 57% in the world. By 2025, the United States will use as much oil as Canada, Western and Eastern Europe, Japan, Australia, and New Zealand combined. The forecasted increase alone in U.S. oil imports will exceed the 2001 total oil use of China, India, and South Korea (Lovins et al., 2004).

Yet the problems of growth are not limited to the United States. Today, only 12% of the world's population own cars. Africa and China currently have the car ownership America enjoyed in 1915. However, China's compound annual car growth was 55% between 2001 and 2005. By 2025, its cars could require the oil output of a Saudi Arabia or two (which now exports one-fourth of world oil).

Such harrowing growth rates in fossil fuel usage will dramatically increase greenhouse gas emissions to a level threatening to derail society's capacity to stabilize atmospheric concentrations below a safe threshold, triggering multi-century catastrophic consequences (Hansen, 2005; Hansen et al., 2008; Romm, 2007). Fortunately, a significant fraction of the growth rate in the global demand for energy and mobility services can be effectively satisfied through smart energy efficiency improvements, at tens of trillions of dollars

An early-morning wave breaks into the sunrise in Ventura, California. There are many ways to tap the energy available in the ocean, including harnessing underwater currents, tidal flows, and wave motion. TODD GLASER

Livestock release methane, and research is showing how to reduce it. At the same time, methane from animal waste can be recycled into a renewable gas. PETER ESSICK

lower cost this century compared to conventional supply expansion. Moreover, as illuminated in Chapter 1: Energy Efficiency, many of the efficiency gains actually enhance the cost-effectiveness of wind and solar energy options.

Renewable resources take diverse forms and include solar, wind, geothermal, biological, and hydrological sources. They can be used to provide any of the myriad applications for which humankind requires: thermal heat; solid, liquid, or gaseous chemical fuels; or even electricity.

Many of these sources are highly cost-effective now and will only become increasingly economical in the coming decades. To facilitate their application and acceptance, we need to stop providing incentives for outdated and unsustainable fuel technologies and focus instead on the most ecologically sustainable renewable sources, notably wind and solar. The combination, in particular, of vehicle-to-grid system efficiencies and expansion of wind and solar energy offers multiple benefits: reduced cost of energy services; dramatic reductions in greenhouse gases, acid rain, and urban air pollutants; deep reductions in oil imports; and significantly less wilderness habitat converted and fresh water diverted to grow fuel crops.

It will also take ambitious research, development, and demonstration initiatives, coupled with market-based incentives and innovative regulatory policies, to ensure the timely availability of economically attractive and affordable renewables on a global scale throughout this century.

Abundant Options

Current global energy consumption is about 15 terawatt-years or 475 exajoules, the equivalent of oil supertanker shipments arriving at the rate of one every ten minutes, or the distribution of fuel to service stations by 437 million delivery trucks per year. Projected energy consumption worldwide from 2000 to 2100, assuming no change in human behavior, is approximately 240 times the current amount—about 3,600 terawatt-years or 113,000 exajoules. Fossil fuels, also assuming no change in human behavior, would account for three-fourths of this sum, releasing several trillion tons of greenhouse gases, while tripling the Earth's atmospheric concentration of greenhouse gases (in carbon-dioxide equivalents) from pre-industrial levels.

Opinion surveys consistently show that more than 80% of citizens prefer solar and other renewables and energy efficiency to the use of fossil fuels. This is not surprising, given the unimaginably vast amount of renewable energy flows worldwide. Consider that global human energy consumption in 2007 amounted to just one hour of sunlight landing on Earth. Expert evaluations conclude that renewables are quite capable over the long term, in combination with extensive energy efficiency gains, to economically provide the current total global energy supply many times over.

Solar. Solar technical potential is conservatively estimated at greater than 50 terawatt-years per year, or more than three times the current annual global energy use. From 2000 to 2100, solar's technical potential of 5,000 terawatt-years is 277% greater than the remaining post-efficiency supply requirements (i.e., after harnessing the large pool of cost-effective energy-efficiency opportunities). This solar technical potential was characterized nearly a decade ago, and faster market developments indicate this potential will increase over time as continuous scientific advancements and technological breakthroughs are able to capture an ever-larger fraction of the theoretical potential of 124,000 terawatt-years, or nearly 4 million exajoules per year.

Wind. Wind technical potential is more than 20 terawatt-years per year, or more than 134% of the current annual global energy use. From 2000 to 2100, wind's technical potential of 2,000 terawatt-years is more than 110% greater than the remaining (post-efficiency) supply requirements. About 1–2% of the energy coming from the sun is converted into wind energy. Wind's theoretical potential is 2,476 terawatt-years, or 78,000 exajoules per year.

Geothermal. Geothermal technical potential is about 160 terawatt-years per year, or more than ten times the current annual global energy use. The Earth's interior reaches temperatures greater than 4,000°C, and this geothermal energy flows continuously to the surface. From 2000 to 2100, geothermal's technical potential of 16,000 terawatt-years is 900% greater than the remaining (post-efficiency) supply requirements. Geothermal's theoretical potential worldwide

differences between different layers of the ocean (called Ocean Thermal Energy Conversion). More research remains to be done on the ecological impacts of the options on marine life, and these technologies may play a niche role for some island and coastal communities.

Hydropower. Hydropower's technical potential is 1.6 terawatt-years per year, or a bit over 10% of current annual global energy use. From 2000 to 2100, hydro's technical potential of 160 terawatt-years is 9% of the remaining (post-efficiency)

is 440,000 terawatt-years, or 14 million exajoules per year. Domestic resources in the United States are equivalent to a 30,000-year energy supply at the current rate of consumption.

supply requirements. This potential is further limited by serious ecological, social, and climatic problems associated with some river sites.

Biomass. Biomass technical potential is 8.6 terawatt-years per year, or 57% of current annual global energy use. From 2000 to 2100, biomass's technical potential of 860 terawatt-years is 48% of the remaining (post-efficiency) supply requirements. On average, plant net primary production (NPP) is about 5 million calories per square meter per year. An important caveat about biomass availability is that global NPP is the amount of energy available to all subsequent links in critical ecosystem services plus the food, fiber, animal feed, and biofuel chain. The Earth's surface area is about 500 trillion m². The net power output stored by plants is thus 19 terawatt-years, or 0.01% (1/100th of 1%) of the sun's power emitted to Earth.

Counting the Costs

Not surprisingly, much of the lively and contentious debate over future energy supplies tends to reduce itself to one key criterion: cost. This is myopic for two reasons. First, assumptions about long-term technological cost and performance data inherently contain a fair degree of subjective judgment. The future is uncertain in too many ways, precluding any technical assessment to claim complete objectivity or certitude. Moreover, current views on technology options are heavily conditioned by the long trail of public interventions and subventions shaping markets and investment patterns. For humanity to avoid catastrophic climate change, and avert conflicts and wars over oil resources, there will need to be a dramatic change in the calculus of energy policy-making and investment decision-making. This means it is a wide-open arena for all energy options, even the current energy giants, since the accumulated rules and subsidies currently in place are now facing a radical makeover to align outcomes for climate-positive, real energy-security results (DeCanio, 2003; Smil, 2003).

Oceans. Ocean power's technical potential (more than 80% from thermal energy conversion) is 5 terawatt-years per year, or one-third of current annual global energy use. From 2000 to 2100, the ocean's technical potential of 500 terawatt-years is 27% of the remaining (post-efficiency) supply requirements. There are various potential ocean technologies, such as harnessing the power of underwater currents, tidal flows, wave motion, and exploiting the temperature

Second, cost and climate emissions are just two criteria among many for ensuring a sustainable smart-energy system worldwide this century. There

The cooling towers of a nuclear power plant frame a traditional windmill in St. Laurent des Eaux in France's Loire Valley. Contemporary wind turbines, designed with state-of-the-art technologies, now deliver electricity at several times lower cost than nuclear power. THOMAS HOEPKER

is a rich literature developed in the wake of innumerable energy crises over the past forty years stressing important attributes that should be sought in energy services to achieve a high probability of avoiding adverse impacts and unintended consequences (Lovins and Lovins, 1982; Lovins et al., 2004; Smil, 2003). A dozen criteria recur as important attributes of energy supplies:

- Is it economically affordable, even for the poorest of the poor and cash-strapped?
- Is it safe through its entire life cycle?
- Is it clean through its entire lifespan?
- Is its risk low and manageable during financial and price volatility?
- Is it resilient and flexible to volatility, surprises, miscalculations, and human error?
- Is it ecologically sustainable, with no adverse impacts on biodiversity?
- Is it environmentally benign in that it maintains air, water, and soil quality?
- Will it fail gracefully, not catastrophically, in response to abrupt surprises or crises?
- Will it rebound easily and swiftly from failures, with low recovery cost and limited lost time?
- Does it have endogenous learning capacity, with intrinsic new productivity opportunities?
- Does it have a robust experience curve for reducing negative externalities and amplifying positive externalities, including scalable innovation possibilities?
- Is it an uninteresting target for malicious disruption, off the radar of terrorists and military planners?

Among the range of available energy options, only energy services from efficiency gains rank at the top in every attribute. All other options are deficient or weak in two or more of these attributes. The vast expansion of energy consumption from coal, oil, natural gas, nuclear, hydrodams, and wood and crops over the past century has revealed a series of grave problems,

some intractable or intrinsic to the energy option, that have been costly to human well-being and ecological health.

For example, hydroelectric power is promoted as the most cost-effective renewable energy solution for climate change. This is grossly misleading and highly inaccurate. Actual measurements of hydrodams in different parts of the world indicate they are responsible for an estimated 8% of total global greenhouse gas emissions, and projected expansion in coming decades, mostly in wilderness areas, could increase this to 15% of total emissions (St. Louis et al., 2000). Hydrodams have also been the major reason why one-fourth of freshwater species have been driven to extinction worldwide (Bräutigam, 1999) This is not to say that all hydro facilities release greenhouse gas emissions. Not all hydroelectric plants require dams, and not all dams generate electricity. And clearly other extenuating circumstances come into play (e.g., the need for irrigation) (WCD, 2000).

This reinforces the point that using multiple criteria to prioritize preferable energy options this century, coupled with the alignment of public policies and regulations towards this end, is imperative given the looming threat of climate catastrophe in need of fast and massive action, while at the same time avoiding wars and conflicts over the accelerating demand for vulnerable oil supplies; avoiding and reversing the contamination of air, water, and soil; avoiding nuclear weapons proliferation; and preventing the destruction of wildlife and biodiversity loss.

In addition, we must now take into account the increasing occurrence of climate-triggered mega-droughts, super-hurricanes, deluge-level floods, larger and longer wildfires, more widespread pest devastation, and the adverse impacts these will have on energy installations. It is also prudent in a post-9/11 world—where nuclear reactors and large refineries now remain on constant alert to possible terrorist attacks—to design energy systems that are uninteresting targets (Romm, 2007).

Proper Investment and the Future of Renewables

In spite of renewables' overwhelming potential, existing public policies—as well as the majority of future-looking global energy assessments—reflect negligible

Moreover, nuclear power continues to receive unprecedented taxpayer-subsidized insurance coverage for reactor disasters. A similar taxpayer burden is now being proposed to underwrite federally assumed liability of a century-long leakage risk from carbon capture and storage projects. Likewise, the fossil fuel industries have received considerable largesse and investment stability as a result of long-standing subsidies, while emerging competitive options like wind power suffer financial instability because the Production Tax Credit is sunset every few years,

roles for solar, wind, and geothermal energy sources or the ambitious efficiency gains posited in Chapter 1. On the contrary, they emphasize massive fossil fuel carbon capture and storage (CCS) operations, aggressive nuclear power expansion, enormous biomass plantations, and large-scale hydro development (Hamrin, Hummel, and Canapa, 2007). This is due less to technical or economic constraints than to institutional and political inertia.

Over the past half century, governments have provided (and continue to provide) several trillion dollars per decade in subsidies—nearly two-thirds have been dedicated to fossil fuels (mostly to coal and oil) and one-fourth to nuclear power. Only 5% went to all non-hydro renewables (solar thermal, solar-electric photovoltaics, solar-thermal-electric "concentrated solar power" systems, terrestrial wind, offshore wind farms, geothermal heat, geothermal-electric) and all efficiency (buildings, transportation, appliances, industry, combined heat and power). For each U.S. tax dollar supporting wind power or solar power research and development over the past fifty years, nuclear power received 100 times more. Even in the U.S. 2008 federal appropriations, wind power research and development funding was $40 million vs. $400 million for nuclear. This makes no sense given the fact that wind power generates electricity already competitive to nuclear reactors and has a global technical potential that could provide twice the level of total global energy needs this century (in combination with ambitious efficiency gains) (GWEC, 2006).

wreaking havoc by disrupting investment flows (Koplow and Dernbach, 2001).

In sharp contrast, however, is the attention that many other nations, as well as a number of U.S. states, have focused on the future of renewables to meet the range of environmental, economic, social, and security criteria noted above. There is a growing body of literature describing that future, including policy targets and shifts in financial incentives based on insights gleaned from socio-economic and technology scenarios, carbon-constrained scenarios, and future social visions. Policy targets for future shares of renewable energy are described for regions, specific countries, states/provinces, and cities. By 2020, many targets and scenarios show a 20–35% share of electricity from renewables, increasing to 50–80% by 2050 under the highest scenarios (Martinot et al., 2007).

Two scenarios with very ambitious efficiency and renewable goals were released in 2007 by the European Renewable Energy Commission (EREC, 2007) and by the American Solar Energy Society (ASES, 2007), the latter limited to the United States. The European Renewable Energy Commission projects 70% renewables in the electric sector (while constraining nuclear and large hydro), and the American Solar Energy Society forecasts 50% renewables in the U.S. electricity sector by 2030 (also ignoring nuclear and large hydro). The high penetration rates are directly due to the fact that both

An electric Smart Car advertises the New York City Marathon in Midtown Manhattan's Times Square. Using plug-in hybrid technology, the electricity infrastructure in the United States could potentially power the daily use of 84% of the nation's cars, pickup trucks, and SUVs. CHUCK PEFLEY

reports estimate half or more of total energy supply being displaced through lower-cost energy-efficiency gains—by a factor of four to one in the case of the EREC projects.

The ASES report is highly transparent and richly detailed and strongly demonstrates that energy efficiency and renewable energy technologies have the potential to provide most, if not all, of the U.S. carbon emissions reductions that will be needed to help stabilize the atmospheric concentration of greenhouse gases (Hamrin, Hummel, and Canapa, 2007). However, while some renewable options accrue multiple benefits and positive externalities and should be encouraged, other renewable options trigger adverse impacts or incur negative tradeoffs. This is especially the case when a supply option like biofuels is vastly expanded over space and time.

High oil prices have driven policymakers to set high production targets and enact lavish subsidies for investors to develop biofuels from agricultural crops. Mobile liquid biofuels—both ethanol derived from corn and sugarcane and biodiesel derived from oil palm, soybean, and rapeseed—are not only more expensive than vehicle efficiency gains by a factor of two to five (Lovins et al., 2004), but also more expensive than system efficiency gains achievable by connecting plug-in hybrid electric vehicles to the national electricity grid system. Genetically modified fuels of the future are likely to lower production costs, but pose many of the same ecological issues associated with current biofuels (Jacobson, 2007).

Preeminent Solutions: Electric Vehicles

Research and developments over the past two decades in the production of electric vehicles and separately in the commercialization of hybrid-electric vehicles have given rise to the recognition that plugging vehicles into the grid system would accrue several remarkable benefits far superior to continuing to run vehicles entirely on mobile liquid fuels. As researchers have pointed out, "The vehicle fleet has twenty times the power capacity, less than one-tenth the utilization, and one-tenth the capital cost per prime mover kilowatt. Conversely, utility generators have ten to fifty times longer an operating life and lower operating costs per kilowatt-hour. To tap Vehicle-to-Grid is to synergistically use these complementary strengths, and to reconcile the complementary needs of the driver and grid manager" (Kempton and Tomić, 2005).

As discussed in the chapter on efficiency and smart energy services, the existing U.S. grid could recharge 80% of America's 200+ million vehicle fleet if they were plug-in hybrid electric vehicles, without having to build a new power plant. This would have the positive effect of eliminating 52% of U.S. oil imports (340 billion liters per year) worth some $350 billion savings at the gas pump, while also reducing total U.S. carbon dioxide emissions by 27% (PNNL, 2007).

As with the market diffusion rate of any major technological innovation (accelerated to some degree by favorable public policies and incentives), declining manufacturing costs and vehicle prices will occur with accumulated experience of scaled-up production. Researchers note another tremendous benefit of vehicle-to-grid over time, as production costs drop: providing battery storage for intermittent wind power and solar electricity generation. Research calculations suggest that vehicle-to-grid could stabilize large-scale (one-half of U.S. electricity) wind power with 3% of the fleet dedicated to regulation for wind, plus 8% to 38% of the fleet providing operating reserves or storage for wind (Kempton and Tomić, 2005). For context, currently half of U.S. electricity is coal-fired.

The vehicle-to-grid technological revolution is driven by many of the same digital electronics and advanced materials that enable production and operation of high-efficiency, lower energy-consuming smart appliances, smart grids, smart buildings, and smart cars. It offers an economic development strategy for developed and developing countries alike. With the majority of the world's population becoming urban-based, electric and hybrid-electric vehicles can accommodate the typical urban driving cycles of 16 to 48 kilometers per day. Longer distances can be provided by the flexible fuel component derived from local and regional biowastes.

The Role of Biofuels

Local and regional biowastes can be converted to biofuels, providing the mobile fuels essential for long-range driving beyond electric battery capacity.

renewable resources; accumulated scientific knowledge also gives good indication they will incur the smallest climate and ecological footprints when scaled up globally and operated over long time periods. Solar photovoltaics and wind power have the added advantage of requiring 95% less water per terawatt-year than coal or nuclear power, biopower or solar-thermal-electric "concentrated solar power" (CSP) systems.

In a vehicle-to-grid connected world, with solar and wind power stored in the mass distribution of plug-in hybrid electric batteries, sixty and thirty times less land area, respectively, would be needed than in the case of biofuels for the same power output (Jacobson, 2007). Roughly 7% of the U.S.'s 50 million hectares of urban land area covered with solar photovoltaic panels at today's 10%-efficient systems could provide 100% of U.S. electricity. Brownfields could provide most of the land area. Building-integrated photovoltaic systems (BIPVs) could provide half of the power (Kazmerski, 2002; Zweibel, 2004). Alternatively, around 2.5% of the North American Great Plains with dispersed wind farms—or roughly 92 million out of 363 million hectares—could provide 100% of U.S. electricity. The actual footprint of the several hundred thousand multi-megawatt turbines, hypothetically squeezed into one spot, would be less than the size of one large Wyoming coal strip mine (Komanoff, 2006; Williams, 2001). Even when spaced out to optimize wind capture, 90% of the 2.5% could still be farmed, ranched, or ecologically restored.

Such a modest use of biofuels would prevent some of the near-intractable problems associated with large-scale biofuel consumption.

Unfortunately, one unintended negative consequence of corn-based ethanol expansion in the United States is that it drives soy production to Brazil and Argentina (where it is grown mainly for animal feed), which leads to deforestation and destruction of biodiversity-rich savannah grasslands and Amazon ecosystems (CARD, 2007; Searchinger et al., 2008; Fargione et al., 2008). Similarly, oil palm plantations in tropical countries, already one of the major causes of biodiversity loss, are the preferred low-cost feedstock for biodiesel. Some of the last remaining intact wilderness habitats for mega-charismatic species like the orangutan and the Sumatran tiger, and also rhino and elephant are threatened with conversion to oil palm. Species extinction will be the outcome of people "putting an orangutan in your tank."

Minimizing biofuel expansion reduces the adverse impacts on ecosystems and biodiversity loss in tropical countries already being caused by ethanol and biodiesel plantation growth (Morton et al., 2006; Fearnside, 2002; Killeen, 2007). It also avoids driving up food prices (CARD, 2007).

Harnessing the Sun and the Wind

Solar, wind, and geothermal energy systems are not only the three largest

Several valuable benefits would accrue to rural communities from such a strategy. Farmers and ranchers can earn, on average, twice as much from wind farm royalty payments than they currently obtain from crop and animal farming. Currently 75% of the Great Plains is farmed or ranched, but only generates 5% of the region's economic output. Shifting to wind farming could produce twice as much economic output on thirty-five times less land area. Similarly, vast wind resources are available in China and

The people of Hveragerdi, in southwest Iceland, use geothermal energy to heat their greenhouses. Geothermal heat in Iceland is also used for swimming pools, to bake bread, and to heat up footpaths, streets, and parking spaces.
ARCTIC-IMAGES/CORBIS

India, as well as along coastal regions throughout the world (Totten, 2007; GWEC, 2006; NREL, 2006). China and India will account for 80% of coal increase by 2030. China annually expands its coal use equivalent to that of the United Kingdom. It surpassed the United States in 2007 as the world's top greenhouse gas emitter. However, China's wind technical potential is estimated at 2 million megawatts, 400% larger than China's total electric generation capacity. In addition, twice as much solar energy lands on China each year than could be produced from its 800 billion tons of coal over the next several centuries.

Economies of Efficiency—Combining Heat and Power

Instead of targeting massive investments into central, large-scale, coal, nuclear, and hydroelectric generating stations, cities around the world should be looking for energy system efficiencies that could enable phasing in use of local and regional biological wastes over the long-term. One of the proven options available globally is decentralized combined heat and power. Whereas central thermal power plants vent 70% of the energy when generating electricity, combined heat and power systems capture this waste heat to cogenerate two, three, or four different energy services (heat, steam, electricity, cooling). Moreover, in being sited close to the point of use, combined heat and power systems require significantly less transmission and distribution investment than centralized power plants, as well as avoiding the 15% transmission and distribution line losses (WADE, 2004). For example, just the waste heat discarded from U.S. power plants is equivalent to 1.2 times Japan's total energy use.

Recent assessments indicate that if China moved to 100% high-efficiency decentralized combined heat and power systems by 2021, retail and capital cost savings could reach $400 billion. At no extra cost, new emissions of carbon dioxide would drop 56%, avoiding 400 million tons of such emissions per year, and nitrogen oxide and sulfur dioxide emissions would decline by 90%. But these results are possible only if the Chinese government adopts key policies enabling a faster rate of implementation than the current annual combined heat and power addition of 3,000 megawatts. Some 100,000 megawatts of combined heat and power could be online in several years if a number of important power sector reforms occur (WADE, 2004).

For nations like China facing water crises, combined heat and power offers a highly cost-effective system efficiency option for combining the delivery of energy and potable water. Water consumes considerable energy throughout the process of extracting, pumping, distributing, heating, and disposing. In California, for example, 20% of the electricity and one-third of natural gas are consumed by the water sector (NRDC and Pacific Institute, 2004). Delivering water services efficiently saves money, reduces air pollution, and cuts greenhouse gases. China faces the additional problem that its water resources per capita may decline to around 1,700 cubic meters by 2050, which is the threshold of severe water scarcity. Water shortage already has become a critical constraint for socio-economic development in northern China, where per capita levels are now below 300 cubic meters. To solve or eliminate water shortage problems, China is now pursuing all water-efficiency opportunities (e.g., drip irrigation) that can cut water use by two-thirds on farms (which consume 80% of all water).

Alternative Water Supplies

Meanwhile, wastewater and seawater desalination are drawing more and more attention from researchers and policy-makers as alternative water supply sources (Zhou and Tol, 2003).

Desalination costs currently vary by a factor of seven or more, depending on the type of feedwater (brackish, waste, or seawater), the available concentrate disposal options, the proximity to distribution systems, and the availability and cost of power. Desalination's primary operating cost is for power. One cubic kilometer (one trillion liters) of wastewater or seawater desalination requires about 500 megawatts of power. The reduction in unit energy use by desalination plants has been among the most dramatic improvements in recent years due to improvement in energy recovery systems. Estimates considered valid for China today range from a cost of $0.60 per cubic meter (1,000 liters) for brackish and wastewater desalination to $1 per cubic meter for seawater desalination by reverse osmosis (Zhi, Totten, and Chou, 2006).

operate reverse osmosis technologies to purify these wastewaters, while also providing ancillary energy services like space and water heating and cooling.

The Final Hope

As the chapter on efficiency and smart energy services describes, ensuring the capture of the immense pool of efficiency opportunities could deliver more than half of the world's cumulative energy services at lower cost and risk than expanding energy supplies, replacing the need for 1,800 terawatt-years or 57,000 exajoules of energy supplies. Envision eliminating the need for 13.8 billion coal railcars this century. However, that still leaves a demand for another 1,800 terawatt-years or 57,000 exajoules of energy supply. A lively debate has ensued as to the best options for satisfying this immense growth.

Smarter delivery of energy services through efficiency gains can effectively satisfy most of this growth, while saving money and reducing emissions provide ancillary benefits. Combining these with steady increases in harnessing energy services powered by wind, solar, geothermal, and biowastes promises society a long-term, clean, safe, secure, and ecologically sound energy system. Achieving this ambitious but feasible outcome is fundamental for resolving climate and energy crises, while bringing all of humanity to health and well-being and preventing the unnecessary extinction of the planet's rich biodiversity of plants and animals.

Extrapolating from technological trends, and given the promise of ongoing innovations in lower-cost, higher-performance membranes, seawater desalination costs will continue to fall. The average cost may decline to $0.30 per cubic meter in 2025. For comparison, China's average (subsidized) water prices are $0.25 per cubic meter for domestic and industrial use, $0.34 per cubic meter for commercial use, $0.60 per cubic meter in Tianjin and Dalian, and approaching $0.80 per cubic meter at full pricing in cities like Beijing.

Desalination of wastewater via combined heat and power can capture double benefits: it reduces contaminated discharges into rivers and, instead, expands the city's freshwater supplies at lower cost than importing remote water resources. The Reverse Osmosis membrane process is universally considered to be the most promising technology for brackish and seawater desalination A model of using reverse osmosis membranes powered by combined heat and power is the Ashkelon plant in Israel, which produces 100 million cubic meters per year of potable water at a highly cost-effective 50 cents per cubic meter. China's total wastewater discharges annually exceed 60 cubic kilometers (60 trillion liters). As of the late 1990s, less than one-seventh of this wastewater was treated. Close to 600 million Chinese people have water supplies that are contaminated by animal and human waste. Harnessing 30,000 megawatts of co-generation available in cities and industrial facilities potentially could

A CLIMATE FOR LIFE

This overly expensive nuclear power plant outside Sacramento was shut down and replaced by solar photovoltaics and other renewables. SARAH LEEN

Technicians in Biosphere 2 place calcareous algae in jars and take periodic water samples to determine the amount of carbon absorbed. Different algae species offer versatile opportunities both to absorb carbon, as in this photo, as well as to clean polluted waters to generate biofuels from waste products. PETER ESSICK

Although coleseed has been dubbed "black gold" and is one of many options for the production of biodiesel, its large-scale use carries with it many adverse ecological implications.
CHRISTOPHER THOMAS

This geothermal power plant in Iceland is able to provide most of the energy needs for the area it serves. Globally, geothermal's technical potential is more than ten times the current annual energy use on the planet. CHRIS LINDER

Biofuels

Despite their recent rise and fall in public perception, biofuels can still play an important role in a diversified energy portfolio, provided that we commit to established best-practice guidelines, strict protection of high-priority biodiversity areas, and the implementation of a system of policies and standards that promote environmentally sustainable production.

A CLIMATE FOR LIFE

A flight from Alta Floresta to Santarem (in the Brazilian Amazon) reveals one of the most biodiverse and carbon-rich regions on Earth. Valuable forests like these are at risk of being converted to biofuel plantations.
DANIEL BELTRÁ

PREVIOUS PAGES:
In a living sea of green, a laborer takes a break from weeding on a sugarcane farm in central Brazil that produces 150 million liters of fuel alcohol each year. Ethanol provides 40% of Brazil's fuel for cars and light trucks. ROBERT CLARK

A CLIMATE FOR LIFE

Enormous fires are ignited to clear the rain forest for soy plantations around Santarem in the Brazilian Amazon. Soy is being used to produce biodiesel. DANIEL BELTRÁ

CHAPTER THREE

Biofuels

Christine Dragisic, John Buchanan, Gustavo A. B. da Fonseca,
Tim Killeen, Andrea Kutter, Laura Ledwith Pennypacker,
Russell A. Mittermeier, Paulo Gustavo Prado,
José Maria Cardoso da Silva, Michael Totten, Will Turner

Soy fields near Belterra, Para State, Brazil, are dotted with
isolated Brazil nut trees, left standing because of their
protected government status, but doomed to perish.
DANIEL BELTRÁ

Initially heralded as environmental saviors, biofuels have endured a rollercoaster ride of popularity. By their supporters, they are billed as a means of tapping nature's abundance to provide clean, renewable energy with the potential to reduce greenhouse gas emissions. Many of these benefits are real. Biofuels do emit lower levels of some pollutants when compared to gasoline or diesel, and, if managed correctly, their feedstocks hold the potential for being renewably harvested. In addition, given that biofuels are derived from the agricultural sector, there is an opportunity to spread economic and employment benefits to rural populations that do not typically participate in the energy economy, while at the same time creating local capacity to generate energy in remote areas.

However, the anticipated growth in the production and consumption of biofuels will not be environmentally or socially cost-free. The fact is that the production of biofuels, especially if not well planned and managed over their entire life cycle, can actually result in a net increase in carbon dioxide emissions, exacerbating global warming. And while biofuels may burn cleaner than fossil fuels, the clearing of habitat for crop production may release additional carbon.

The greatest threat to biodiversity, meanwhile, is that converting natural landscapes to agricultural areas, particularly in tropical hotspots and high-biodiversity ecosystems, can destroy critical plant and animal habitats. For example, Malaysian oil palm plantations have only a quarter of the bird species found in their neighboring old-growth forests. Meanwhile, orang-utans in Borneo and Sumatra have lost at least 50% of their habitat to oil palm plantations and face serious threat of extinction over the next decade. So much of the lowland rain forests have been cleared for oil palm that the Sumatran rhinoceros and Sumatran tiger are now classified as Critically Endangered.

Despite these concerns, biofuels can still play an important role in a diversified energy portfolio and help reduce climate change-inducing emissions, provided that careful attention is paid to location, crop selection, management of plantations and processing plants, environmental impacts, and especially carbon neutrality (zero net emissions). This will require faithful

adherence to established best-practice guidelines, strict protection of high-priority biodiversity areas, and the implementation of a system of policies and standards that promote environmentally sustainable production.

In this chapter, we give a brief history of global biofuel development, describe the most common types and sources of biofuels, and examine the potential economic, social, and environmental benefits and costs associated with biofuel production and use. In particular, we focus on exploring the impacts that increased demand for biofuels and associated agricultural expansion will have on global CO_2 emissions, biodiversity, and ecosystem health. Finally, we offer recommendations and criteria to help ensure that the biofuels produced, processed, and consumed have a net positive (or non-negative) impact on climate, biodiversity, and human well-being.

The Promise of Renewable Fuel

Biofuels may lead to greater energy and economic security for producer countries, many of which are developing nations located in the tropics. They represent an opportunity to increase export earnings and foreign investment while generating employment in rural regions. Given adequate policies and support, small farmers may benefit from linkages to global energy markets. Small-scale production of biofuel feedstocks may also allow energy to be generated in isolated areas, improving living conditions and facilitating economic development.

For importing countries, a greater diversification in energy suppliers may be possible. This would allow importers to hedge against instability in oil-producing regions, as well as fluctuations in the supply of fossil fuels.

However, biofuels are not an easy solution to the world's energy needs. The production and use of biofuels is associated with several important risks, which must be included in any evaluation of the costs and benefits of biofuel use, but which are often left out of the analysis. In many cases, these risks—and the costs they imply—may outweigh the benefits associated with biofuels.

Form and Function

The term biofuel is a very complex one to define. While the two predominant fossil fuels, oil (petroleum) and coal, are biological in origin, they are not included in most modern definitions of biofuels. Other traditional sources of energy such as charcoal are also derived from biomass, and biomass waste is increasingly being used to generate electricity or heat at industrial facilities. These uses are sometimes included within the modern definition of a biofuel. Here, however, we limit our discussion to those fuels that are derived from animal by-products or crops, either naturally occurring or planted, and used as liquids or gases to fuel transportation or for heating purposes. These biofuels represent a rapidly growing sector with a large potential for contributing to reduced greenhouse gas emissions, but also for creating new and poorly documented impacts that may offset any potential benefits.

Today, the principal biofuel products are ethanol and biodiesel. Ethanol is a simple two-carbon molecule that can be produced by petroleum refineries via the chemical hydration of ethylene. However, ethanol biofuel is produced via the biological fermentation of simple molecules such as glucose and fructose (monosaccharide). Sucrose from sugarcane is the major feedstock for

Amber waves of corn sprawl across a storage lot in Fremont, Nebraska. Previously used to feed California dairy cows, this crop is headed for one of sixteen ethanol plants that will consume a third of the state's crop this year. ROBERT CLARK

ethanol in Brazil, while starch from corn (maize) is the major feedstock in the United States. Ethanol has been used as an additive to gasoline, as well as an alternative fuel for standard gasoline-powered internal combustion engines.

Biodiesel is a diesel-equivalent fuel produced from vegetable oil or animal fats that are converted by a relatively simple chemical process known as "transesterification." Although animal fats can be converted to biodiesel, in mass production the feedstocks will likely be limited to crops, including soy in the United States and Brazil, rapeseed in Europe, and oil palm in the humid tropics. Biodiesel can be used in unmodified diesel engines for motor transport or replace fuel oil in some furnaces. Vegetable oils that have not been modified by the transesterification process can be used in modified diesel engines.

Although current ethanol feedstocks are limited to starch- or sucrose-producing plants, future technological development is expected to lead to "second-generation biofuels" that will have greatly improved the efficiency in the conversion of biomass into biofuels. The most promising of the next generation of biofuels may be cellulosic ethanol; in this case, the monosaccharide sugars that are the raw material of the fermentation process are derived from cellulose rather than starch or sucrose. Cellulose is similar in structure to starch, but is much more difficult to break down into its constituent sugars. However, cellulose is the most abundant plant fiber on Earth, and, once its technological limitations are overcome, cellulosic ethanol will likely be produced at efficiencies several times greater than with current technologies.

The production of cellulosic ethanol is still an immature technology and faces multiple challenges, including technical difficulties in converting associated organic molecules known as lignin (e.g., wood) to liquid biofuels, as well as costs that are currently prohibitive on an industrial scale (U.S. Department of Energy, 2006). Some experts predict that lignocellulose technologies will become economically competitive with existing biofuel technologies within ten years (ibid.).

The economic impact of second-generation technologies will radically change the production of biofuels. Since much greater amounts of energy can be derived from the same amount of biomass, less land will be needed to produce the same amount of energy. Since cellulose is overwhelmingly abundant in all plants in all ecosystems, the options for cultivation of biofuel feedstocks will likewise be greatly expanded.

Supply and Demand

While global public attention to biofuels is a recent phenomenon, biofuels have actually been around for thousands of years. Ethanol is essential alcohol, which has been fermented from fruits and grains since ancient times (Roach, 2005). In addition, people have used oils derived from plants and animal fats as a heating source for millennia. Biofuels have powered transportation from the earliest days of the automobile. The Ford Model T, produced between 1908 and 1927, was capable of running on both ethanol and gasoline. The growing supply of inexpensive gasoline from the 1930s onward, however, condemned ethanol to an almost non-existent role in the transportation-fuels market until the first oil crisis of 1973. In response to that crisis, Brazil became a pioneer in boosting a significant domestic ethanol industry associated with the production of cars that ran solely on this biofuel. That earlier experience was instrumental in preparing the country for this recent reemergence of biofuels in the international arena.

More recently, global attention has again turned to biofuels, this time in response to an increased awareness of climate change, rising oil costs, and a desire for energy independence, among other factors. The ease with which biofuels can replace fossil fuels with only minimal changes to the world's energy, transport, and industrial infrastructure has contributed to their popularity among corporate and government decision-makers.

A Case Study—Biofuels in Brazil

Responsible for more than half of all of the world's ethanol production, Brazil is at the epicenter of the modern biofuels revolution. With centuries of experience in sugarcane production and as a world leader in refinement technology, the country has achieved a scale in the use of biofuels in the transportation sector unmatched by any other country on Earth. Building on

An Astroturf-covered Volkswagen in Corvallis, Oregon, is powered with used vegetable oil. The use of waste material is one of the best options for fueling transportation with minimal environmental cost. SARAH LEEN

the "ProAlcool" program of the early 1970s, which was designed in response to the first OPEC-led oil supply crisis, Brazil has shifted its automobile fleet to "flex-fuel" engines that can run on gasoline, ethanol, or a mixture of the two fuels. Since about 2000, when these cars were introduced by all major manufacturers in Brazil, motorists have learned to make spot calculations to decide which fuel to purchase, tracking the price of ethanol and gasoline in relation to their respective fuel efficiency (ethanol is 27% less fuel efficient per liter than gasoline). Such flexibility has proven popular; today 80% of cars in Brazil are flex-fuel.

The prevalence of ethanol in Brazilian gas stations is facilitated because Brazil is one of the countries with the greatest potential for biofuels in general, and ethanol in particular. With the realization that global warming is a reality, and a real threat to ecosystems and economies, Brazil became the poster child for displacing oil-based transportation fuels with biofuels. Between 2006 and 2007, investors from the United States and Europe flocked to Brazilian sugarcane production/trade associations, government offices, research laboratories, and ethanol refineries for quick lessons on the experience accumulated there over the past three decades. Emerging partnerships among Brazilian mills, refinery equipment manufacturers, government-funded agricultural technology agencies, and foreign investors have led to new ventures to export the Brazilian biofuels technology to suitable countries in Africa and Asia.

However, this leadership in biofuels is coming at a heavy expense to Brazilian ecosystems. The land planted in sugarcane alone is expected to expand from 6 million hectares today to 10 million hectares by 2010 and perhaps as many as 35 million hectares within 20 years. Increased water use, habitat clearing, and local reductions in biodiversity are all being blamed on the expansion of sugarcane. In the Atlantic Forest region, sugarcane has replaced traditional crops such as coffee, while in the Cerrado it is being planted on former soy fields and pastureland, and is heavily dependent on irrigation. In turn, the soy farmers and cattle ranchers are moving farther north and west, clearing new lands on the Amazonian agricultural frontier. The expansion of soy cultivation in Brazil is being exacerbated by the displacement of U.S. soy by

corn for ethanol. Other crops, including oil palm, jatropha, and castor beans, are also making inroads. Recently, proposed legislation would allow oil palm to replace part of the native habitat reserves required on Amazon properties, potentially magnifying greatly the impact on the world's largest rainforest.

Demand

The global demand for biofuels has increased sharply in recent years, with an annual growth rate of 15% to 20% expected over the next two decades. While biofuels currently represent about 3% of the total global transportation-fuels market, that proportion is expected to reach 8.5% by 2015. Taking into account technological innovation and a favorable policy environment, biofuels could constitute 30% of the transportation fuels market by 2030 (New, 2007).

Much of the current demand is being driven by government regulations, subsidies, or policies that have mandated biofuel use (Koplow, 2007; Kutas, Lindberg, and Steenblik, 2007). Investors are rushing to take advantage of the financial incentives. Brazil was one of the first countries to aggressively promote ethanol as a transportation fuel, and the country's biofuels industry is one of the most advanced in the world. Today eight out of every ten new cars in Brazil are flex-fuel vehicles that can run on a variable mixture of ethanol and gasoline or pure ethanol, which is available at nearly all gas stations. Current rules mandate a 25% ethanol mixture, as well as a 2% biodiesel blend that will increase to 5% by 2013 (Reuters, 2007).

Other countries have also begun to require a blend of biofuels with traditional fossil fuels for transportation. A 2005 law passed by the U.S. Congress obligated gasoline producers to gradually increase the use of ethanol and other alternative fuels to 28.4 billion liters. A new energy law enacted at the end of 2007 further obligates gasoline producers to increase the use of ethanol and biodiesel from 19 billion liters in 2007 to 140 billion liters by 2022. In support of this objective, total U.S. subsidies to the biofuels sector are expected to reach $92 billion from 2006 to 2012 (Koplow, 2007).

In 2003, the European Commission set a target of 5.75% biofuels use by 2010, and heads of state increased that goal to 10% by 2020. Some member

states have also established minimum blend levels (Kutas, Lindberg, and Steeblik, 2007). In order to support European production of biofuels, the Commission originally set a 45 Euro per hectare subsidy for biofuel feedstocks to promote the development of the biofuels sector. As it turned out, the area eligible for these subsidies was scaled back as the incentive proved too popular and the goal was surpassed (World Business Council for Sustainable Development, 2007).

Many other countries have also set national biofuel goals for transportation fuels. Examples include: Colombia requires 10% ethanol blending for gasoline, gradually increasing to 25% by 2025; India requires 5% biofuels; five provinces in China require ethanol blends of 10% in all gasoline; and Japan requires a 10% ethanol blend by 2010 (Reuters, 2007). Malaysia has decreed a 5% blend using palm oil, but the country has delayed implementation until the price of palm oil falls by approximately 25% (Khorana and Bhattacharya, 2007).

Supply

Producers are racing to keep pace with demand. According to the Renewable Fuels Association, in the United States alone there are thirty-four new ethanol plants under construction, eight of the ninety-five existing plants are expanding, and 150 new plants or expansions are in the planning stages (Blum, 2006). The United States is not alone in this trend.

Driven by expected economic benefits, developing countries are increasingly expressing interest in converting arable lands to biofuel crops in order to participate in what is perceived as a new global market. As noted above, Brazil has long been a leader in the biofuels industry, and both the land dedicated to feedstocks and the number of processing plants are in quick expansion.

As governments and private companies compete to take advantage of emerging opportunities, biofuel processing plants are springing up in countries from Cameroon to China to Thailand. In just one example, Thailand has recently approved 45 ethanol-processing plants with a capacity of 10.9 million liters a day (Khorana and Bhattacharya, 2007). One critical concern associated with this rapid biofuels expansion is the potential trade-off between long-term economic, social, and environmental costs and short-term economic benefits. As those trade-offs are often not immediately obvious, they may not always be taken into account. For example, when biofuel feedstocks with multiple uses are sold on the biofuels market without investment in additional production capacity, there will be an inevitable impact on other markets and an increase in prices that will be expressed at the local, national, or global scale, depending on the circumstances.

The United States and Brazil are currently the largest consumers and producers of ethanol, with China, India, and Spain rounding off the top five producers (New, 2007; Renewable Energy Policy Network for the 21st Century, 2006). The European Union is the largest consumer and producer of biodiesel (New, 2007). Germany, France, and Italy produce the largest amount of biodiesel by volume, followed by the United States and the Czech Republic (Renewable Energy Policy Network for the 21st Century, 2006). Malaysia and Indonesia are also important producers of palm oil for biodiesel; both are quickly expanding their production and processing capabilities.

The production and consumption dynamics noted above may change in the

next decade as additional technologies and species complement, or even replace, current biofuels and feedstocks. As mentioned above, some of the most promising research and development efforts currently focus on cellulosic ethanol, which uses abundant cellulosic plant fibers to produce a highly energy-efficient liquid fiber.

In addition, research is currently under way focusing on the development of new crop varieties and processing techniques that would allow for expanded options in the biofuels market. For example, researchers in Africa and South America are working to produce ethanol from cassava, a widespread traditional crop favored by small farmers and highly adaptable to marginal climates. Investments are also being made to produce biodiesel from algae on a commercial scale. These developments may have a transformational effect on global agriculture; but until technologies and crop variety development are more advanced, it will be difficult to predict accurately the extent of future crop cultivation or potential impacts on the natural environment.

Impact on Land Use

As the demand for biofuels grows, the land dedicated to growing biofuel feedstocks will also expand. This expansion is associated with a diverse set of environmental and socioeconomic impacts. An estimated 20% of the U.S. corn harvest in 2007 was used for ethanol production, amounting to 7.3 million hectares. By 2012, ethanol production will be consuming one-third of the harvest. Crops planted for biofuels in the European Union grew from 0.31 million hectares in 2004 to 2.84 million hectares in 2007. Sugarcane production in Brazil is projected to expand from its current 6 million hectares to as many as 35 million hectares in twenty years (Inovação Unicamp, 2006). In Sumatra and Borneo, some 4 million hectares of forest have been converted to oil palm plantations (Buckland, 2005). It is projected that a further 6 million hectares in Malaysia and 16.5 million in Indonesia could be cleared

(Dros, 2003). Other crops such as jatropha and castor beans, although planted in smaller quantities, are expected to become much more prevalent in rural landscapes, especially in regions with pronounced dry seasons.

While significant land areas are currently dedicated to biofuel crops in North America (corn) and Europe (rapeseed), the tropics represent the greatest opportunity for the expansion of the biofuels industry. Plant growth is influenced by water, solar radiation, and soil nutrients. Two of these three elements (water and solar energy) are at a maximum in the tropics, but soil nutrient levels tend to be lower, often requiring higher levels of chemical inputs. Tropical climatic conditions also provide the potential for multiple harvests each year. Ecosystems in the tropics are likely great candidates for capitalizing on the second generation of biofuel crops based on converting not just the starch but plant fiber as well. Yet despite the competitive advantages of tropical ecosystems, the growth in biofuels production in temperate regions will continue as well.

How will the increased demand for biofuels be met? In some cases, the expansion of biofuel crops will occur on unproductive or degraded land without displacing other land-based activities. Cellulosic crops will be competitive at least on marginal lands not suitable for food production, and government subsidies may stimulate additional production. This is the ideal situation, with low social or environmental opportunity costs, and may be

A farmer sits atop a cart loaded with sugar cane at the Bajaj Hindustan Limited Sugar mill, whose distillery will produce ethanol in Kinauni, India. The Indian government may begin mixing ethanol with automobile fuel to reduce crude oil dependence. AMIT BHARGAVA

easiest with crops such as jatropha that are suited to marginal environments.

Producers, however, may not follow this ideal situation, even where marginal land is available. This may happen because economics often plays a dominant role in biofuels-production decision-making, particularly when alternative environmental and social costs are not taken into account. Often the financial cost to a biofuels producer of restoring degraded land to the point where it can support crops may be greater than the cost of clearing new land. In other cases, infrastructure may be lacking or knowledge of suitable areas may be insufficient. Potential biofuels producers may choose to plant on existing pasture or cropland. In this case, the indirect effects of biofuel production could lead to a reduction in the supply of the crop available for other uses or shift crop production farther towards the agricultural frontier.

As prices for feedstocks rise due to increased demand for biofuels, additional land will be slated for production. This is not surprising, as the relationship between commodity prices and deforestation has been heavily studied. In just one example, a study of the Brazilian State of Mato Grosso identified a direct correlation between the price of soy (all markets) and the area deforested for cropland (Morton et al., 2006).

Direct clearing of natural habitat for biofuel feedstock production is perhaps most common for oil palm. For example, it is estimated that the expansion of oil palm plantations was responsible for an 87% deforestation rate in Malaysia between 1985 and 2000 (Rosenthal, 2007). While most of that palm oil production was destined for the food and cosmetic markets, the expansion of the biodiesel market may exacerbate the phenomena.

For crops such as soy and sugarcane, the link between feedstock production and deforestation is more often indirect, but is no less important. Since most suitable farmland in North America and Europe is already occupied, a shift towards biofuel production in these places can lead to a displacement of crop production to other continents with available land—often the tropical agricultural frontier. As the price of corn rises due to increased ethanol demand, for example, U.S. farmers are shifting their cropland from soy to corn. However, global demand for soy has not decreased; rather, soy plantations are increasing along the agricultural frontier in places like the Brazilian Amazon. As most

of the direct and indirect clearing of natural habitats for biofuel feedstock expansion occurs in tropical or semi-tropical regions, many of which are areas of extremely high biodiversity and/or areas that store globally important carbon reserves, the worldwide implications of this expansion are grave.

Impact on the Environment

In terms of protecting ecosystems and biodiversity, what is particularly worrisome is the expansion of biofuel crops taking place in forests or other natural habitats. Clearing of land to grow crops for biofuels can today be considered one of the greatest threats to tropical forests, peatlands, grasslands, and wetlands. While mitigating the environmental risks posed by biofuels could be achieved by adhering to rigorous biofuel "best-practice guidelines," poorly managed expansion of biofuel crops could exacerbate the very problem it is intended to alleviate.

Carbon

Experts suggest that the burning and clearing of intact ecosystems for biofuel crops threatens the very habitats that store much of the Earth's carbon, thereby releasing stored carbon into the air and fueling climate change. An increase in CO_2 emissions from the clearing of tropical ecosystems is one of the least recognized, and perhaps most insidious, impacts of biofuels expansion. While it is true that biofuels in general emit less CO_2 during combustion than fossil fuels and that the plants that produce biofuel feedstocks do absorb and store carbon during growth, the carbon equation is not that simple. To date, most studies on biofuels show a positive carbon balance (net removal of CO_2 from the atmosphere), but these studies do not take into account the land conversion caused by producing biomass for biofuels, nor account for foregone carbon sequestration potential.

When tropical forests, peatlands, shrublands, and grasslands are cleared to plant crops, the carbon stored in the native vegetation is released through burning or decomposition of organic material, and additional carbon is emitted as the soil is exposed to the sun and plowed for planting. To aggravate the matter, the crops that replace the native vegetation almost always have less

The annual migration of Monarch butterflies in Michoacan, Mexico, may be threatened as their habitats are cut down. Illegal deforestation of their overwintering grounds in Mexico, as well as crop expansion for biofuels along migration routes, have already led to drastic reductions in butterfly populations.
FRANS LANTING

carbon sequestration potential than native ecosystems, and soil carbon usually continues to decline over several years. To some extent, these losses can be mitigated. Avoiding burning and also applying appropriate soil-management techniques can help reduce carbon loss, while perennial tree crops such as oil palm have higher carbon sequestration capacity when compared to annual crops. In most cases, however, the clearing of natural habitat and planting with biofuel feedstocks results in a net negative carbon balance. This means that the production, processing, and burning of biofuels associated with newly cleared land actually emit more CO_2 into the atmosphere compared to a scenario without biofuels, resulting in an exacerbation of climate change.

Research that incorporates CO_2 emissions due to land-use change into total carbon calculations is just now emerging. Although there are discrepancies in the final calculations, studies suggest that the payback period for biofuels—the period required for reductions in CO_2 emissions from biofuel use to compensate for increased CO_2 emissions from production and land-use change—can be measured in generations. One analysis indicates that when biofuels are directly produced on former rainforest that has been burned or drained, the payback period could be in the hundreds of years (Searchinger, 2007). Even considering only direct land conversion for sugarcane (the most energy-dense feedstock to date), the estimated payback period may be up to forty-five years (ibid.). Calculations for oil palm plantations in tropical rainforests place the payback at approximately fifty years (T. Killeen, personal communication). Most emerging studies make it clear that the CO_2 emissions caused by land conversion associated with biofuel feedstocks are not compensated for in either the short or medium term by the slight reduction in CO_2 emissions that results from the replacement of fossil fuels by biofuels.

Even without taking land conversion into account, the conventional wisdom that biofuels are a good strategy for reducing CO_2 emissions is being called into question. One recent analysis compared the emissions avoided by biofuel use (without including land conversion) with the sequestration potential of forest or grassland restoration. They found that "in all cases, forestation of an equivalent area of land would sequester two to nine times more carbon over a 30-year period than the emissions avoided by the use of the biofuel. Taking

this opportunity cost into account, the emissions cost of liquid biofuels exceeds that of fossil fuels" (Righelato and Spracklen, 2007).

Another report found that "the minimum subsidy cost per tonne of CO_2-equivalent reduced over the 2006–2012 period is \$295 for corn ethanol; \$239 for biodiesel; and \$109 for a hypothetical cellulosic ethanol case. For each one tonne of reductions obtained via current subsidies to biofuels, 89, 75, and 33 tonnes of carbon offsets respectively could have been purchased on the Chicago Climate Exchange" (Koplow, 2007).

European numbers are similar. An assessment submitted to the European Parliament concluded that the subsidies amounted to € 575 to € 800 per ton of CO_2 reduction for ethanol made from sugar beets, around € 215 for biodiesel made from used cooking oil, and more than € 600 for biodiesel made from rapeseed. By comparison, using the biofuels subsidies to purchase reductions in the marketplace would have accrued twenty times more CO_2 offsets just on the European Climate Exchange (Kutas, Lindberg, and Steenblik, 2007). There is little doubt that alternatives such as habitat conservation and restoration (especially on forest land) are a less expensive and more effective means of sequestering atmospheric carbon and mitigating climate change in the short to medium term than is the use of biofuels. Although markets for such activities have been limited to date, this situation may be modified by recent developments in the climate-change dialogue.

Biodiversity

CO_2 emissions are not the only environmental issue associated with biofuels production. Inappropriate plantation location and management practices can also threaten natural habitats, biodiversity, water quality, soils, and even local climates and precipitation patterns (Clay, 2006; Killeen, 2007). Converting diverse landscapes including natural ecosystems to agriculture also destroys the habitat of the plants and animals that live there. In some cases, especially in tropical hotspots and high-biodiversity wilderness areas rich in endemic species, the threat posed to endangered species may be very high.

In one example, the diversity of bird species in Malaysian oil palm plantations was found to be just 23% of that in old-growth forests and substantially lower

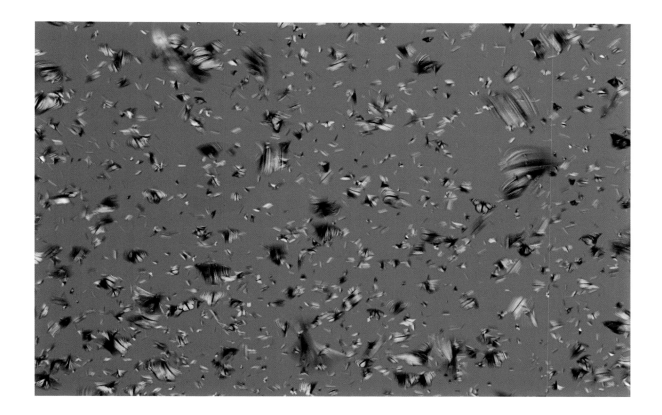

than in logged forests or rubber plantations. The number of butterfly species found in oil palm plantations in Borneo was just 17% of the corresponding level for old-growth forests (Peh et al., 2005; Hoh and Wilgrove, as cited in Koh 2007c). Although not all the oil produced was for biofuel markets, the biodiversity impact of these plantations is clear.

Similarly, orangutans (*Pongo pygmaeus* and *Pongo abelii*) face serious threat of extinction over the next decade as a result of habitat loss due, in large part, to expanding oil palm plantations (Nellemann et al., 2007). Between 1992 and 2003, orangutan habitat declined by more than 5.5 million hectares, while the plantation area across Borneo and Sumatra increased by almost 4.7 million hectares. Oil palm plantations could be responsible for at least 50% of the observed loss in orangutan habitat during this period. (Buckland 2005; Singleton et al., 2004). Other flagship species of the lowland rainforests of Sumatra and Borneo threatened by expanding oil palm plantations include the Asian elephant (*Elephas maximus*), the Sumatran rhinoceros (*Dicerorhinus sumatrensis*), and the Sumatran tiger (*Panthera tigris sumatrae*), the latter two classified as Critically Endangered.

Even the conversion of small areas may eliminate connectivity between remaining fragments of habitat, which would lead to a decline of species on a local or broader scale, or even extinction. Given the complex web of biological interactions, the consequences of land-use change—and landscape conversion

in particular—are difficult to predict. Resulting species loss could lead to failure of important crops (in the case of a decline in pollinators), a surge in agricultural pest species due to the removal of a predator, or other unforeseen problems.

As mentioned earlier, most of the regions with the greatest potential for biofuel crop expansion are tropical or semi-tropical regions. The Amazon, the Brazilian Cerrado, the Atlantic forest, the Congo Basin, Indonesia, and tropical South Asia, for example, enjoy conditions that promote rapid plant growth, and each has unique features that are suitable for at least one biofuel feedstock. All also fall within biodiversity hotspots or high-biodiversity wilderness areas. Given that these areas together contain the last remaining fragments of habitat on which nearly 70% of the world's plants and more than 50% of its terrestrial vertebrates depend, any conversion of forests, savannas, grasslands, or wetlands to agricultural use represents an increased risk to the world's biological support system.

Ecosystems

Management practices for biofuel crops vary greatly among species, producers, and regions. While some producers follow environmental best-management practices for their crops and safeguard water, soil, and biodiversity, many others employ less optimal practices. This is especially true on the agricultural frontier in places like the Brazilian Amazon, where land values are low, regulatory regimes non-existent, credit expensive, and the scramble to obtain short-term profit in high-risk environments paramount. Given the forecasted expansion of the land dedicated to biofuel crops in the coming years, these practices will multiply.

The removal of vegetation from riparian zones leads to reduced filtration capacity, which affects water quality near the source and further downstream. Removing native vegetation on slopes can also lead to problems involving erosion and nutrient runoff, reducing soil productivity and creating problems

As wheat prices steadily climb in North America, the cost of bread in Nigeria has risen by 50% in the last year.
BENEDICTE KURZEN

with sedimentation and nutrient pollution. The large-scale conversion of land from native habitat to cropland may even have an impact on local climates and precipitation, given the role vegetation plays in water cycling and air cooling (Malhi et al., 2007). At the scale at which biofuel crop expansion is being discussed, these impacts might be problematic regionally, and perhaps disastrous locally.

When biofuel crops are grown as monocultures, they bring with them all associated positive and negative aspects. In most cases, the use of pesticides and herbicides is necessary to combat insect pests and reduce weed-crop competition. To ensure maximum yield, fertilizers are frequently applied in large quantities, often above the amounts necessary to achieve those maximum yields. Both pesticides and fertilizers can negatively affect soil and water quality in the production area and downstream. Production in countries located in arid and semi-arid climate zones will impact scarce freshwater resources, adding a new dimension to the debate on the environmental costs and benefits of biofuels.

Some of the effects of the cultivation of biofuel feedstocks on the environment are beginning to be seen. According to the U.S. National Academy of Sciences, biofuel growth in the United States has probably already contributed to a decline in water quality because of the large amount of nitrogen and phosphorus fertilizers required to produce corn. The extent of hypoxia "dead zone" (oxygen deprivation) in the Gulf of Mexico in 2007 is among the three largest mapped to date, and the amount of nitrogen fertilizer applied to the land is also at or near a historical high point. "If projected future increases in the uses of corn for ethanol production do occur, the increase in harm to water quality could be considerable" (NAS, 2007).

Impact on Society

The social ramifications of biofuels are also very important to consider. Much discussion has focused recently on the issues of food security, involving both the availability of food and its cost to consumers. Where crops with multiple uses are shifted towards biofuel production without additional agricultural intensification or production elsewhere, alternative markets may experience

a reduction in supply leading to higher prices. A shift in the pattern of palm oil sales towards biofuels, for example, could reduce the supply available for food oil and also drive up the cost of personal care products, where palm oil is a common ingredient.

The shift of corn production from food to ethanol markets in the U.S. has driven up the cost of numerous food products that depend on corn, both in the U.S. and abroad. There have been many anecdotal reports of rising prices for everything from corn-fed pork and high-fructose corn syrup to tortillas in Mexico. Wheat and rice prices also rose to decade highs as farmers chose to increase corn acreage at the expense of other crops. This, of course, meant additional income for farmers, but higher costs for consumers.

A rise in the price of staple foods affects the poor most severely. Concerns recently raised by agricultural experts writing in *Foreign Affairs* magazine make it clear that: "Biofuels have tied oil and food prices together in ways that could profoundly upset the relationships between food producers, consumers, and nations in the years ahead, with potentially devastating implications for both global poverty and food security" (Runge and Senauer, 2007).

As the land dedicated to biofuel feedstocks increases, additional impacts are likely to become more evident. Crops destined for biofuel production may compete for drinking water and irrigation with food crops in arid areas or for scarce arable land for living space in densely populated regions. While the impacts will vary from region to region, in all cases there will be winners (e.g., individuals employed in biofuel transformation, or farmers who earn additional income by producing biofuel crops) and losers (e.g., those who must pay higher prices for food). These shifts in the distribution of wealth among producers and consumers need to be taken into account in any discussion of the social impacts of biofuels.

Prospects for the Future

Future developments will determine the scope, scale, and location of impacts related to the biofuels sector in coming years. Each of these developments will carry with it a new set of benefits, as well as associated environmental impacts. At the moment, heavy investment is being made in developing the next

However, if development is carefully monitored, and safeguards and best practices are incorporated into the implementation of the next generation of biofuels, it may be possible to minimize negative impacts while capturing the associated benefits.

Conclusions: Potential and Limitations

The current trend towards biofuels brings with it several benefits and numerous challenges. Biofuels emit lower levels of some greenhouse gases during combustion when compared to gasoline or diesel and hold the potential for being renewably

generation of biofuels. For instance, certain algae are being studied intensively and may represent promising future feedstock for biodiesel; nonetheless, an industrial-scale production system might stress existing water resources.

New refinement technologies may make traditional crops like cassava and sorghum more attractive as biofuel feedstocks. These crops have traditionally been grown on marginal lands and offer not only a new source of biofuels, but also economic opportunity to small farmers. Nonetheless, expanding production of annual crops on fragile marginal lands carries with it a high risk of environmental degradation.

As mentioned previously, cellulosic ethanol has great potential and may transform the biofuels market in the medium term. Should sources for cellulosic ethanol be limited to excess crop waste or wood-processing by-products, for example, the benefits could be high. However, the search for efficiencies may cause an unsustainable level of crop waste to be converted to ethanol, leading perhaps to a reduction in soil fertility. Alternatively, corn or soy fields that have been established on marginal lands could be planted with a perennial grass species and harvested for cellulosic ethanol. This "pasture" could be organized to mimic the original grassland ecosystem and would generate other environmental benefits.

It is impossible to accurately assess the risks associated with potential technologies and feedstocks until they are fully mature and implemented.

harvested. For countries in the developed world, biofuels offer greater energy and economic security whether they are produced domestically or imported from other countries (Colchester et al., 2006). Since the countries with the greatest production potential are located in poor areas of the tropics, biofuels represent a rare opportunity to stimulate economic growth and create jobs, while increasing export earnings and foreign investment. Contingent on public policies, rules, and regulations ensuring socially equitable practices, small farmers may benefit from linkages to global energy markets, as many biofuel feedstocks can be produced on a small scale (Colchester and Jiwan, 2006).

However, the rapid expansion of biofuels brings with it a number of risks. Biofuels may exacerbate climate change when they directly or indirectly cause the destruction of natural habitats and emit greenhouse gases throughout the production chain. Even when best practices are followed, the restoration of forest ecosystems is usually a more cost-effective strategy for mitigating climate change than is biofuel use, at least in the short to medium term. Another key risk is an increased loss of species and landscape diversity, and especially natural habitat, with the associated reduction in the provision of ecosystem services. Related to this is the loss of biodiversity, which depends on the habitats at risk of degradation or destruction. Finally, the greater demand for land for biofuel feedstocks may also cause reduced supply and

higher prices in alternate markets, which often places a disproportionate burden on the poor.

Fortunately, opportunities exist to resolve many of these issues. By completing an in-depth analysis of potential areas for biofuel crop expansion and overlaying this information with regions of high value for biodiversity conservation, carbon storage, and protection of water resources and other ecosystem services, it is possible to identify areas that should be avoided during expansion, as well as opportunities for growth onto abandoned or degraded lands. The development of industry-wide sustainability standards, as well as comprehensive national policies and regulatory frameworks for biofuel crop expansion, will increase the likelihood that expansion complies with comprehensive land-use plans, and that producers follow recognized best practices in the production and processing of biofuels. If total energy use is minimized and biofuels are produced in accordance with the recommendations below, the negative impacts associated with them may be minimized while benefits are generated for both producers and consumers.

Recommendations

Before any recommendations for environmentally sustainable biofuels can be made, three preliminary criteria that should underlie any strategy relating to biofuels must be met:

- Avoid clearing natural habitat for biofuel plantations. From a conservation perspective, the highest-priority recommendation must be to avoid clearing any areas of natural habitat to establish biofuel plantations. Many countries have within them large areas of already degraded or deforested land, and these should be top priority for future biofuel plantations. Associated with this is the need to create more parks, reserves, and other protected areas in the highest-priority regions for biodiversity, removing

them as possible targets for biofuel plantations and ensuring that their existing carbon stores are maintained.

- Use material that would otherwise be wasted. By taking advantage of materials that would otherwise be disposed of (crop residues beyond that needed for maintaining soil fertility, wood by-products, etc.), it is possible to produce biofuels with lower environmental and social opportunity costs while avoiding pollution and emissions from burning the crop residues. The potential to utilize waste will likely be much higher with second-generation biofuels.

- Reduce energy use and increase energy efficiency. While this falls partially outside the scope of influence of the biofuels industry, it must remain on the forefront in any broader discussion of energy options. Reducing overall energy use would be the most effective means to reduce the impact of all types of energy on the environment. Efficiency is key to this, with energy efficiency gains capable of cost-effectively satisfying half or more of the energy services desired or needed by society now and for decades to come. Research has shown that energy-efficiency measures may be more effective in lowering overall energy and fossil fuel demand, and thus CO_2 emissions, while forest protection and restoration are often a more cost-effective means of reducing net global carbon emissions and delivering biodiversity and

Volunteers collect native prairie seeds from the Polk City (Iowa) cemetery to restore the nearby Neal Smith National Wildlife Refuge. The cemetery has one of the few remaining stands of virgin prairie in Iowa. JOEL SARTORE

livelihood benefits (Righelato and Spracklen, 2007). Removing market barriers that constrain beneficial efficiency gains should be an integral step in any strategy for resolving climate change or energy use (see Chapter 1: Energy Efficiency). This should include promoting system efficiencies, which have the added benefit of expanding the market for cost-effective wind power and solar power (see Chapter 2: Renewable Energy).

Beyond these fundamental steps, certain minimum criteria are necessary to ensure that the location, production, and processing of biofuels are environmentally sustainable and socially acceptable and that they pose no threats to biodiversity. These include the following:

• Ensure that biofuels have a net positive carbon contribution (i.e., lower life-cycle emissions compared to displaced gasoline or diesel), including accounting for emissions from land-use change.
• Avoid converting or degrading existing intact ecosystems including forests, grasslands, wetlands, mangroves, and peatlands.
• Site biofuel crops on previously cleared land that has been abandoned, degraded, or underutilized.
• Use available biodiversity information and planning tools to help determine suitable locations for biofuel crops, including avoiding identified areas of high-biodiversity importance and the immediate buffer zone of protected areas.
• Avoid locating biofuel processing and refinery plants in areas at risk from land-use change.
• Protect ecosystem functions in production landscapes by positioning crops in a manner that conserves natural vegetation in riparian areas and on steep slopes and establishes biodiversity corridors of natural vegetation linking remaining fragments of natural habitat.
• Favor perennial crops, which are inherently more carbon efficient and ecologically sustainable when compared to traditional annual crops.
• Require and continuously apply best practices in siting, growing, and processing biofuel crops, including cropping systems that incorporate appropriate environmental safeguards; minimal use of chemical inputs;

and ongoing monitoring of impacts of production on biodiversity, water quality, and soil.
• Certify or verify both practices and results.
• Offset negative ecological impacts through public- or private-sector funding for protection of key biodiversity areas.

Applying these criteria to all biofuels everywhere in the world will not be easy. It will take a long-term, concerted effort from all stakeholders. Governments need to examine regulations requiring biofuel additives to gasoline and subsidies for biofuel feedstocks, and ensure that land-use planning and legislative and regulatory frameworks encompass basic sustainability criteria and that important areas for biodiversity and ecosystem services are protected.

The private sector must promote industry standards that guarantee sustainability, incorporate sustainability criteria into operations and purchasing decisions, and develop new techniques and feedstock species that maximize energy output while minimizing environmental impact.

Civil society and academia should cooperate to make sure that cutting-edge information on issues like biodiversity, carbon stocks, and land suitability is available to inform public debate and decision-making. They should also support local capacity-building to manage biofuel development, promote conservation in areas of feedstock expansion, and insist that benefits from the biofuels market be accessible to small-scale farmers and have positive impacts on rural communities.

Finally, consumers must take time to understand the full range of implications of biofuels, and make their decisions accordingly.

If all stakeholders see that the basic recommendations for sustainability are met, it may be possible to produce biofuels that do not contribute to climate change and that do help maintain biodiversity and safeguard important ecosystem services. This could, indeed, be a "triple win," providing the economic benefits associated with biofuels, guaranteeing a renewable supply of carbon-neutral energy, and helping to secure rich and diverse ecosystems.

A CLIMATE FOR LIFE

Two workers watch the soy harvest in Nova Mutum, Brazil. Brazil is the second largest soy producer in the world. ALEX WEBB

The Pantanal: A Threatened Haven for Wildlife

A jabiru stork eats a piranha in the Brazilian Pantanal, one of the world's largest wetlands.

LEFT:
An aerial view shows the Pantanal at full flood in May, seen flying into a wildlife reserve near Poconé. Small planes are the fastest way to get around during the flood season, when many of the roads are covered in water.

Photographs by Joel Sartore

SO PRECISE ARE THE HYDRAULICS of South America's Pantanal that a change in rainfall may throw a unique habitat out of equilibrium. To photographer Joel Sartore, it would be a paradise lost.

"This is a fantastic place for viewing wildlife," he said. "It's a crossroads of ecosystems, where grassy savannah and triple canopy jungle meet, so you get a high variety of species. There are copses of trees but it is basically flat and the animals are easily seen. I've worked in Africa and other parts of South America where you can hear birds and animals, but you often can't see them in the thick cover.

"In the Pantanal's savannah there are parrots and macaws in view most of the time, and you see maned wolves, capybara, and giant anteaters with no trouble at all. When the main road into the area was graded up it left ditches that fill with water, which become habitat for all kinds of birds. I saw tons of birds without having to leave the road."

Not only is the Pantanal flat, it is also a pan. That pan, half the size of Montana and touching Brazil, Paraguay, and Bolivia, becomes one of the world's largest wetlands during the rainy season from October through April.

When land along the Paraguay River and its tributaries becomes saturated, the streams spill onto the savannah. In January, February, and March during a very wet year the only solid ground is on hummocks and in sinuous forests where deer, jaguars, ocelots, crab-eating foxes, and cattle keep their feet dry. The rest is under water. Then the water slowly dries, after which cattle graze on lush grasses in ranching operations that have existed since the late 19th century.

"The Pantanal has become dependent on seasonal, adequate rain that falls on the highlands and drains into this flat pan, where it stays for months," said Sartore. "As the waters gradually recede, lagoons trap fish that feed a host of predators, including water birds, caimans, anacondas, and the big cats. Birds time their migration so they can be here when the lagoons are full of food."

As in other parts of South America, heightened agriculture and river dredging offer their own threats to the Pantanal. Forests in the highlands are being cleared for vast fields of soybeans, corn, and cotton, so streams that carried forest-filtered

RIGHT: An anaconda constricts an egret in Brazil's Pantanal.

A maned wolf in the Pantanal takes its own picture by triggering a camera trap's infrared beam.

water are now freighted with silt and farm chemicals that alter ecosystems. Multinational corporations that own the farms are pressuring the governments of Brazil, Paraguay, and Bolivia to deepen the Paraguay River so ocean-going ships can hasten their products to market. Deepening the river would rush water past the pastures and diminish the overflow that has long fed the land.

"These effects are drastic," said Sartore, "but the long-term change would come from global warming. Changes in rainfall and temperature would be disastrous for species that have adjusted to a seasonally flooded plain."

Scientific evidence of diminished rainfall is lacking, but already scientists have observed that the dry season in the Pantanal is starting earlier and lasting longer. A recent drought was so severe that some perennial rivers dried out completely in the summer months.

If that happens on a larger scale, the fragile hydraulics of the Pantanal will be disrupted, and the human footprint may forever change a verdant ecosystem.

EYEWITNESS TO CHANGE

During the wet season in the Pantanal, a flooded cattle pasture at Barra Mansa Ranch becomes a resting spot for a freshwater stingray. Annual flooding allows stingrays and a host of fish to patrol farmland looking for places to feed and spawn.
JOEL SARTORE

Forest Conservation

Tropical forests provide important mechanisms for carbon storage and local ecosystem products and services. Forest conservation and management therefore represent an immediate and highly cost-effective means of preventing catastrophic climate change, as well as a solid strategy for alleviating poverty and enhancing biodiversity conservation.

An aerial view reveals the extent of deforestation for an oil palm plantation in Sabah, on the island of Borneo.
FRANS LANTING

PREVIOUS PAGES:
Ecuador's San Rafael Falls (Coca Falls) tumble down the Quijos River in the Amazon. Although reforestation can be used to restore watersheds and reduce erosion, there is no comparison to the additional benefits provided by an intact forest ecosystem. PETE OXFORD

Red meranti is logged heavily in the territory of Jeli in Kelantan, Malaysia. It is endemic to the region and is critically endangered as a result of habitat loss. STUART FRANKLIN

CHAPTER FOUR

Forest Conservation

Frederick Boltz, Aaron Bruner, Claude Gascon, Russell A. Mittermeier

As already indicated elsewhere in this book, immediate and aggressive reductions in anthropogenic greenhouse gas (GHG) emissions are urgently needed to prevent catastrophic climate change. Preventing the deforestation and degradation of the world's remaining forest cover is an immediate and highly cost-effective means of achieving this daunting goal. Indeed, as Lord Stern pointed out in the Stern Report, maintaining tropical forests is one of the most cost-effective methods of mitigating climate change available to us (Stern, 2006). What is more, if policies and economic incentives for forest conservation are provided at the scale we believe possible, and at a fair price, they could go a long way in helping to redress some of the huge imbalances that currently exist between the rich and poor.

The knowledge, technology, and financing exist to conserve an extraordinary wealth of carbon and biodiversity under policies and markets for Reducing Emissions from Deforestation and Forest Degradation (hereafter referred to as REDD) (ibid.). Moreover, if designed and implemented effectively and equitably, REDD activities could provide important benefits to indigenous and forest-dependent rural communities, as well as help conserve plant and animal biodiversity. Forest conservation and management therefore present not only an immediate and substantial opportunity to mitigate climate change, but also to alleviate poverty and enhance biodiversity conservation.

Tropical deforestation currently accounts for 18 to 25% of total human-induced GHG emissions, including carbon dioxide (CO_2), methane, nitrous oxide, and other reactive gases (Houghton, 2005; Stern, 2006; IPCC, 2007). Tropical deforestation accounts for the majority of current land-use GHG emissions and is expected to remain the principal land-use emissions source through 2050 (IPCC, 2007). Consequently, conserving forests and improving forest management must be a substantial component of mitigation strategies if dangerous climate change is to be avoided.

This chapter describes the importance of tropical forests in carbon storage and CO_2 emissions and the potential contribution of REDD to climate-change mitigation. It describes the importance of REDD as an incentive for forest conservation and notes its immediate additional benefits, such as maintaining other ecosystem services and processes vital to the long-term well-being of

A golden-crowned sifaka hugs a tree at the edge of a gold-mining area in Daraina in northern Madagascar. PETE OXFORD

Motubile Kasipa carries planks out of the Ituri Forest in Congo. The planks are cut from trees on site with only one working chainsaw. RANDY OLSON

humanity and biodiversity. It presents the principles underlying REDD as a mechanism for climate-change mitigation and the issues and challenges surrounding its implementation. Lastly it notes the particular opportunity presented by protected areas as sound carbon offsets. Throughout, the chapter highlights the enormous potential of REDD as a means of confronting three major crises facing humanity: climate change, biodiversity loss, and poverty.

Forests as Sources and Sinks of Carbon

Forests play a fundamental role in the natural global carbon cycle, absorbing atmospheric carbon dioxide through photosynthesis and serving as the principal terrestrial carbon sink (storage repository). Carbon is the building block of biomass and is present in leaves, branches, trunks, roots, litter, and in soils. There are several trillion tons of carbon stored terrestrially worldwide, including about 550 petagrams (PgC, or billion metric tons) in aboveground biomass (vegetation), 300 PgC in litter, and 1,500 to 2,000 PgC in the top meter of soils (Houghton, 2007). Per unit area, forests hold twenty to fifty times more carbon in their vegetation than the land uses that commonly replace them (Houghton and Hackler, 1999).

Of the diverse forms of vegetation on Earth, tropical forests are the most complex and rich in biomass and, consequently, store the greatest amount of aboveground carbon in their vegetation. Although they cover only 22% of potential vegetation by area, tropical forests represent an estimated 59% of this aboveground carbon (Dixon et al., 1994) and store about as much carbon in their vegetation and soils as temperate and boreal forests combined (Houghton, 2005). This is due to their extraordinary productivity. Annual net carbon production of tropical forests has been estimated at 17.8 billion tons, or 32% of the Earth's potential terrestrial net primary production (NPP) (i.e., the production of new biomass by plants [Field et al., 1998]). Tropical forests plus tropical woody savannahs comprise some 61% of terrestrial NPP and 33% of total global potential NPP, oceanic and terrestrial (Field et al., 1998).

Current global forest cover is nearly 4 billion hectares (ha) or about 30% of the world's land area (FAO, 2007). Forest cover is decreasing due to the conversion of intact forests to agricultural land, the expansion of infrastructure and settlements, and unsustainable logging. Current net deforestation rates are approximately 7.3 million ha or about 0.2% per year, most of which occurs in the tropics. When forests are cleared or degraded, significant quantities of stored carbon are released into the atmosphere in the form of CO_2.

Deforestation occurs when forests are converted to agriculture, pasture, infrastructure, and settlements, or when ground fires destroy entire forest stands. Such activities result in a release of stored carbon in the form of CO_2 emitted by burning, decomposition, and soil oxidation. Burning biomass results in other greenhouse gas emissions, including methane (CH_4) and nitrous oxide (N_2O). The burning also releases chemically active gases, including carbon monoxide (CO), non-methane hydrocarbons, nitric oxide (HNO_3), and methyl chloride (CH_2Cl_2). These gases, as well as methane, trigger the chemical production of tropospheric ozone (O_3, another greenhouse gas) and mediate the concentration of the hydroxyl radical, which regulates the lifetime of almost every atmospheric gas. Subsequent to biomass burning, biogenic emissions of nitrous oxide, nitric oxide, and methane are significantly enhanced (Levine, 1996).

Tropical forests typically store 75 to 150 tons of carbon (tC) per ha in aboveground biomass (Mahli et al., 2006), with an additional storage of 10% to 20% in belowground live biomass (Cairns et al., 1997). Beyond the important contribution from belowground live biomass, even greater carbon is stored in soils, particularly in mangroves and peat forests. Soil carbon in tropical mangroves has been estimated to reach 700 t C per meter depth per ha (Ong, 2002). In addition to uncertainties concerning soil-carbon storage in tropical ecosystems, there are further uncertainties about the level of soil-carbon emissions after clearing. Soil loss and oxidation of carbon beyond roots is a problem in mangrove and peatland systems, the former through aquaculture development that removes soil 1 to 2 meters deep, and the latter through the peat-burning for establishing plantations that burn off and oxidize underground peat. These are not trivial problems. Moreover, there is a long-term threat of soil carbon beyond root systems being oxidized (Canadell et al., 2006; Lenton et al., 2008).

dioxide emissions from tropical forest degradation have been estimated to range from 4.4% of total emissions from tropical deforestation during the 1990s (Achard et al., 2004) to 26.4% of total deforestation CO_2 emissions for tropical Asia for the period from 1850 to 1995 (Houghton and Hackler, 1999). Although not as important in carbon loss per unit area as deforestation, forest degradation is often a precursor to deforestation, as it facilitates access by humans and cattle to previously intact forests and may increase susceptibility to fires (Nepstad et al., 1999). Reducing the degradation of forests is, therefore, essential for reducing further greenhouse gas emissions.

The estimated global total net flux of carbon to the atmosphere from deforestation and land-use change in the period from 1850 to 2000 was 156 billion metric tons of carbon, about 60% of which occurred in the tropics (Houghton, 2000). This is just over half of the amount of carbon emitted from fossil-fuel use during the same period (Houghton, 2007). During the 1990s, the contribution of only tropical deforestation to greenhouse gas emissions was estimated to be between 3 billion (Achard et al., 2004) and 8 billion (Houghton, 2003) tons of CO_2 per year. This latter estimate (8 billion tCO_2) substantially exceeds total emissions produced by the global transport sector, which, in 2004, emitted 6.3 billion tons of CO_2 and accounted for 23% of global energy-related CO_2 emissions (IPCC, 2007).

Degradation, the long-term reduction of forest biomass density and carbon stocks, affected tropical forests at a rate of 2.4 million ha per year in the 1990s. (Nabuurs et al., 2007). Forest degradation results from any extractive use of forest resources, such as logging or non-timber forest product (NTFP) harvest, ground fires, livestock grazing, and progressive fragmentation of intact forest ecosystems. The biomass loss and CO_2 emissions from such activities vary greatly from the modest impacts of resin collection (rubber tapping) to severe impacts of activities such as logging and fires. The magnitude of impacts is related to the level of biomass extraction, of course, as well as the level of effort taken to minimize unplanned damage to vegetation and soils. Carbon

REDD Potential in Global Climate Change Mitigation

Any disturbance of natural forest in extraction or conversion to alternative land uses results in CO_2 emissions. The principle of reduced emissions from deforestation is that such emissions can be avoided by an explicit decision to conserve areas that would otherwise be converted to non-forest land uses and by taking the measures necessary to ensure forest conservation. Deforestation can be reduced through diverse means, from creating and improving the management of protected areas, to providing incentives to forest landowners for conservation such as stewardship payments and subsidies for alternative livelihoods, improving law enforcement, controlling fires, and regulating logging and the forest conversion that often follows in its aftermath. From a broader economic perspective, deforestation and degradation are likely to continue in most developing regions until structural shifts in economies reduce direct and indirect dependence on forest use and conversion as a basis of subsistence and economic development. Compensation for the "carbon services" obtained through maintenance of standing forests facing the threat of deforestation provides an important opportunity to catalyze such shifts.

Future REDD initiatives should also include efforts to create new protected areas at strategic locations within the expanding agricultural frontier. Changing the behavior of an individual or enterprise seeking short-term economic benefit on the agricultural frontier is a daunting problem and one that may prove insoluble in some locations, even in a policy environment replete with the financial resources from a REDD mechanism. Individuals will continue to make decisions that are best for their families. A REDD mechanism may help landholders and communities to set aside larger areas of less productive land, thus maintaining forest cover and reducing greenhouse gas emissions (Killeen, 2007).

There are also proven means for reducing forest degradation caused in extractive use. Research has demonstrated that improved planning and efforts to minimize damage from logging in tropical forests through the adoption of Reduced-Impact Logging (RIL) practices can result in substantial reductions of disturbance to vegetation and soils (Johns et al., 1996). RIL systems have proven to reduce forest canopy loss and ground disturbance and, thus, to reduce carbon loss in extractive forest use (Pinard and Putz, 1996). In some cases, the financial gains from more efficient extraction are sufficient incentive for the adoption of RIL systems (Holmes et al., 2002), while in others, given the high level of harvest, additional costs are incurred in RIL implementation (Pinard, Putz, and Tay, 2000; Boltz, Holmes, and Carter, 2003). Moreover, any effort to maintain timber stock for future harvest or to conserve intact forest set-asides in managed areas for biodiversity conservation result in an opportunity cost that will not be undertaken by most commercial operators without regulatory controls or financial incentives. Income from REDD could be used to improve sustainability by lessening the opportunity costs of adopting improved harvesting practices and longer harvest rotations to ensure that natural forests retain economic value over centuries. REDD financing for the reduced emissions of CO_2 in improved planning, reduced extraction levels, longer rotations, and the creation of set-asides is a promising means of covering this opportunity cost and promoting the conservation of forests allocated for extractive use.

Gains in the conservation of forests under REDD policies would make a substantial contribution to climate-change mitigation. Per estimates conducted for the Third Assessment Report of the IPCC, the forest sector has a biophysical mitigation potential of 5,380 million tons (Mt) CO_2 per year on average until 2050 (Kauppi, 2001). This estimate is for all forestry actions including afforestation, reforestation, improved forest management, and reduced deforestation. REDD is the land-use option with the greatest potential for emissions reduction in the short-term, given that deforestation is the single most important land-use source of CO_2 emissions (Nabuurs et al., 2007). In the immediate future (2008 to 2012), more than 90% of total mitigation potential in the tropics is estimated to be in the form of REDD (Jung, 2005). REDD investments would make an immediate and substantial contribution towards achieving CO_2 emissions-abatement targets. CO_2 emissions from current annual deforestation in Brazil and Indonesia alone equal four-fifths of the emissions reductions that could be achieved under the Kyoto Protocol (Santilli et al., 2005).

Future deforestation is expected to remain high in the tropics in the absence of REDD or other incentives and regulatory mechanisms providing

Cattle are herded on a ranch near Cachimbo in Brazil. Brazil is the largest beef producer in the world, and the destruction of rain forests to provide areas for cattle ranching is having profound impacts on biodiversity. ALEX WEBB

for its mitigation. Continued deforestation to 2050 is estimated to result in the loss of nearly 600 million ha of forest across all regions, with particularly high rates in the tropics (Sathaye et al., 2007). At today's rates of tropical deforestation, another 312 to 477 billion tons of CO_2 will be emitted over the next hundred years (Houghton, 2005) if no action is taken. This would increase the atmospheric concentration of CO_2 by nearly 130 parts per million, much more than previously estimated (Stern, 2006). Thus REDD is not only an important mitigation option in the short-term, but is a critical element of climate-change stabilization efforts long-term and an important complement to other GHG emissions reduction measures.

REDD payments and regulatory policies represent a decisive opportunity to achieve emissions reductions and great gains in the conservation of the Earth's remaining tropical forests. According to current global forestry model estimates of carbon sequestration by 2020 under different CO_2 prices at a cost of US\$5.40 per ton CO_2 and increasing at 3% per year, 11.7 billion tons of CO_2 (cumulative) could be sequestered and approximately 28 million ha of forest conserved in the tropical regions alone (Sohngen and Sedjo, 2006). At more aggressive pricing of \$27.20 per ton CO_2, deforestation could be virtually eliminated through payments for avoided deforestation emissions. For context, the projected commercialization cost for carbon capture and storage of CO_2 emissions from coal-fired power plants is estimated at \$40 to \$50 per ton CO_2 (MIT, 2007).

REDD Policies and Incentives

Forests provide a wealth of goods and services of critical value to humankind, from timber, gums, fibers, fruits, and medicines to maintenance of hydrological processes and regulation of the global carbon cycle. These benefits have conventionally been considered free goods and consequently unvalued or dramatically undervalued, which has resulted in both their overexploitation and their seemingly costless decline both in extent and integrity. Awareness of the importance of GHG emissions from land-use change and broad recognition of the magnitude of the climate-change crisis have created a radically new understanding of the role of forests as truly scarce resources

critical to the maintenance of the global carbon balance. This recognition has resulted in an increasing demand for afforestation and reforestation carbon offset credits in the rapidly growing compliance and voluntary carbon markets. It has, moreover, prompted greater attention in the regulatory arena to include prevention of forest emissions as well, most prominently in efforts to credit REDD in developing countries.

Reducing Emissions from Deforestation and Forest Degradation refers to policies and mechanisms that provide positive incentives for the prevention of probable deforestation or damage of intact natural forests. REDD regulatory policies and financing are now under intensive discussion by the UN Framework Convention on Climate Change (UNFCCC), following an agreement in principle at the Bali Conference of Parties in December of 2007. Incentives to encourage REDD will likely come from both international and national regulatory mechanisms, as well as market-driven sources. However, new and existing carbon markets are likely the only means by which to access the level of financial capital necessary to implement REDD actions at meaningful scale (Stern, 2006).

Under current Clean Development Mechanism (CDM) standards established under the Kyoto Protocol, reducing emissions from deforestation and degradation was excluded as a creditable carbon-mitigation option. In the absence of recognition by this international compliance market, it has been voluntary market investments that have catalyzed development of REDD projects. The voluntary market in 2006 generated a transaction volume of approximately 4.8 million tons of CO_2 in forestry projects. This represented 36% of the estimated voluntary market volume, excluding transactions of the Chicago Climate Exchange, at prices of US\$10 to \$18 per ton CO_2 for avoided deforestation projects (Hamilton et al., 2007). Investment in REDD projects is increasing, given the growing acceptance by the international community of the critical need to recognize avoided deforestation as a major contributor to emissions reductions, particularly in the short term.

REDD is based upon the principle that protecting existing forests under threat of deforestation or degradation results in a net decrease in future GHG emissions. Assigning market value to the avoidance of emissions from forest

Jaime is a boy whose family is working to protect their forest home and ensure a sustainable living. Here he holds up a piquiá fruit he has collected in Quiandeua, Brazil. JOEL SARTORE

loss and degradation presents an extraordinary conservation opportunity to provide financial incentives for the maintenance of intact forests for their value as carbon storage systems. A basic tenet of forest economics is that a forest will remain forested as long as its value as forest (timber and non-timber products, water flows, biodiversity, recreational uses) is greater than the opportunity costs of alternative, non-forest land uses. Establishing a financial value for the conservation of forest in avoided CO_2 emissions or as retained carbon stocks would change the economic decision on forest exploitation and conversion. Creating this value for standing forest carbon would increase the proportion of forests that are now economically marginal by creating a value for their preservation that would have to be considered a cost of revenue foregone in any economic decision for forest use, and thus rendering their benefits exploited inferior to their benefits intact.

The Poverty Reduction and Biodiversity Conservation Potential of REDD

Forests are the Earth's richest terrestrial sanctuaries of plant and animal diversity, of sources and storage of freshwater flows, and a myriad of ecological services fundamental to life. Consequently, projects reducing emissions from deforestation and degradation will have important additional benefits beyond their carbon storage value. Preventing deforestation will contribute to conserving freshwater resources, reducing flooding, controlling erosion and siltation, and safeguarding ecosystems and biodiversity vulnerable to direct climate-change impacts. REDD markets would not explicitly provide financial compensation for the maintenance of these additional positive externalities of intact forest ecosystems; however, independent verification systems for capturing market preference for multiple benefit carbon projects are available, such as the carbon project standards of the Climate, Community and Biodiversity Alliance (www.climate-standards.org). To maximize REDD benefits, offset investments should be selected on their ability to provide the greatest biodiversity, ecosystem service, and human-welfare benefits.

REDD financing can greatly benefit rural communities of the forest frontier and contribute to poverty reduction. More than 800 million indigenous and local people live in or near tropical forests and savannahs (Chomitz et al., 2007).

These people depend upon the goods and services provided by forests. Efforts to halt forest loss must prioritize equitable participation of and the provision of financial incentives to those people most directly linked to and dependent on them. REDD has the potential to generate annual financing of several billion dollars for tropical developing countries, even under relatively conservative assumptions. This could create important alternative development options for many developing countries and their forest-dependent populations.

REDD financing could also provide recognition of the important role that indigenous people have had in maintaining intact forests. Especially in Latin America, where there is a substantial amount of land in legally recognized indigenous territories, there are huge synergies to REDD, which could support livelihoods and self-determination while simultaneously protecting carbon stocks. Indigenous reserves cover 12% of Brazil's total land area and approximately 21% of the Amazon. The fate of the Amazon may well depend on how indigenous people manage their reserves, the links between these lands and government protected areas, and the ability of both to jointly resist threats from road construction, colonization, and fire (Schwartzman and Zimmerman, 2005; Nepstad et al., 2006).

Governance issues such as weak land-tenure regimes, limited market access, elite capture, and corruption are major hurdles to the pro-poor realization of REDD, and should be addressed in the design of policies and financial incentives. With appropriate means of distributing their benefits to residents of the forest frontier, REDD mitigation projects can generate employment opportunities and financial capital to support sustainable development actions in rural landscapes currently at the very margins of the global economy. Lastly, forestry actions intended to mitigate climate change, from reforestation to REDD, can make compatible contributions to human adaptation for those most vulnerable to climate-change impacts. Prioritizing benefit distribution to vulnerable populations and realizing their potential as long-term stewards of the Earth's richest forests in carbon, biodiversity, and other valuable ecosystem services should be a guiding principle of international REDD efforts.

Turning to biodiversity conservation, a massive investment in maintenance

importance of securing the vast stocks of forest carbon and the wealth of biodiversity contained in the less-threatened wilderness areas of the planet (Mittermeier et al., 2003) and particularly those countries with current high forest cover and low deforestation rates (da Fonseca et al., 2007). The volume-weighted average price of carbon in voluntary markets in 2006 was US$4.10 per ton of CO_2 (Hamilton et al., 2007), while the average price of carbon in compliance markets in 2006 was US$10.90 (Capoor and Ambrosi, 2007). According to Sohngen and Sedjo's model

of the tropical forest cover under REDD would irrefutably lead to great gains. REDD policies should target the most biodiverse forests to maximize such gains. Under present policy considerations, REDD investments would target those forests under substantiated threat of generating CO_2 emissions due to deforestation and degradation. In most instances, the areas most readily qualifying for REDD, given the high threat of their deforestation, will be forests located in the biodiversity hotspots that are the priority for conservation efforts (Mittermeier et al., 1999; Myers et al., 2000; Mittermeier et al., 2004). Estimates prepared for the Stern Review on the economics of climate change indicate that the opportunity costs of forest conservation required to eliminate deforestation in Brazil, Bolivia, Cameroon, Democratic Republic of Congo, Ghana, Indonesia, Malaysia, and Papua New Guinea in the next decade would be $US5 to 6.5 billion per year or around $1 per ha per year (Grieg-Gran, 2006). Drawing upon the projections of Sohngen and Sedjo (2006), at an economically competitive price to many other mitigation options of US$27.20 per ton of CO_2, nearly all of the 190 million ha in the twenty-two tropical forest hotspots could be conserved by 2020 if REDD policies provide not only for the avoidance of pending forest loss but for the conservation of carbon in all intact forests.

However, efforts to advance international commitments to REDD as a foremost climate-change mitigation option should also focus on the

(2006), at an offset price of US$5.40 per ton of CO_2, which is on par with the voluntary market price, approximately 440 million ha of tropical forest could be conserved through REDD payments during the twenty-first century. This conserved area could include all tropical forest hotspots and an important proportion of the nearly 714 million ha of tropical forest in the high-biodiversity wilderness areas of the Congo, New Guinea, and Amazonia. While these projections are as yet unsubstantiated, pending more rigorous analysis, it is certain that a significant proportion of the remaining tropical forests of the planet could be conserved with REDD investments.

Case Study: Mexico—La Selva Lacandona

Covering approximately 1.8 million ha, the Selva de Lacandona region of southern Mexico is home to several indigenous people, including the Lacandon Maya that number fewer than 2,000 members. The Selva de Lacandona is also one of the biologically richest protected areas in Mexico, with a number of endangered vertebrates and at least fifteen vulnerable or endangered plants. The diverse forests of Lacandona are under pressure from illegal land incursions for agriculture, unsustainable cattle ranching, and unauthorized logging. Local conservation and community organizations, in partnership with Conservation International, have undertaken a mixed REDD and reforestation project to create a new indigenous forest reserve and reforest

To ease crowding on the islands of Java and Bali, the government offers five acres, a year's worth of rice, and a one-way air ticket to anyone who will move to an undeveloped region—in this case a freshly cut rain forest in Irian Jaya (West Papua), the most eastern province of Indonesia.
GEORGE STEINMETZ

degraded agricultural lands.

The focus of the conservation efforts is La Cojolita, a forested mountain chain that is a natural corridor between national parks in Mexico and Guatemala. The project will reduce deforestation and associated greenhouse gas emissions in the 40,000 ha Sierra la Cojolita and undertake reforestation on 10,000 ha of communal lands, resulting in a net increase in the amount of sequestered carbon on the landscape. The project will provide jobs to local inhabitants, train farmers in improved grazing and cropping practices that enhance productivity, and promote sustainable tourism in the local communities and their protected forests.

REDD Approaches and Issues

While the critical role of forests in the Earth's carbon cycle and the approximate magnitude of forests' contribution to atmospheric CO_2 increases were known during the negotiation of the Kyoto Protocol, uncertainties and risks prevented their inclusion in the Clean Development Mechanism (CDM). Specifically, negotiation of the UNFCCC's Marrakech Accords led to the exclusion of "avoided deforestation" projects under the CDM due to concerns by several parties related to issues that must be resolved for REDD to be a legitimate carbon offset for regulatory frameworks and markets. These include the following:

- Leakage—The indirect effects of a mitigation project on GHG emissions outside the project or country boundaries, which engenders emissions from threats abated by the project such as displacement of logging pressures from one forest area to another
- Non-permanence—The result when the carbon "protected" through REDD is released to the atmosphere at a future date due to natural or human disturbance

All carbon-offset projects under the CDM must meet the criterion of "additionality," demonstrating that the carbon offset would not have occurred in the absence of the explicit project/investment. In the case of REDD, additionality requires substantiation that emissions from deforestation or degradation would have occurred in the absence of the REDD project. This issue has been a particularly vexing one for conservationists and for countries with historically low rates of deforestation and high forest cover, as the leading proposals for methodologies demonstrating REDD additionality are linked to demonstration of historic evidence of deforestation threat (da Fonseca et al., 2007).

Referring to historical trends and threats is methodologically incorrect, as it ignores legitimate current and future threats to intact forest areas that have not been historically threatened. In countries with an expanding agricultural frontier, such as Bolivia, reference to a historical precedent could underestimate deforestation rates in the next period by as much as 50% (Killeen et al., 2007). Historical baselines may also create the perverse incentive to establish credible threats of deforestation and degradation in areas that have been historically conserved, simply so that these areas may qualify for compensation for forest protection. More progressive proposals suggest compensation not only for the avoidance of emissions, but for the preservation of forest carbon stocks (Prior, O'Sullivan, and Streck, 2007; da Fonseca et al., 2007) so that those countries and landowners that have historically conserved their forests may benefit from their contribution to conservation of this global public good.

In the face of the human-driven climate change crisis, tropical forests are gaining market value, not for the full suite of carbon storage and other ecosystem services they provide, but for the avoidance of costs to humanity of increased GHG emissions from their loss. Markets emerging for forestry mitigation actions are payments to regulate the flux of carbon, both to increase stored carbon through reforestation and restoration and to prevent further carbon loss through deforestation and degradation. This is an important step in overcoming traditional undervaluing of tropical forests, but is incomplete. A more aggressive policy and market approach favoring equivalent carbon offset values for all remaining forests is warranted. For the 50- to 100-year time frame in which we must pursue all options to stabilize atmospheric CO_2 levels at 400 to 450 ppm, all forests will be under threat of conversion and degradation. To the extent that it would be economical to log, mine, or transform them to alternative uses, much of the remaining tropical forests are under such threat now.

(ibid.). To put this into perspective, whereas it will require $40 to $50 billion to capture and store one billion tons of CO_2 from new coal plants, the same amount of money would prevent the release of eight times this amount of carbon dioxide through avoided deforestation. Moreover, whereas alternative energy technologies and emissions reduction alternatives for many industrial sectors may require years of research and development, the technology required to successfully implement REDD mitigation activities exists today.

The low costs for REDD are encouraging, given the call by climate scientists for stabilizing atmospheric concentration of GHGs at 350 to 400 ppm in order to provide a high probability of not exceeding a global average temperature rise beyond 2 degrees Celsius. The availability of a large pool of REDD enables committing to more aggressive cuts that will be necessary to achieve these more rigorous stabilization targets.

REDD will require a significant global effort to establish regulatory frameworks, build capacity, and generate and sustain financing of forest conservation. Relative to other emissions-reduction options, however, REDD is expected to be relatively less expensive, at least in the immediate future. Current economic models suggest that including REDD and other forestry actions could reduce the overall costs of climate stabilization by 40% by 2050 compared to abatement measures without forestry (Tavoni, Sohngen, and Bosetti, 2007). Other modeling studies, using alternative methodologies, have suggested that, while there are significant opportunities to protect forests in some regions at low costs, the marginal abatement cost curve could rise from very low costs up to around $30 per ton of CO_2 were deforestation to be eliminated completely (Stern, 2006).

The opportunity costs of forest conservation in rural landscapes of the developing tropics are in many cases quite low, most notably when the alternatives are largely subsistence activities such as shifting cultivation, smallholder livestock, and selective logging for fuel, timber, and fiber. REDD costs are expected to be among the lowest for CO_2 emissions-mitigation options. Research commissioned by the Stern Review suggests that REDD compensation in tropical forest nations could yield CO_2 reductions for under $5 per ton and possibly for as little as $1 per ton of CO_2 in some regions, based upon the opportunity costs of land no longer available for agriculture

The potential for a new development paradigm, linked to and financed by REDD, has appeared at a point in time when many developing countries are experiencing unprecedented economic growth. The global demand for agricultural commodities, biofuels, and minerals, accordingly, has placed extraordinary pressure on existing transportation infrastructure, and governments are upgrading highway systems to improve the competitive position of their export sectors. In South America, for instance, governments hope to create a regional economy by integrating transportation, energy, and communications infrastructure, but such investments also threaten the ecological integrity of the Amazon Wilderness Area (Killeen, 2007). This combination of market conditions increases the challenges and imperatives to making REDD effective.

For a REDD mechanism to be successful in slowing deforestation on frontier landscapes, it must deal with—and alter—the economic calculus of individuals acting in their own short-term economic interest. The agricultural frontier is populated by individuals who view deforestation as part of the legitimate development process of securing land tenure, the monetization of capital assets (timber exploitation), and access to credit and the ability to commercialize production (Fearnside, 2001; Margulis, 2004; Killeen, 2007). In order to deal with the extremely difficult challenges of the agricultural frontier, REDD initiatives should incorporate: 1) A focus on the individual landholder, as well as the community. 2) Interventions by the state designed to manipulate market mechanisms, rather than reliance on statutory regulations that attempt to dictate the actions of individuals. 3) Legitimate and secure land-titling as a priority and prerequisite to REDD financing. 4) Alternative production systems that provide decent jobs and successfully compete with deforestation-based traditional development. Finally, income from REDD should not be used to pay "rents" to governments or communities, because these will eventually be viewed as entitlements rather than as payment for ecosystem services. REDD mechanisms should avoid burdensome bureaucratic requirements, such as those that characterize the CDM of the Kyoto Protocol, as they will exclude the very actors that are essential for reducing deforestation (Killeen, 2007).

Complementary Strategies: Protected Areas and REDD

Protected areas are the cornerstone of the global community's strategy for conserving intact forests, grasslands, and other natural habitats for their rich biodiversity, cultural and spiritual values, and the myriad ecosystems, goods, and services that they provide. Indeed, there are now more than 100,000 protected sites worldwide covering more than 12% of the Earth's land surface (Chape et al., 2005). In addition to being the most effective tool for maintaining Earth's unique diversity of plants and animals and critical ecosystem services (e.g., freshwater supplies), the global protected area system should also be seen as an extremely effective and cost-effective means of mitigating climate change. Protected areas provide a very robust way to mitigate forest conversion and degradation in otherwise threatened landscapes and thereby prevent millions of tons of CO_2 from entering the atmosphere annually, and their role can and should increase dramatically in the future.

Under additionality requirements, forests must be shown to be under threat of deforestation or degradation to be eligible for carbon credits and potential REDD funding. It may be therefore argued that their legal protection status and historical investment in their conservation would preclude additionality through REDD investment in the management of existing protected areas. That is, because existing protected areas are already legally protected and therefore theoretically not under threat of deforestation or degradation, REDD funding could not reduce CO_2 emissions. However, a closer look at the global protected area system suggests that categorizing existing protected areas as ineligible for potential REDD funding is unjustified. Despite their legal protection status, most protected areas are under threat of deforestation or degradation, even those that have historically been well-protected. Investment is often insufficient, and funding for staff, infrastructure, and operations is therefore required. Rather than being off the table, investments in protected areas should be a top priority for REDD funding. They represent a large and increasing area of the land sequestering carbon, and much of the work to ensure their demarcation and continuity has already been carried out. Furthermore, given their high biodiversity and ecosystem service values, protected areas should be given preferentially high priority in REDD funding.

Case Study: Madagascar—Mantadia-Zahamena Conservation Corridor

The thin rainforest band covering the central-eastern escarpment of Madagascar is some of most threatened real estate on the island. Forests of the Mantadia and Zahamena protected areas, and the newly designated Conservation Area that connects them, lie between the capital city of Antananarivo and the principal eastern port of Tamatave and are bounded on their northwestern end by Madagascar's most productive rice-producing region. These forests are also among the most biologically rich and important for conservation of Madagascar's unique fauna and flora, including some of the most endangered lemurs and many other threatened species.

The Mantadia-Zahamena Conservation Corridor project is designed to protect forests, mitigate climate change, and contribute to local livelihoods. Conceived and implemented in close partnership with the government of Madagascar and local communities, the project combines REDD activities in a core forest area, reforestation on degraded lands, and the expansion of agroforestry systems in communal gardens. The project's climate change mitigation goals are to prevent deforestation of the threatened forest corridor and sequester carbon in reforested and agroforestry areas. Under the project, more than 400,000 ha of standing rain forest are being protected, while 3,500 ha are being reforested with native species and fruit gardens. It will generate carbon offsets eligible for both Certified (under the CDM of the Kyoto Protocol) and Voluntary Emissions Reductions. Over the 30-year life of the project, the forest conservation and reforestation components of the project are expected to generate a net emissions reduction benefit of over 4.5 million tons CO_2. Income generated by the carbon offsets will provide direct funding to the government and to local communities for conservation of the remaining forests. The project is expected to create 200 jobs over a seven-year period, improve agricultural production, and further diversify local livelihoods.

Case Study: Madagascar—Makira Conservation Area

In Madagascar's northeastern rainforest region, Conservation International, the Wildlife Conservation Society (WCS), and the Malagasy government have launched a voluntary REDD initiative aiming at conserving the Makira Conservation Area, which is the core area of the largest contiguous tract of pristine rain forest remaining on the island. More than 50% of Madagascar's floral biodiversity can be found in the greater Makira region. Among its various terrains and diverse bioclimatic zones, Makira is an important stronghold for the endangered lemur (*Indri indri*) and the Madagascar serpent eagle (*Eutriorchis astur*). In addition, the forests of Makira maintain connectivity between the Masoala and Anjanaharibe-Sud protected areas, providing an important genetic corridor and ensuring the ecological integrity of one of the most diverse and intact areas of Madagascar.

The WCS-GOM-CI partnership aims to promote conservation and sustainable development in the 460,000 ha region through sustainable financing for conservation, promotion of community-based resource management in buffer areas, and funding for sustainable development initiatives. The REDD project was formulated on the principle of preventing deforestation of the 350,000 ha Makira forest, which is under active pressure for shifting agriculture. By protecting the remaining forests and reducing the rate of forest loss, the quantity of CO_2 released into the atmosphere will be significantly reduced. An assessment by Winrock International suggested that that the emission of over 9 million tons of CO_2 will be avoided through the Makira forest protection activities over the life of the project. Activities intended to reduce deforestation include participatory management of buffer zones and boundaries of the conservation area, improved patrolling and protected area management, financing of alternative livelihood initiatives, and training in sustainable agriculture. Investors benefiting from emissions offsets through the project include Mitsubishi Group, NavTech, and the music group Pearl Jam.

Research at a range of scales and using a range of methodologies has demonstrated that, in general, protected areas reduce deforestation (Bruner et al., 2001, Sánchez-Azofeifa et al., 2003; Naughton-Treves, Buck, and Brandon, 2005; Nepstad et al., 2006). However, this does not mean that simply creating protected areas will ensure the protection of forests within their boundaries. On the contrary, numerous protected areas do not have the financing necessary to ensure their effective protection, and quite a few are in a state of crisis (van Schaik, Terborgh, and Dugelby, 1997; Curran et al., 2004).

Good management (along with factors such as political and legal support, good governance, etc.) plays a central role in determining protected area effectiveness. Sufficient and experienced staff, good community relations, and well-demarcated borders are broadly identified as being particularly valuable (Terborgh et al., 2002, Dudley et al., 2004). Supporting these and other important management activities requires sufficient and stable financing. Adequately funded protected areas (assuming they spend efficiently) are more likely to prevent deforestation than inadequately funded ones. Currently, funding is far from sufficient, especially in developing countries (James, Gaston, and Balmford, 2001; Bruner, Gullison, and Balmford, 2004). Moreover, many protected areas suffer from damaging fluctuations in funding (Emerton, Bishop, and Thomas, 2006). REDD financing to prevent such fluctuations

would further reduce the amount of deforestation that takes place within the global protected area system and could go a long way in ensuring long-term sustainable funding sources for these areas.

A number of factors suggest that investments in new and existing protected areas would be both cost effective, and relatively low-risk, in terms of options for decreasing carbon emissions. Protected areas are, by definition, a tool for maintaining natural habitats such as standing forests. As a tool designed for that purpose, they are one of the few land allocations that provide a legal framework designed to prevent forest from being cleared. Further, where funding is available, protected areas have the management structure in place to ensure protection; they are likely to be one of the most secure means for protecting standing forests and their carbon.

The cost per ton of avoiding CO_2 emissions through support for protected areas is also likely to be far lower than the cost per ton of other climate-change mitigation strategies. For a REDD agreement to be economically attractive to a private actor, it would generally need to cover not only the entire cost of forest management for conservation (unless complementary subsidies are available), but also the opportunity cost of foregoing logging or conversion to non-forest land uses. In a protected area, in contrast, REDD funding would need to cover only management costs to be both worthwhile for protected area managers and effective in reducing carbon emissions. In fact, covering full management costs in a protected area is likely to represent a maximum cost, as most protected areas already receive at least some funding from other sources. Finally, protected areas are typically far larger than individual private lands. Given that the per-ha cost of management for conservation decreases rapidly as conservation areas increase in size (Balmford et al., 2003), private conservation initiatives that cannot aggregate large areas will likely be far more expensive in terms of per-ha management costs and, thus, per-ton costs of reducing CO_2 emissions.

Which countries and areas would potentially benefit most from REDD investment in protected areas? Potential revenue from REDD depends on factors such as deforestation and degradation levels, carbon densities, and protection effectiveness. Protected area management costs, in turn, depend on factors including protected area size, national and local cost levels, and the types and magnitudes of threat. While some of these factors would cause management cost and potential REDD funding to increase together (e.g., level of threat), others (e.g., carbon densities or lower management costs in developing countries) suggest high potential for protected areas to generate carbon revenues that meet or exceed their management costs. A back-of-the-envelope bounding exercise using deforestation and carbon-density data for tropical countries from the UN Food and Agriculture Organization (FAO, 2007) and protected area costs modeled by Bruner et al. (2004), suggests that those protected areas that could generate the greatest revenue streams beyond their management costs are likely to fall disproportionately among the world's poorest countries, especially in Africa. These countries have some of the highest deforestation rates and lowest protected areas management costs in the world.

Case Study: Liberia—National Protected Area System

Liberia contains 4.5 million ha of lowland tropical forest, giving it by far

A quetzal rests in the rain forest in the El Triunfo Biosphere
Reserve of the Sierra Madre range of Chiapas, Mexico.
THOMAS D. MANGELSEN

the largest areas of forest in the highly threatened Guinean Forests of West Africa hotspot. These forests are immensely important for their biological diversity, containing the last long-term viable populations of several endemic species, including the pygmy hippopotamus (*Hexaprotodon liberiensis*), the zebra duiker (*Cephalophus zebra*), Jentink's duiker (*Cephalophus jentinki*), and the Liberian mongoose (*Liberiictis kuhni*). As the country recovers from the devastating impacts of a fourteen-year civil war, the government of Liberia has been working to increase funding and capacity to manage its natural resources effectively. This has focused on designing a national forest strategy, known as the "3C" approach, to include areas zoned for Community, Conservation, and Commercial uses.

Liberia's Carbon Working Group, co-hosted by Liberia's Forestry Development Authority and its Environmental Protection Agency, is leading the integration of REDD and carbon financing into this national forest strategy. This working group, which includes several international NGOs and lending institutions and the U.S. Forest Service, is collaborating with the government to identify pilot sites for project implementation, build capacity within the Liberian government with respect to carbon financing, and analyze deforestation trends and future land-use scenarios. Financing from the sale of REDD credits would be the funding mechanism through which protected areas would be managed. The project involves effective management and monitoring of protected areas to reduce emissions from deforestation. The potential protected areas include up to 1.5 million ha of intact tropical forest, representing a very significant reservoir of stored carbon. Managing the forests of Liberia for carbon storage will provide a sustainable income stream for protected areas management, employment, and direct benefits for forest-dependent communities.

Numerous and substantial benefits would be gained in allocating REDD financing to the effective management of protected areas. This approach would reduce the cost of meeting emissions targets and would result in relatively lower risk and greater permanence of emissions reductions in many cases. In all instances, it would generate income for poor countries with limited resources for protected area conservation and secure the biodiversity, ecosystem services, and cultural and historical value of those natural areas recognized as most valuable. If properly designed, it would also ensure resource flows to the local communities living in proximity to these areas.

Conclusion: An Opportunity We Cannot Afford to Miss

If current trends continue, tropical deforestation will release about 50% as much carbon into the atmosphere by 2100 as has been emitted from fossil-fuel combustion since the start of the Industrial Revolution (Houghton, 2005). By far the greatest and most immediate CO_2 emissions potential in the forestry section lies in reducing emissions from deforestation, which continues at a gross rate of some 13 million ha per year (FAO, 2007). What is more, we already have the knowledge and market willingness to capture this great mitigation potential and to virtually eliminate deforestation within a generation. What are urgently needed are the policies and secure, efficient financial instruments necessary to fast track such activity immediately and at a global scale.

The Earth's richest terrestrial habitats are sanctuaries for the majority of biological diversity and serve as the principal terrestrial carbon stocks and regulators of carbon flux between the Earth and the atmosphere. Global recognition of the carbon value of forests and the consequences of GHG emissions from unabated forest loss and degradation is a long overdue change in the modern economic view of tropical forests. Capturing the immediate potential for climate-change mitigation under REDD is a necessary step in the required, aggressive pursuit of CO_2 stabilization targets, and it offers a historic, time-sensitive opportunity to provide long-term financial incentives for the conservation of intact tropical forests. Given the dire consequences of carbon release, diminished freshwater supply, exhaustion of forest products and services directly beneficial to humanity, and the massive species extinction that would result, continued tropical deforestation simply cannot continue. While we must acknowledge that, in the very short term, tropical forests will be lost due to a multiplicity of drivers and human needs, the opportunity now exists to turn the tide from short-sighted destruction to conservation for a vast majority of the remaining tropical forests of the planet.

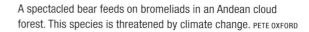

A spectacled bear feeds on bromeliads in an Andean cloud forest. This species is threatened by climate change. PETE OXFORD

Hope for Borneo's "People of the Forest"

An adult male orangutan named Jari Manis rests in a tree in Gunung Palung National Park, in Indonesia.

LEFT: Rhinoceros hornbills perch in a tree high in the Dipterocarp rain forest of Gunung Palung National Park in Indonesia.

Photographs by Tim Laman

TIM LAMAN REMEMBERS a scene that seemed to typify the dilemma of Indonesia's orangutans.

"We were traveling upriver from the nearest village by boat to our study area," said the photographer, who is also a field biologist. "It used to be a 12-hour trip through lush forests, because the 90,000-hectare Gunung Palung National Park where we observe orangutans was once surrounded by rain forest many times the size of the park. But through the years along the route the forest has been burned, cleared, and turned into fields.

"This particular year there had been a big drought, so huge fires burned the dry forest. Along the river there remained a thin strip of trees, and a single orangutan was hanging out in that little strip, with charred wasteland behind him. You knew that he had survived when many others had probably been wiped out, and you just hoped that he could make it to a bigger patch of forest."

For Laman, who has been observing and studying orangutans in the wild for more than 20 years, it was like the loss of family. He came to know more than 30 individuals by following them from dawn to dusk, trying to get in position to get good photographs to record their life in the wild. Orangutans spend 90 per cent of their time in trees, where they move rather slowly, so it was fairly easy to follow them from the ground. After first trying to get away from him, they eventually grew accustomed to the human far below and tolerated his presence.

"It's amazing to spend time with them," he said. "I remember one big male who came down to the ground fairly near me to eat termites. It started to rain, and he pulled a large leaf off a tree and held it over his head like an umbrella. I thought, wow, we're looking at real intelligence here."

In fact researchers consider orangutans among the most intelligent of the great apes, more intelligent than chimpanzees. So human-like are they that their name in Indonesian means "person of the forest." More solitary than the communal chimps, they spend most time alone, males and females getting together only to mate. Only two or three orangutans may occupy a square kilometer.

A one-year-old orangutan named Bekti and her mother, Beth, share a tree in Gunung Palung.

That space is shrinking due to the same forces that cause climate change—deforestation and conversion to agriculture. Illegal logging within the park forced Laman and his wife, Cheryl Knott, assistant professor of anthropology at Harvard University, to close down their research several years ago. The future of orangutans looked bleak.

"Fortunately, the Indonesian government is now doing a better job of protecting the park," Laman said, "and Cheryl and her collaborators have rebuilt the research site and are back there conducting studies.

"About 2,000 orangutans now live in Gunung Palung, one of 5-10 places where that many can be found. I think there is a reasonable chance that we can save enough habitat for them to continue to exist."

Brazilian laborers walk past burning fields cleared for cattle pasture. RON HAVIV

Years of Watching the Rain Forest Disappear

Photographs by Daniel Beltrá

SINCE 2001, photographer Daniel Beltrá has been traveling to the rain forests of Brazil, recording their destruction. He wonders how long it can continue before the entire Amazonian forest is no more.

"I've been going there regularly, about two to four months a year," said the Spanish-born photographer. "I can't tell the rate of forest loss just by looking because we're talking about devastation on a huge scale, and I only look at one location at a time. I have to rely on statistics, and the statistics say that it is going away very fast."

Destruction follows a pattern, he said. Individuals move into an area, log it, and clear the land to graze cattle or grow crops. After they've occupied an area for a time they try to get the paper to prove they own it, saying 'look, we've lived here for several years so it's our home.'

Aiding the process are big corporations, big farm owners, and many individuals that buy up huge areas or log illegally on what are designated as Indian lands. After logging it they clear the remainder and often plant huge fields of soybeans. A few years ago a downturn in the soy market slowed forest destruction, Beltrá said, but the current high price of soy has heightened clearing again.

The building of roads also facilitates settlement of an area, especially if the roads are paved and can be used in the rainy season. Indigenous people are seen as an impediment and often forcibly removed.

"There's a lot of violence," said Beltrá. "It's a situation similar to the Old West in the United States."

Even he has not felt safe recording the devastation, shooting many of his pictures from aircraft. "Access to ground being cleared is very difficult. If they hear you are working with environmentalists and doing photography, you are not very welcome."

The Brazilian government is trying to implement policies to slow down the process, he said, but it is not strong enough to have much effect over such a wide area. Local headquarters of IBAMA, the government organization that polices the environment, have been burned, and government agents have been fired upon by land developers. Beltrá thinks the international community should offer help to the Brazilian government in implementing their policies, before it's too late.

A blue-and-gold macaw perches above Ariau, near Manaus in the central Brazilian Amazon.

LEFT: An Enawene-Nawe boy swims in a river near Juina, in the Brazilian state of Mato Grosso. The survival of these people is now threatened by logging and large-scale agriculture.

149

A flight between the Brazilian cities of Manaus and Santarem exposes an area of 1,645 hectares illegally logged to plant soy. Scenes like this repeat themselves in many places in Amazonia. DANIEL BELTRÁ

Reforestation
and Agroforestry

With the appropriate design
and management, planting and
conserving trees in agricultural
landscapes offers significant
and immediate opportunities
to absorb carbon dioxide from
the atmosphere and to store it
in the vegetation and soil, all
while conserving biodiversity
and providing sustainable
livelihoods.

A CLIMATE FOR LIFE

The Synya River winds through the Yugyd-Va National Park near Pechora, Komi, Russia, the largest tract of old-growth boreal forest left in Europe. Although reforestation can be a positive conservation tool, the best way to protect healthy ecosystems is by avoiding deforestation in the first place.
PETER ESSICK

PREVIOUS PAGES:
Reforestation with non-native species can sequester carbon, but it does not provide the biodiversity benefits of intact forest.
DANIEL BELTRÁ

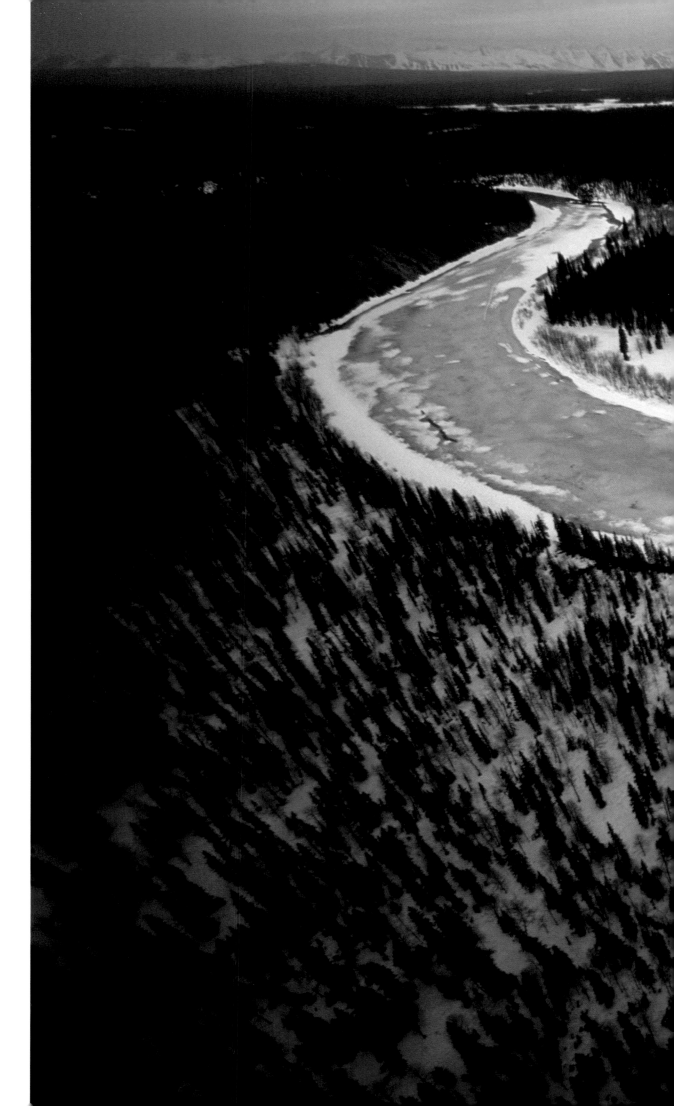

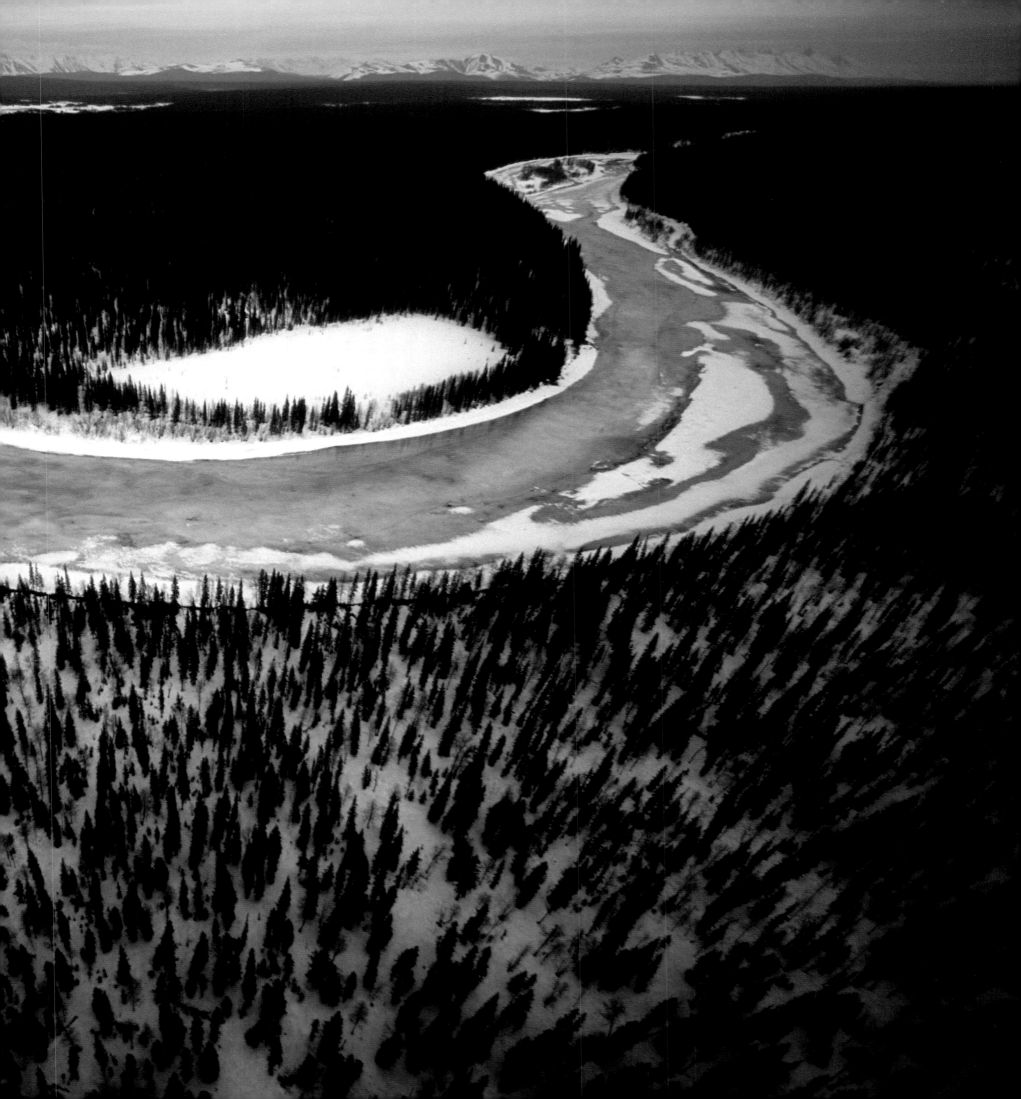

A CLIMATE FOR LIFE

This second-growth forest near Jokkmokk, Sweden, is sustainable if it is replanted following a timber harvest. When carefully managed, plantation forests can serve as reliable sources of timber and other wood products for local use.
PETER ESSICK

CHAPTER FIVE

Reforestation and Agroforestry

Celia A. Harvey, Goetz Schroth, Lorena Soto-Pinto,
Olaf Zerbock, Jon Philipsborn

Planting and conserving trees in agricultural landscapes—whether as mixed-forest plantations or as diverse agroforestry systems—can help mitigate climate change while achieving additional conservation and livelihood benefits. Reforestation and agroforestry offer significant and immediate opportunities to absorb substantial quantities of carbon dioxide from the atmosphere and store it in the vegetation and soil. In addition, both activities can potentially help to reduce deforestation and land-use changes that release greenhouse gas emissions, thereby further mitigating climate change.

Agroforestry and reforestation can also make significant contributions to biodiversity conservation and sustainable livelihoods. Both have enormous potential to conserve biodiversity by providing habitats and resources, reducing stress on existing forests, and maintaining natural corridors between ecosystems. These corridors will become increasingly important as species are forced to shift their habitats in response to climate change. At the same time, agroforestry systems and mixed-forest plantations can contribute to sustainable development by diversifying employment opportunities and providing sustainable supplies of goods and ecological services. With appropriate design, management, and strategic placement, diverse agroforestry systems and forest plantations are therefore poised to play a critical role in climate-change mitigation, biodiversity conservation, and preservation of human welfare. As such, they are particularly attractive options for global mitigation efforts.

This chapter first examines the potential of forest plantations and agroforestry systems to sequester carbon dioxide and reduce the emissions of greenhouse gases from land-use changes and deforestation. It then highlights the ways in which diverse forest plantations and agroforestry systems can contribute to conserving biodiversity and improving human livelihoods and provides two case studies illustrating how these benefits can be achieved. Finally, the chapter discusses some of the challenges to scaling up reforestation and agroforestry activities to their full mitigation and conservation potential.

When forest plantations, like the one being planted here, and agroforestry systems are newly established, the growing trees sequester and accumulate significant quantities of carbon in their biomass and, depending on the previous vegetation cover, also in the soil. PETER DENNEN

Contrasting eucalyptus and natural forests divide the land above the Jaguari River watershed in Brazil. It is part of the Serra da Cantareira that provides 50% of São Paulo's drinking water. SCOTT WARREN

Key Definitions and Units

Before highlighting the role of reforestation and agroforestry as mitigation and conservation tools, it is important to clearly define what each of these activities entails. Reforestation refers broadly to the conversion of non-forested land to forest land through planting, seeding, or promoting natural seed sources. The Kyoto Protocol makes a technical distinction between the reforestation of land that was previously forested (reforestation) and land that was not under forest during the last fifty years (afforestation), but aside from differences in the types of land being replanted, these two activities are essentially identical. Consequently, this chapter uses the term reforestation broadly to refer to both of these activities, but, where appropriate, it highlights differences in the impact of reforesting both kinds of areas. Reforestation can occur at different scales (from small areas of a few hectares planted by farmers to massive industrial plantations covering many kilometers), may consist of either a single species or multiple species, and may involve native or exotic species or a mixture thereof. These differences can have important implications for mitigation, conservation, and livelihood outcomes.

Agroforestry refers to the intentional integration of trees with agricultural crops, pastures, and/or livestock production (Nair, 1993). Common agroforestry systems include windbreaks, shaded perennial crops (such as coffee and cacao), shaded annual crops, silvopastoral systems (where trees are integrated with livestock production), home gardens, and diverse agroforests, among others. Like plantations, agroforestry systems can differ in their structure, composition, and management and these differences influence their ability to mitigate climate change and conserve biodiversity.

Another important clarification is required on the units used to quantify carbon sequestration and greenhouse gas emissions. When plants take up carbon dioxide from the atmosphere, they store it in their leaves, stems, trunks, and roots as sugars. The stored carbon within plant biomass is measured as the number of tons of carbon present in the biomass per hectare of land (one ton = 1,000 kg). When this plant biomass is burned or decomposes, the carbon is emitted in the form of carbon dioxide (CO_2, a greenhouse gas), with every ton of carbon stored within plant biomass releasing the equivalent of 3.67 tons of

CO_2. These emissions are measured in terms of the number of tons of carbon dioxide emitted. Throughout this chapter and book, all references to the carbon stored in plant biomass refer to the tons of carbon per hectare, whereas all information on emissions from deforestation and other land changes are given in tons of carbon dioxide per hectare.

Mitigating Climate Change through Carbon Sequestration

Reforestation and agroforestry can help mitigate climate change in two ways—by directly removing carbon dioxide from the atmosphere and by reducing the emissions of greenhouse gases from land use changes and deforestation. When forest plantations and agroforestry systems are newly established, the growing trees sequester and accumulate significant quantities of carbon in their biomass and, depending on the previous vegetation cover, also in the soil.

According to a meta-analysis of carbon sequestration studies conducted by Richards and Stokes (2004), forest plantations can store anywhere between 0.6 to 18.75 tons of carbon per hectare per year, and may accumulate between 15 to 175 tons of carbon per hectare over their lifetime. In contrast, agroforestry systems, which tend to be planted less densely than plantations to allow crops or grass to grow among the trees, are reported to store from 1.5 to 3.5 tons of carbon per hectare per year (Montagnini and Nair, 2004), and may have a total carbon storage potential of 12–228 tons of carbon per hectare over fifty years (Albrecht and Kandji, 2003; Kandji et al., 2006). The specific rate of carbon accumulation and total carbon storage varies across individual forest plantations and agroforestry systems, reflecting differences in species composition, planting density, management regimes, and the initial site conditions of the land on which trees are planted, among other factors.

The choice of species and planting density is particularly important in determining how much carbon is stored. Individual tree species differ in the rate of carbon accumulation, as well as the total carbon they sequester over their lifetime. Fast-growing trees such as *Cordia alliodora*, *Eucalyptus* spp., and *Pinus* spp. generally sequester carbon more quickly than plantations of mixed native forests or natural regeneration of abandoned land, reaching peak

systems to prevent extensive shading of adjacent crops or pastures. Selective harvesting or thinning of plantations may temporarily reduce the biomass present at a site, but sometimes leads to higher overall carbon sequestration rates per unit area over time, as periodic removal of aboveground biomass can stimulate accelerated growth of the remaining trees. Fertilization of plantations may encourage tree growth and carbon uptake, but also increases the emission of nitrous oxide (a greenhouse gas), thereby reducing the plantation's overall mitigation impact (Mosier, 1998; Mutuo

carbon sequestration rates early in their growth cycles (Montagnini and Nair, 2004). In contrast, slower-growing hardwood species in both temperate and tropical regions may not reach their peak carbon capture rate until several years or even decades later (Richards and Stokes, 2004), but may accumulate more carbon over the long term, as these trees have longer life spans and often reach greater sizes. Consequently, while rapidly growing pioneer species can sequester more carbon than slower-growing species in the first decade of growth, in the long term it is the slower-growing species that may ultimately sequester more carbon due to their higher wood densities (Redondo-Brenes, 2007). Because species may also differ in how much carbon they store in their aboveground versus below-ground biomass (Lugo, 1992), the amount of carbon stored in a particular agroforestry system or forest plantation will depend on what mixture of tree species is planted. Carbon-capture rates also vary with plantation age, with younger plantations generally sequestering carbon at a higher rate than mature forests (Montagnini and Porras, 1998).

Management practices—such as selecting planting density, thinning, using fertilizers, tilling, and following harvesting and rotation schedules—also significantly influence carbon uptake and storage (Albrecht and Kandji, 2003; Conant, Paustian, and Elliott, 2001). Plantations or agroforestry systems with dense planting arrangements will generally sequester more carbon than those with fewer trees. However, lower tree densities may be desirable in agroforestry

et al., 2005). The rotation schedule or permanence of agroforestry systems or forest plantations will also impact carbon storage: Permanent agroforestry systems or forest plantations with long rotation times accumulate larger average amounts of biomass over a rotation cycle than systems that need to be replanted more frequently because of low productivity, disease, or harvesting (Schroeder, 1993).

The net contribution of newly planted forest areas and agroforestry systems to climate change mitigation also depends on the initial site conditions of the area that is replanted, particularly its existing carbon stocks. If trees are planted on degraded agricultural lands with little aboveground biomass and depleted soil carbon stocks, the net carbon uptake and storage can be considerable. However, if agroforestry systems and forest plantations replace land uses with high carbon stocks (such as old-growth tropical forests or native grasslands), the result will be a net loss of carbon from the system, exacerbating the climate-change problem. For example, old-growth tropical forests typically store 120 to 400 tons of carbon per hectare in aboveground vegetation (Laurence, 2007), compared to the range of 15 to 175 tons of carbon per hectare stored in forest plantations (Richards and Stokes, 2004). Consequently, it is critical that forest plantations and agroforestry never replace intact forests, native grasslands, or other carbon-dense habitat (e.g., peat lands or swamps), as such land conversions would negatively impact both the global climate (increasing

the emissions of greenhouse gases into the atmosphere) and the rich biodiversity associated with these ecosystems.

Other factors that will influence carbon sequestration and storage rates are the overall site conditions. In general, trees will grow faster in areas with favorable soils and microclimatic conditions (Silver, Ostertag, and Lugo, 2000). Establishing agroforestry and forest plantations in areas with suitable soils and microclimatic conditions is therefore likely to result in greater mitigation benefits than similar activities in areas where tree growth is slower.

Reducing Emissions through Conservation and Reduction

Planting new agroforestry systems and multi-species forest plantations is just one way in which agroforestry and reforestation can help mitigate climate change. Another approach is to avoid the conversion of land uses with high carbon stocks (e.g., traditional agroforestry systems, diverse plantations, or intact forests) to land uses with low carbon stocks, such as agriculture and pastures. Conserving diverse traditional agroforestry systems and preventing their conversion to other land uses helps prevent the release of carbon dioxide into the atmosphere, thereby reducing greenhouse gas emissions.

Many of the traditional agroforestry systems, such as the famous cabruca systems for cocoa-growing in Brazil or the multi-strata rubber agroforests of Indonesia that have high carbon stocks and high species diversity, are threatened by intensification, simplification, or outright conversion to land uses with lower carbon stocks, resulting in the additional emission of greenhouse gases. For example, the shade-grown coffee systems that were once wide-spread in Central and South America have widely been converted into plantations with monospecific shade and far lower biomass in an effort to increase coffee yields and accommodate modern, more productive coffee varieties (Perfecto et al., 1996). Many shaded cocoa plantations (cabrucas) in Brazil have lost much

of their stocks of large timber trees to logging during the cocoa crisis of the 1990s when farmers were desperate for alternative sources of revenue (Johns, 1999), and traditional agroforests in Indonesia are widely under pressure from conversion into industrial oil palm and rubber plantations. These processes result in net losses in biomass as well as habitat for native species. Countering these threats to traditional land-use systems remains a challenge, but needs to be priority for climate-change mitigation efforts.

Agroforestry and forest plantations can also potentially help reduce greenhouse gas emissions by reducing the pressure on nearby forests for timber and wood products. The clearing and burning of forests currently account for roughly 20% of all greenhouse gas emissions, with most of these emissions occurring in the tropics (Gullison et al., 2007). Agroforestry practices that allow farmers to cultivate a single piece of land over the long term, by maintaining high levels of soil fertility and productivity and generating higher profits per hectare, can help governments as well as local communities conserve forests and reduce greenhouse gas emissions from deforestation. Similarly, the establishment of small-scale, diverse forest plantations can provide alternative sources of timber, firewood, and other products to local communities, reducing their need to obtain these products from nearby forests and thereby reducing both the deforestation and degradation of adjacent forests (Schroth et al., 2004).

A worker waters seedlings at the edge of Maowusu Desert in Lingwu, China. With more than a dozen sandstorms occurring annually, such plantings are an attempt to control the desert from expanding. JASON LEE

Industrial forest plantations also play a key role in meeting society's need for timber and fuelwood, thereby potentially creating opportunities for enhanced forest protection and conservation elsewhere. Already, forest plantations supply about 35% of the global round-wood harvest, and this percentage is expected to increase (FAO, 2006). If these industrial plantations are established on degraded, non-forested land and result in reduced pressure on native forests, then the net climate benefit could be considerable. However, currently almost half of the 1.9 million hectares of forest plantations planted each year in tropical countries are established by converting natural forest ecosystems to managed forest plantations (Brown, 2000), and these activities result in the release of large quantities of greenhouse gases.

Potential for Global Mitigation

The establishment of new agroforestry systems and diverse forest plantations, coupled with the reduction of emissions from the conversion of established agroforestry systems to agricultural and low-carbon land uses, could make a significant contribution to global mitigation efforts if these activities were conducted at scale. The potential to sequester carbon through reforestation and agroforestry activities is particularly high, given the vast areas of degraded land globally. It is estimated that approximately 585 to 1,215 million hectares of degraded land in Africa, Asia, and the Americas are available for agroforestry and reforestation activities (Dixon et al., 1994). With agroforestry systems able to sequester an estimated 12 to 228 tons of carbon per hectare over 50 years, this translates into an estimated (rough) global potential for 1.1 to 2.2 billion tons of carbon that could be stored in terrestrial vegetation over the next fifty years (Albrecht and Kandji, 2003).

Another study suggests that 10.5 million hectares of land could be converted to agroforestry, assuming that 20% of the 15 million hectares that are annually deforested is put into agroforestry every year and that 3% of the 250 million hectares of degraded lands at the forest margins is converted to agroforests every year (i.e., 7.5 million hectares per year; Sánchez, 2000). If this were to happen, the global contribution of agroforestry to carbon sequestration would be on the order of 105 to 525 million tons of carbon per year, with

a modal value of 315 million tons of carbon per year (ibid.). If reforestation and agroforestry efforts are combined with efforts to reduce emissions from deforestation and degradation (i.e., the so-called REDD activities), the total mitigation potential is even greater. For example, the IPCC Fourth Assessment estimates that the global mitigation potential of all forestry and land-based activities could contribute to the net reduction of 1.3 to 4.2 gigatons (or billion tons) of CO_2 per year (Nabuurs et al., 2007).

Biodiversity and Sustainable Development

In addition to their important roles as carbon sinks, forest plantations and agroforestry systems can be carefully designed and managed to provide synergies with biodiversity conservation and sustainable development. In fact, diverse agroforestry systems in particular (and, to a lesser degree, multi-species forest plantations) are being widely touted as key examples of win-win situations, where the multiple objectives of carbon sequestration, biodiversity conservation, and sustainable livelihoods can be met simultaneously, without compromising any of the goals (Garrity, 2004; Makundi and Sathaye, 2004; Garrity et al., 2006). For these reasons, they are also widely recognized as potential tools for achieving many of the Millennium Development Goals, a global agenda to combat poverty, environmental degradation, hunger, and other global humanitarian challenges (Garrity et al., 2006). Both agroforestry systems and diverse forest plantations are also recognized as providing critical ecosystem services to human communities (Millennium Ecosystem Assessment, 2005). However, the extent to which agroforestry and reforestation activities provide these additional benefits is a function of several factors, including their design, management, and implementation.

Biodiversity Conservation

Agroforestry systems and small-scale, mixed forest plantations can potentially help conserve biodiversity by offering valuable resources and habitats to forest fauna and flora, maintaining landscape connectivity, and reducing pressure on intact forests (Schroth et al., 2004; Harvey, 2007). They may also serve as important genetic reservoirs for useful tree and plant species

A split-level perspective shows the roots and shoot of a young mangrove sapling in Cuba. Mangrove reforestation in degraded areas both protects coastlines and serves to store carbon.
JURGEN FREUND

that provide timber, food, fibers, and other materials to local communities. Other ways in which these systems can contribute to biodiversity conservation include restoring forest cover in existing protected areas, serving as buffers, and providing additional habitat for some species, provided that safeguards against their expansion into forest are in place. When located in agricultural landscapes, they may serve as corridors or stepping stones for animal movement across the agricultural matrix (Noss, 2001). This connectivity function will become increasingly important as climate change occurs and species must move to find new habitats and climates appropriate for their survival (Hannah, Midgley, and Millar, 2002). Thus, if diverse agroforestry and forest plantations are strategically positioned and managed, they can play an important role not only in mitigating climate change, but also in helping plant and animal species adapt, or cope with, climate change (Verchot et al., 2007).

However, not all reforested areas will confer these biodiversity benefits. In contrast to small-scale plantations and diverse agroforestry systems, the vast majority of industrial plantations are monocultures of fast-growing exotic species such as *Pinus* (which represents 20% of global forest plantations), *Eucalyptus* (10%), *Hevea* (5%), *Acacia* (4%), and *Tectona* (3%), that provide neither habitat nor resources to wildlife and plant species (FAO, 2001) and often have significant negative impacts on both terrestrial and aquatic ecosystems (Cannell, 1999). Large contiguous expanses of monoculture plantations lead to the homogenization of landscapes and the consequent loss of biodiversity (Wagner et al., 2006). These industrial plantations can also have significant impacts on runoff, stream flow, groundwater recharge, and water-table levels, affecting the amount of water available for both humans and aquatic ecosystems (Farley, Jobbágy, and Jackson, 2005). Consequently, the expansion of industrial forest plantations should be heavily scrutinized and assessed to avoid or minimize potential negative impacts on biodiversity conservation and local communities. In addition, if agroforestry or forest plantations are established on land that was never previously forested (e.g., grasslands, swamps, or native savannahs), their establishment is likely to lead to the loss of plant and animal species associated with the original ecosystems.

Sustainable Development

Reforestation and agroforestry activities can also be designed to contribute to sustainable development and can help countries achieve their Millennium Development Goals, particularly if they use multiple native species that provide direct benefits and services to local people (Sánchez, 2000; Garrity, 2004). Forest-based mitigation activities can serve as key sources of local employment and generate new sources of income through the sale of carbon credits, thereby helping to alleviate poverty in rural areas where these activities are implemented. Diverse agroforests are also important for the local economies due to the variety of products that they produce (Laird, Awung, and Lysinge, 2007). Diversified agroforestry systems, such as home gardens and agroforests, contain high numbers of edible plant species, as well as species that provide fibers, firewood, medicines, construction materials, and other commercially important products (Sánchez, 2000; Watson and Eyzaguirre, 2002). If carefully managed, they can serve as sustainable sources of timber and other wood products for local use, though sustainability hinges on the land being immediately replanted following harvesting. By virtue of combining trees with agricultural production, agroforestry systems can also play a key role in ensuring food security, as the trees help maintain yields, reduce soil erosion, and prevent losses in soil fertility. In addition, these systems provide many of the ecological services on which rural communities depend, such as water and nitrogen cycling, soil regeneration, and pollination, among others. Last, but not least, establishing agroforests and forest plantations can be a way for communities to ascertain their right over the land against competing claims from national governments (Michon, 2005; Millennium Ecosystem Assessment, 2005).

However, in contrast to diverse agroforestry systems and multi-species plantations, industrial plantations rarely provide direct benefits to local communities (except potentially as sources of employment). Because the exotic species are typically of little use to local people, much of the revenue typically stays within the forest company, and forest products are usually destined for export or use outside of the community (Nabuurs et al., 2007). In addition, the potential negative impacts of large-scale reforestation projects

Harvey, 2007). Key management practices that can enhance biodiversity conservation of forest plantations and agroforestry systems include minimal management and disturbance, careful and restricted use of pesticides and other chemical inputs, and long rotation periods that allow the forested areas to become key features of the agricultural landscapes (Harvey and Villalobos, 2007). In general, those systems that are the most floristically and structurally diverse, least managed and most forest-like, are likely to harbor the greatest diversity of plant and animal life. For example, monoculture plantations tend to have much lower animal diversity than either structurally complex plantations or intact, primary forests (Cannell, 1999; Barlow et al., 2007).

The location of reforested and agroforestry areas within the broader landscape is another key consideration for conservation planning (Schroth et al., 2004; Harvey and Sáenz, 2008). Agroforestry systems should only be established on existing, degraded agricultural and pasture land that has little biodiversity value and low biomass. Conversely, if they are established in areas that were previously forest habitats, both biomass carbon stocks and biodiversity will decrease, while the afforestation of native grasslands may increase aboveground biomass but lead to a loss in biodiversity, ecosystem services, underground soil carbon and root biomass, and freshwater decline (Jackson et al., 2002; Farley, Jobbágy, and Jackson, 2005).

The positioning of the plantation or agroforestry system can also determine its value for biodiversity conservation. If the reforested areas are positioned near remaining natural habitat, they may also serve as buffers to protected areas and native habitat remnants, as long as safeguards are included to ensure that they do not encroach on the remaining forest. Similarly, planting trees on degraded lands between isolated, remnant forest patches can create biological linkages or stepping stones for certain species, facilitating their dispersal and movement within agricultural landscapes (Harvey, 2007) and enabling them to

on water resources can also undermine sustainable development outcomes. Consequently, the expansion of industrial plantations should be avoided in regions where biodiversity is under direct threat (Donald, 2004) or where local community development is a priority, but may be appropriate in other contexts (e.g., where there is an urgent need to reduce pressure on existing forests by establishing plantations as alternative sources of timber; Brown, Palola, and Lorenzo, 2006). Last, but not least, care must also be taken to ensure that the establishment of these systems does not result in the displacement of economic or subsistence activities that will lead to forest clearing elsewhere, thereby effectively cancelling any potential climate benefits from carbon sequestration.

Multiple Benefits

While agroforestry systems and some small-scale, diverse plantations have the potential to deliver multiple benefits, these benefits do not automatically appear. Instead, they depend on the specific ways in which the systems are designed, managed, and located in the landscape.

To ensure the greatest value of these systems for biodiversity conservation, it is important to use a diverse mix of native tree species, including both slow-growing and fast-growing tree species and both timber species and species that provide habitat and food resources for wildlife (SCBD, 2003;

migrate more easily in response to climate change. Locating woodlots, plantations, and agroforests in degraded lands or fallow areas near communities and development poles may also mitigate threats to forests in other areas by meeting demands for wood products and diversifying or strengthening livelihoods.

In addition to designing agroforestry systems and forest plantations for biodiversity conservation, specific measures can also be taken to enhance their ability to alleviate poverty and improve human livelihoods. There are four essential design elements to include. First, it is important to incorporate species that provide multiple products to farmers, thereby increasing their resilience to market fluctuations and reducing vulnerability to crop losses. Second, farmers must plant high-value crops that can serve as sources of cash (and that can be sold or bartered) as well as crops for self sufficiency. Third, it is imperative to plant tree species that improve the productivity of crops and livestock (e.g., by fixing nitrogen, conserving soil, improving water infiltration, or serving as fodder for cattle). Finally, it is essential to include a diverse array of locally adapted crop varieties that farmers know and favor (Harvey, Schroth, and Zerbock, 2007). When possible, these systems should be based on local or indigenous knowledge and technologies, thereby reducing the dependence on often unreliable external services (Soto-Pinto et al., 2007). They should also be designed to generate sources of income and employment through value-added crops and products and to allow easy management.

While both the biodiversity and sustainable livelihood benefits are attainable in agroforestry systems and small, multi-species plantations, it is important to realize that there are some tradeoffs involved between mitigation, conservation, and livelihood goals (van Noordwijk et al., 1997). Designing agroforestry systems or plantations to maximize a particular objective (e.g., biodiversity conservation) may be distinct from how these systems would be designed if climate change mitigation were the only goal. For example, a monoculture of exotic tree species may provide substantial carbon benefits, yet be unacceptable from a conservation and livelihood perspective due to the associated negative impacts on biodiversity and local communities (Perfecto et al., 2005; Wagner et al., 2006). Win-win situations are possible, but win-lose situations and even lose-lose situations may also occur. Consequently, it is extremely important that all mitigation projects be carefully scrutinized in terms of not only their carbon benefits, but also their potential impacts on biodiversity and communities. Application of the Climate, Community, and Biodiversity Standard can also help ensure that projects are designed in ways that generate these multiple benefits and avoid any potential negative impacts on biodiversity and communities (CCBA, 2005). The following two case studies show ways in which successful projects have achieved multiple goals.

Case Study 1: Restoring Forests in the Rain forests of Ecuador

The coastal rain forests of northwestern Ecuador are exceptionally rich ecosystems, harboring more than 2,000 species of plants, more than 450 species of birds, and a wide array of reptiles and mammals, including many threatened species. Unfortunately, this unique biodiversity is highly threatened by logging and agricultural expansion. More than two-thirds of the region's original forest cover has been lost during the last thirty-five years. In addition to negatively impacting the region's plant and animal species, this widespread

Women from villages near Karatina in Kenya, part of Wangari
Maathai's Green Belt Movement, walk home past a nursery
of tree seedlings. Community livelihoods have flourished
under this successful, large-scale, reforestation movement.
GARY BRAASCH

deforestation has also resulted in the release of significant quantities of greenhouse gases as forests are cut and burned to make way for agriculture.

In order to conserve biodiversity and help mitigate climate change, Conservation International and its partner, Fundación Maquipucuna, initiated the Chocó-Manabí Corridor Reforestation project in 2005. The project aims to restore 265 hectares of degraded pasture lands overgrown with invasive pasture grasses and shrubs. Using a methodology approved by the Clean Development Mechanism, the project will plant a mixture of up to fifteen native tree species, including Pacche (*Nectandra acutifolia*), Nogal (*Juglans neotropica*), and Spanish cedar (*Cedrela odorata*). It is expected that the project will result in the mitigation of at least 80,000 tons of CO_2.

In addition to providing climate benefits, the reforestation will provide conservation benefits by buffering an adjacent private reserve, reforesting degraded areas, and restoring forest cover across an altitudinal gradient, thereby helping facilitate species migration. Local communities are also benefiting from the project through employment and training opportunities associated with reforestation activities.

Case Study 2: Sequestering Carbon in Chiapas, Mexico

Deforestation and land-use changes are a major source of greenhouse gas emissions in Mexico. Agroforestry systems have the potential to help reduce the country's carbon footprint and help mitigate climate change, both by sequestering carbon and reducing the emissions of gases from land burning. In Mexico, the agroforestry systems with the greatest mitigation potential are improved fallows, taungya systems consisting of trees integrated with corn production, and coffee agroforestry systems with timber species. These systems have high carbon-sequestration potential and are also compatible with the customs and cultures of local people. In addition, all of these systems can help conserve natural resources, while also protecting biodiversity and other environmental services.

The "Scolel té" project in Chiapas, Mexico, is a novel forest carbon project that aims to develop a prototype scheme for sequestering carbon in sustainable forest and agricultural systems. The project is one of the few worldwide

to work directly with small farmers on the establishment of a diverse suite of agroforestry systems (e.g., improved fallows shade coffee, silvopastoral systems, conservation and restoration) for carbon sequestration. The systems were selected in accordance with local and scientific criteria and differ in their carbon sequestration potential, depending on the numbers and types of trees incorporated into the system. For example, where coffee agroforestry systems in the region sequester carbon at an annual rate of 2.8 tons of carbon per hectare per year and can accumulate an average total of 115.9 tons of carbon per hectare, improved fallows accumulate carbon at a faster rate (6 tons of C per hectare per year) and have greater total carbon stocks (an average of 276.8 tons of carbon per hectare) (De Jong et al., 1997).

The carbon credits from the agroforestry systems are sold via a trust that consists of the following organizations: the Fondo Bioclimatico, managed by AMBIO, an organization in charge of the operative aspects and monitoring of the project; ECOSUR, which is responsible for undertaking research and forestry/agroforestry system design; and ECCM, which has extended the Mexican experience to Uganda and Mozambique and intends to create a voluntary carbon trade with sales of "credit prototypes in emissions reduction." All carbon credits are paid through the voluntary market.

In addition to helping mitigate climate change, the selected agroforestry systems also aim to solve other problems, such as low productivity related to slash-and-burn farming, sub-utilization, land scarcity and degradation, lack of forest products (timber, firewood), and the need for cash. The combination of timber species with crops has contributed to the re-evaluation of corn, coffee, and livestock farming systems; a better exploitation of limited space; an increase in products and services; and the intensification of land use, biodiversity conservation, and carbon capture.

The farmers benefit directly from the project, as they obtain payments for carbon sequestration as well as additional benefits from products such as posts, palm leaves, and pine needles. Other important benefits acquired through the project have included the acquisition of new management capacities, knowledge, and the rediscovery of a production system based on a culture of protection and conservation.

Women from 65 families in the Girka Pally community nuture 43,500 seedlings in this Hyderabad, India tree nursery every 6 months. The trees are used as part of a massive project involving 108 locations, 1579 women, and over 1.5 million saplings every year. STUART FRANKLIN

Barriers and Opportunities for Reforestation and Agroforestry Activities

Despite the potential for reforestation and agroforestry activities to sequester and store significant quantities of carbon, the current scale of these activities—and, consequently, their contribution to climate change mitigation—is still limited. Worldwide, there are an estimated 140 million hectares of forest plantations (primarily industrial plantations), and an additional 2.8 million hectares are reforested each year (FAO, 2006). The total area under agroforestry systems is unknown, although an estimated 1.2 billion rural people currently practice agroforestry in their communities and depend upon agroforestry products (Garrity et al., 2006). It is clear, however, that as the current rate at which new forest plantations and agroforestry systems are being established pales in comparison to the additional 585 to 1,275 million hectares of land deemed appropriate for reforestation (Dixon, 1995).

The limited scope of these activities is also illustrated by the disappointingly small number of A/R projects under the Clean Development Mechanism (CDM) of the Kyoto Protocol, which allows industrialized countries to meet their emissions reductions targets partially by offsetting their emissions through the enhancement of land-use sequestration in developing countries. Although reforestation activities (including agroforestry) are eligible for carbon trading under the CDM, these activities currently account for much less than 1% of all CDM credits, and only one project has been registered (UNFCCC, 2007). In addition, reforestation projects have to date been pursued in only a limited number of developing countries, primarily China and India. Initial estimates that as much as 5.3 million hectares of land in Africa, Asia, and Latin America could potentially be reforested under the CDM in the first commitment period [2008-2012] of the Kyoto Protocol have proven to be wildly optimistic (Waterloo et al., 2003).

The lack of large-scale plantations and agroforestry activities is due less to the challenges of establishing and planting trees than to the barriers that make these activities financially or logistically unattractive (Brown et al., 2000). Foresters have centuries of experience of successfully establishing and managing plantations, with detailed knowledge of the requirements and growth rates of individual timber species. However, experience with diverse, multi-species plantations is more recent and still an area of research (Evans and Turnbull, 2004; Piottoa et al., 2004). Farmers have traditionally used diverse agroforestry systems to meet both their agricultural and forestry needs and have detailed knowledge of how to integrate trees optimally into agricultural and pastoral activities (e.g., Conway, 1999; Soto-Pinto et al., 2007). There is consequently a vast scientific literature available about how to design, plant, and manage both plantations and agroforestry systems for carbon sequestration and timber production (e.g., Evans and Turnbull, 2004; Pearson, Walker, and Brown, 2005).

The problem in scaling up these activities is one of financial constraints, market access, administrative and political barriers, and lack of institutional capacity to organize and promote these activities. One of the greatest challenges for broader adoption of forest plantations and agroforestry systems is the lack of sufficient funding and financial incentives. Both types of activities require significant up-front investment to collect seeds and saplings, establish tree nurseries, prepare sites for planting, and plant trees, in addition to costs incurred during subsequent management activities such as weeding and pruning.

It is estimated that forestry sequestration projects in developing countries cost in the range of $0.50 to $7 per ton of CO_2, compared to $1.40 to $22.00 per ton of CO_2 for forestry projects in industrialized countries (Nabuurs et al., 2007). The range in costs is due to differences in the price of labor, opportunity costs, and land tenure. Landowners and investors are often risk-averse to financing these up-front expenses, especially since the carbon and associated co-benefits typically accrue gradually over many years, financial returns may not be apparent for decades, and there is uncertainty of whether they'll get a return on the future sale of carbon offsets. In addition, other land uses may provide greater financial returns than reforestation. The unfortunate result is that investors are much more likely to invest in large-scale industrial plantations consisting of a single timber or pulp species, which guarantee the delivery of significant revenue when the timber is later harvested (regardless of whether or not carbon credits are generated and sold), than in small-scale, diverse forest plantations or multi-strata agroforestry systems that typically

financial investment for compliance and often dissuade potential investors from implementing forestry projects (Masripatin, 2005). If the CDM process were simplified and streamlined, it would be much easier for tropical countries to be able to access the carbon credits for reforestation and agroforestry activities and these mitigation activities would likely be more common. In addition, the Kyoto Protocol imposes a capricious limit to the number of forest carbon credits that industrialized countries can offset each year (currently 1% of the countries' annual emissions reduction target during the commitment period), which places forestry at a disadvantage relative to other offsets, such as the use of renewable energy or industrial-emissions avoidance.

A related issue is that forestry credits are considered to be temporary under the current Clean Development Mechanism guidelines, due to the perceived risk that the carbon stored in forest plantations and agroforestry systems could be lost if the system was harvested, burned, or subject to natural disturbance such as fire or pest outbreaks. Carbon credits generated by forestry projects have to be replaced after a certain number of years, and, consequently, prices paid for forest carbon credits are often significantly lower than prices paid for other certified emissions reductions resulting from industrial mitigation activities (i.e., switching to lower carbon-emitting fuels, methane capture technologies) and less attractive from a risk perspective than these alternative options. For example, during the first commitment period of Kyoto, the price of a temporary carbon credit from forestry is estimated to be between 14 and 35% of the price of permanent credits from other mitigation activities (Dutschke et al., 2005). Obtaining similar prices, or, preferably, even a premium price for forest carbon credits, would help achieve mitigation goals while having the added benefit of accruing multiple benefits that are particular to forest carbon projects.

A final obstacle for scaling up is that many countries lack the proper

generate much more significant biodiversity and livelihood benefits, but may provide smaller financial returns.

Uncertainty about the future price of carbon and access of forest carbon credits to different markets also affects both the quantity and timing of reforestation and agroforestry activities. High prices for carbon will likely result in significant early mitigation through carbon-sequestration projects, while lower prices may delay or even prevent these activities from occurring. Restricted access to certain carbon markets (e.g., the European Union's greenhouse gas Emissions Trading Scheme [EU ETS], which does not currently accept carbon credits from land-based projects) may also stymie reforestation activities, adding uncertainty as to whether it will be possible to sell the carbon credits generated (Ellis and Kamel, 2007). The outlook for reforestation activities on the smaller voluntary market is more promising, however, as forestry-based credits currently account for 46% of all credits sold and there is considerable interest in multi-benefit forestry credits (Hamilton et al., 2007).

Another obstacle for reforestation and agroforestry projects is the complexity of the Clean Development Mechanism under the Kyoto Protocol. While reforestation projects are eligible for carbon credits under the CDM, the CDM modalities and procedures for reforestation projects are highly complicated, time-consuming, and require sufficient technical capacity and

Coffee is a valuable commodity for many tropical countries, providing livelihoods for millions of people in rural areas. When coffee is grown under a diverse canopy of shade trees, it can serve as important habitat for plant and animal species, while also sequestering significant quantities of carbon.
CHRISTIAN ZIEGLER

policies, incentives, and institutions that could promote reforestation and agroforestry activities more broadly. For reforestation and agroforestry systems to be implemented at significant scale, it will be necessary for local governments to support these activities actively and provide the necessary capacity-building and infrastructure (tree nurseries, seedlings, etc.), as well as access to information on carbon markets and project development opportunities. Much of this information is available on the Internet and can be used to overcome education, training, and capacity-building needs, but this information needs to be made more broadly accessible to farmers, technicians, and field staff who often lack access (Atkinson, Beniest, and Rao, 2006).

Incentives for establishing plantations could come in the form of reforestation grants, subsidies, tax exemptions for forestry investment, or investment in infrastructure required to support reforestation, among others. The amounts required to stimulate farmers to reforest agricultural lands may be quite small. For example, in Mexico, 65% of the farmers surveyed said they would be willing to transfer at least half of their agricultural land to forestry with a one-time payment of $400 per hectare, and 10% indicated that they would be willing to transfer at least three-quarters of their land. If the incentive were raised to $800 per hectare, 90% of farmers would be willing to change their land to forestry (De Jong et al., 1998). Strong political support is also required to move these efforts forward. In areas where land is communal or where land tenure is unclear, governments will need to play a leading role in defining land and tree tenure and benefit sharing before reforestation and agroforestry systems can be implemented as mitigation options.

Hope for the Future

If designed and managed appropriately, diverse forest plantations and agroforestry systems have the potential to play an important role in climate-change mitigation, while also providing significant benefits to biodiversity conservation and sustainable development. Even if only a portion of the estimated 585 to 1,215 million hectares of currently degraded land is

planted with diverse forest plantations or agroforestry systems, this could represent an important carbon sink and have a positive, immediate impact on climate change, with benefits continuing to accumulate over decades as the trees grow. In addition, preventing the conversion of existing diverse agroforestry systems and small-scale plantations to other land uses can also help to reduce greenhouse gas emissions from land-use changes. The relative ease of establishing and conserving agroforestry systems and diverse forest plantations, combined with their ability to make significant contributions to biodiversity conservation and improved human welfare, makes these activities particularly attractive options for addressing climate change, especially in the tropics, where large areas of deforested land could be easily replanted at relatively low costs. However, in order to achieve the full mitigation potential of these land uses it will be necessary to overcome the financial, policy, and institutional hurdles that currently prevent implementing these activities at scale.

A CLIMATE FOR LIFE

Young Kayapó men spend most days out on the river fishing. The livelihoods of forest people, like the Kayapó Indians of the Brazilian Amazon, depends on healthy forests and rivers.
CRISTINA MITTERMEIER

Kayapó Indians Adjust To A Changing World

Photographs by Cristina Mittermeier

A Kayapó woman collects the fruits of the Açai tree. Kayapo land is under constant threat of deforestation by illegal loggers, ranchers, and miners.

LEFT: A young Kayapó warrior oversees 360 degrees of unbroken rain forest in the 11.5-million hectare Kayapó Indigenous Territory, which is threatened by hydroelectric dams being built outside the reserve. Hydro dams are responsible for an estimated 8% of global greenhouse gas emissions.

THE TRADITIONAL WAYS of indigenous people around the world usually suffer in confrontations with modern civilizations. The Kayapó Indians, however, one of many indigenous groups in Brazil, have proactively taken their destiny into their own hands, says photographer Cristina Mittermeier.

As loggers and miners infringe on their rain forest and hydroelectric dams threaten to dramatically alter their lands, the tribe of some 5,000 in the southeastern Amazon basin has been forced to react. In their 11.5 million hectares, an area about the size of Virginia, the nearly two dozen villages of the Kayapó have organized and agreed that they want to preserve their forest and their way of life.

So far, they've been able to fend off the worst incursions with public protests and appeals to the Brazilian government, but challenges persist. Looming large is the possibility of huge dams that would alter the rivers that provide them a livelihood.

"I've been with many indigenous people," said Mittermeier, "and I've never seen a group as capable and as politically organized as the Kayapó when it comes to dealing with outside threats. They're very egalitarian, and very good at working together. The tribal chiefs must agree that any decision they make will be beneficial to them all, not just a few."

Twenty years ago the Kayapó reacted to incursions as native people have for centuries. Each village acted independently, using traditional weapons in trying to drive out the invaders. Over time, they have learned that unified political action is far more effective.

To deal with the threat of dams just outside their territories, the Kayapó nation has come together to discuss tactics and act cooperatively. Indians patrol their own borders and report illegal activity to the federal government. They stage protests, one of which was attended by the rock star Sting and drew international media attention. They use movie cameras to record conversations with public officials and hold them to their promises.

In a modern world concerned with global warming, keeping their huge forests standing may create an opportunity to make money from standing forests. An intact forest prevents the release of millions of tons of carbon and maintains a sink for greenhouse emissions produced in the industrialized world. Companies that produce carbon dioxide can offset their emissions by buying carbon credits from large areas of

LEFT: The Kayapó have a rich ritual life. Here, the men prepare for a hunt, led by chief Pukatiri. The women watch from afar as they make a circuit around the village.

BELOW: These young Kayapó children will grow up to become leaders and warriors in their community. Like them, indigenous people around the world are often responsible for protecting large traces of forest, thus preventing the release of carbon into the atmosphere.

rain forest. By selling those credits, the Kayapó could derive an income and maintain their lifestyle.

"They know something about western markets," said Mittermeier, who speaks Portuguese and is able to communicate with those Kayapó who also speak Brazil's national language. "Over the years they have made trade agreements with companies like the cosmetic producer Body Shop to provide them with forest products. They have also logged and sold some mahogany.

"Some villages have satellite TV and some of the men have visited Europe and America, so they're aware of other cultures and they understand the perils of bringing some of our western attitudes into their community life. They've banned alcohol from their villages, and they are looking for sustainable ways of supporting their lifestyle.

"They're very proud of the way they live, and they want to preserve it. Given the amount of Amazonia that is held by indigenous people and local communities, it is clear that we must work with them if we want to mitigate climate change. The Kayapó are a great example of an indigenous group that is maintaining their culture while shrewdly participating in the benefits of the global economy."

A CLIMATE FOR LIFE

Kayapó women carry traditional baskets through the forest. The Kayapó depend on the forest for most of their everyday needs. CRISTINA MITTERMEIER

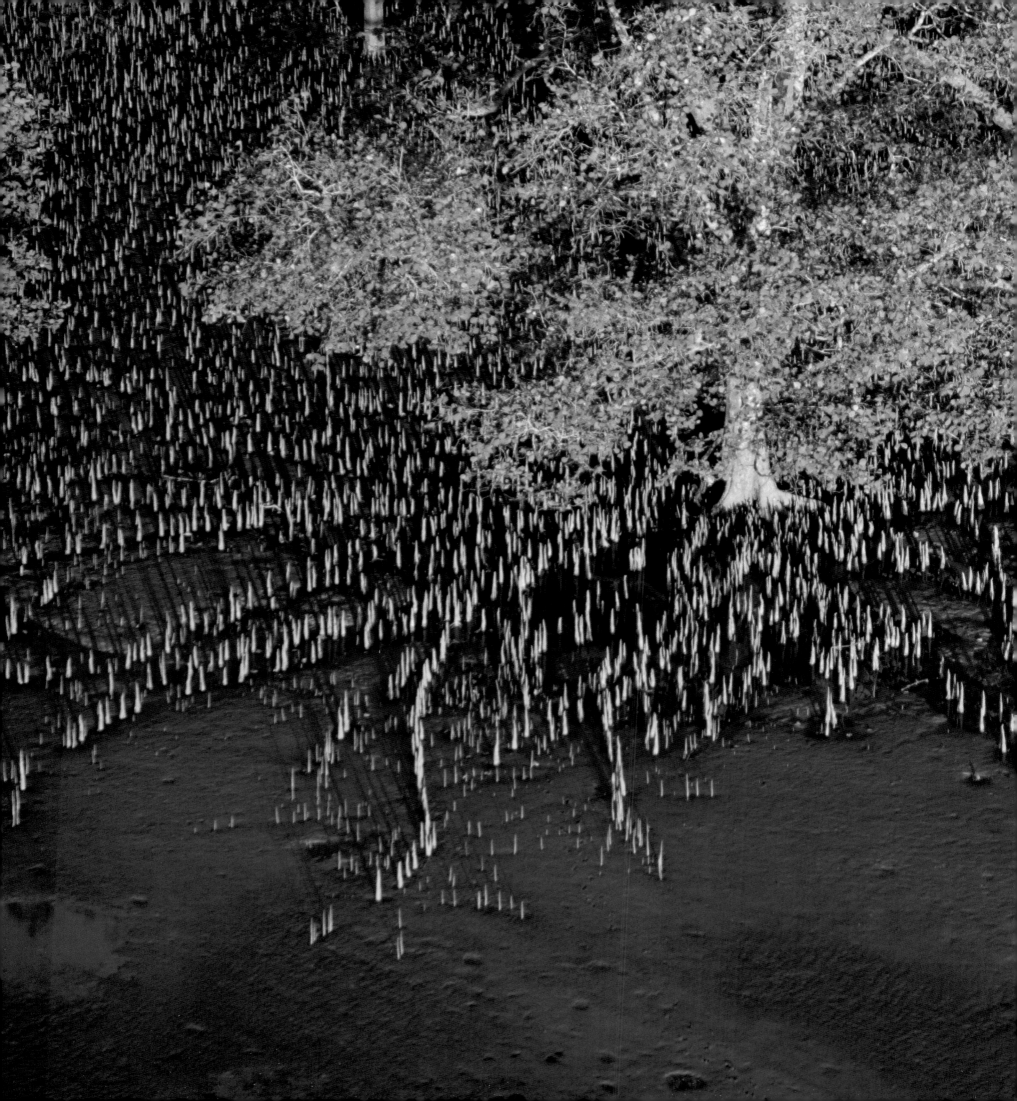

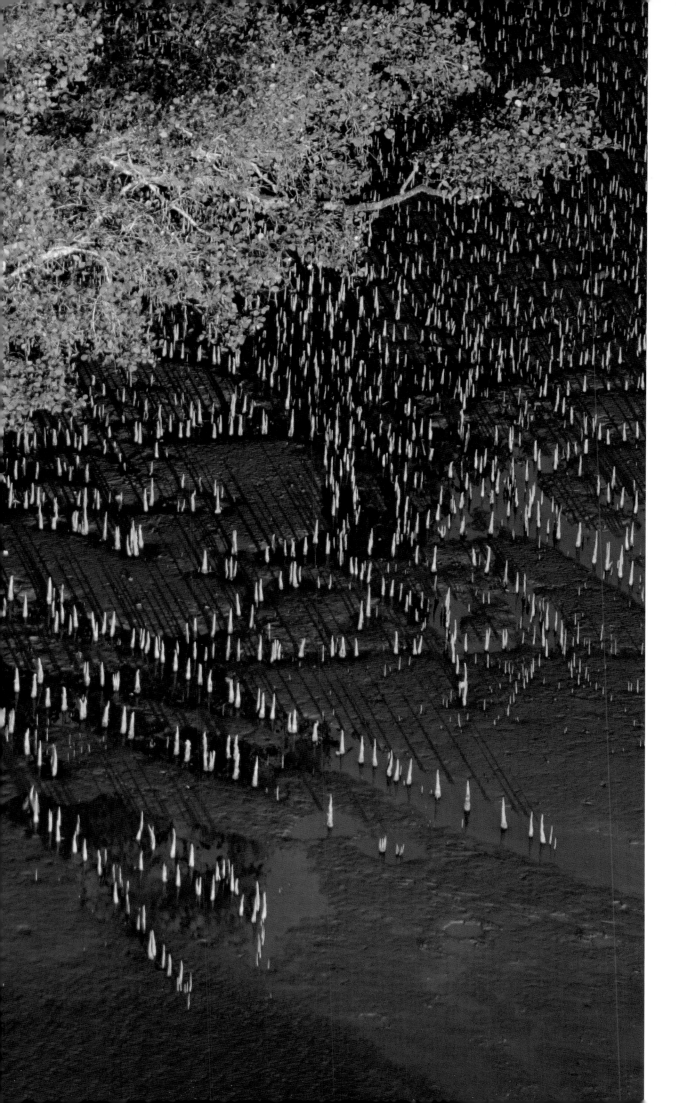

Lines of mangrove roots protrude from the mud flats in Bako National Park, Malaysia. Encouraging mangrove planting and other natural buffers to protect against increasing numbers of storms and typhoons will be critical in the decades ahead.
TIM LAMAN

183

PART II

Adapting to Climate Change

The evidence is unequivocal. Our climate system is changing. Increasing atmospheric greenhouse-gas concentrations are triggering a warming of the Earth's surface and the oceans, sea-level rise and acidification, changes in weather patterns, and an increase in the frequency and magnitude of extreme weather events, from floods and hurricanes to heat waves and droughts. These changes affect the very foundations of our economic and physical well-being and the integrity of the biosphere. In addition to efforts to reduce greenhouse gas emissions and mitigate climate change, we must immediately develop the knowledge and predictive capacity to adapt to climate change now and for the foreseeable future. This has been called "Adaptation," which refers to "the adjustment in natural or human systems in response to actual or expected climatic stimuli or their effects, which moderates harm or exploits beneficial opportunities" (IPCC, 2007).

Climate change will profoundly affect human health and welfare, from food production on land and in the sea, to the value of real estate, to the spread of diseases. Climate change will require agriculture to adapt to changing rainfall; industries to changing water and energy availability; governments to increase disaster prevention, relief, and aid; and vulnerable rural communities to adapt to increases in the frequency of disease outbreaks. Humans are part of and are dependent upon the productivity, function, and resilience of both their local ecosystems and the global biosphere. Human vulnerability is thus tied to the vulnerability of the ecosystems we rely upon.

Developing countries are particularly vulnerable, given their high dependence on climate-sensitive natural resources for livelihoods and economies. The changes in climate projected for the tropics and subtropics are generally adverse for agriculture, the principal livelihood in much of the developing world (IPCC, 2001; IPCC, 2007; Cline, 2007). Furthermore, the institutions, resources, and capacities necessary to adapt to climate change are scarce in many developing countries due to low levels of institutional, human, and economic development, exacerbating their vulnerability and the urgency of adaptation needs (Leary et al., 2008).

Although many effects of climate change on freshwater ecosystems remain uncertain, researchers generally agree that marked changes will occur

Volunteers work to plant beach grass in a sand dune along the Louisiana coast. The dune was eroding rapidly due to storm surges and rising ocean levels. JOEL SARTORE

(Gleick, 2000; Kiparsky and Gleick, 2003; Lorenz et al., 2007). As climate change progresses, several components of the hydrological cycle—evaporation, condensation, precipitation, and collection—will be modified, leading to erratic or failed water flow. As the foundation for several critical ecosystem services such as clean water, nutrient cycling, and flood mitigation (Millennium Ecosystem Assessment, 2005), how the world conserves freshwater ecosystems in the face of changing climate has implications for the very survival of the human species. Resolute progress in planning and regulating integrated water resource management is necessary to ensure water availability and prevent freshwater biodiversity loss. This holistic approach to watershed management accounts for trade-offs between development (agricultural expansion, building dams), human welfare (health, food provision), and biodiversity needs (intact habitats) and can permit adaptation with conservation of freshwater systems and their service flows.

Across the globe, from the tropics to the poles, there is evidence of climate change's impacts to biodiversity. Climate change has already caused range shifts, altered migrations and reproductive patterns, and driven species to extinction (Pounds et al., 1999; Parmesan and Yohe, 2003; Root et al., 2003; Pounds et al., 2006). The effects of climate change on nature are projected to get much worse, particularly in combination with the dominant ongoing threats of habitat loss and fragmentation. As a result of changes in habitat, between 18–35% of the planet's species are predicted to face extinction by 2050; the IPCC refined this estimate to 20–30% of species by 2100 (IPCC, 2007). Biodiversity hotspots are at significant risk, based on models of habitat types, which indicate that up to 43% of the endemic species unique to individual global biodiversity hotspots might be lost due to climate changes that will take place this century. The challenge of conserving Earth's remaining freshwater biological diversity in the face of changing climate may be the greatest facing the conservation community. The IPCC has predicted altered precipitation patterns around the world, the melting of mountain glaciers and icecaps, and increasing intensity and extremes of both droughts and floods in certain geographies, many of which appear to overlap with areas identified as biodiversity hotspots (IPCC, 2007; Mittermeier et al., 2004).

We must urgently conserve the planet's most biodiverse ecosystems both to avoid the loss of species and to ensure the resilience of natural ecosystems. Ecosystems harboring the majority of their endemic biodiversity are likely to be more resilient to climate impacts on environmental conditions and stressors. For instance, genetic diversity in eelgrass (*Zoster marina*) meadows was found to increase resilience of these ecosystems to changes affected by the European heat wave of 2003 (Reusch et al., 2005). Reducing habitat fragmentation, maintaining connectivity across ecological gradients, and conserving endemic species diversity and landscape-scale ecological processes moderate vulnerability and increase the resilience capacity of natural systems to climate change and related disturbances (Battarbee et al., 2007). Special attention should also be given to protecting, understanding, and benefitting from species that have shown resilience to climate change.

As temperatures rise, many species undergo changes in abundance, changes in timing of biological events, and range shifts (Parmesan and Yohe, 2003; Root et al., 2003). These effects of climate change have been observed in both terrestrial and marine environments. New protected areas extending protected habitat, enhanced connectivity for natural migration and dispersal, and proactive modeling and management all will be required to ensure that range shifts may be accommodated and ecological processes maintained under global change. Ensuring that human development does not limit these shifts or disrupt ecosystem function can provide species with the space they need to adapt and ecosystems the ability to adapt to change.

The preservation of biodiverse, resilient ecosystems decreases the vulnerability of human communities to climate change impacts. Biodiversity (and the ecosystems it sustains) provides products and services to humanity, from timber and fibers to pharmaceutical products and critical services, including the purification of water and air, disease and natural-disaster mitigation, pest control, and pollination. By protecting these ecosystems, we can improve our own resilience and increase options for adaptation to climate change. For example, mangroves can prevent salinization of freshwater as sea levels rise, mangroves and coral reefs can buffer coastal areas from increasingly intense storm surges, and forests can recharge aquifers and maintain water flows even as precipitation patterns change. While some of these services can be provided artificially (i.e. through water purification plants), the cost is usually much higher than that of protecting the ecosystems that can do the work for us.

The good news is there is much we can do to help humans and the ecosystems we depend on adapt to climate change. One of the most important actions is removing other stressors. Scarce and degraded natural resources increase the vulnerability and decrease the adaptive capacity of human and natural communities. Habitat loss, degradation, pollution, and over-harvesting, among other anthropogenic pressures, are driving ecosystems to the brink of collapse. Climate change is a compounding stressor, which augments extinction threats and the likelihood of ecosystem collapse. By lessening other pressures, we can promote healthy ecosystems that are more resilient to changes and variations in climate.

Alternative development paradigms, such as "poverty-oriented energy strategies for sustainable development" (Reddy, 1993), have been effectively used to show government officials how to deliver much cleaner, safer, and affordable energy services more rapidly per dollar of investment through the end-use-oriented approach than from the conventional large-scale power plant model. A critically important, core component of this strategy is utility regulatory reform. Utility regulators of electricity, natural gas, and water need to shift the utility's incentives by decoupling utility revenues and earnings and allowing utilities to recoup the lost revenues from reduced sales of kWhs of electricity, liters of water, or therms of gas when they help their customers adopt energy- and water-saving technologies and designs.

The Jiangsu, Shanghai, and Beijing provinces in China are moving in this direction, finding they can deliver five times more kWhs of electricity service through end-use efficiency improvements than they can for the same investment in new power plants (Totten, 2007). The approach has demonstrated powerful opportunities for purifying contaminated water in poor villages in developing countries. For example, the UV Waterworks device developed in the 1990s uses ultraviolet light to disinfect community drinking water supplies inexpensively. The device can treat the drinking-water

demand of a community of 1,000 people at an annual total cost of just $US 10 cents per person (Gadgil et al., 1998; Waterhealth International, 2007). Such highly effective ways of simultaneously supporting economic growth with declining greenhouse-gas emissions is a robust means of ensuring that climate-change mitigation and adaptation measures do not disproportionately impact developing countries.

The following chapters provide an indication of the magnitude of the climate-change threat and the adaptation challenge both for human communities and for terrestrial, freshwater, and marine biota. The climate-change impacts anticipated in these biomes have profound implications for all life on Earth. Adaptation will require responses that encompass and leverage nature's services, and not merely limit actions to human-engineered tactics, if we are to avoid undermining the very integrity of the planet upon which we depend. Since human responses will be diverse, addressing the threats of climate change will require coordination across the environment, development, and other sectors. It will also require integrated scientific approaches that incorporate both physical and biological sciences. Adaptation will require new scientific understanding, aggressive implementation of response measures, and a flexible and adaptive management approach. However, by focusing on ecosystems and the benefits they provide us, we can improve resiliency and ensure that we and the many other species that make up our ecosystems are around for generations to come.

Terrestrial Biodiversity

Climate change could have enormous impacts on biodiversity over the course of this century, resulting in large-scale extinctions in some of the world's richest and most diverse regions. To protect against such impacts, we must create more protected areas, increase connectivity through corridors of natural habitat, and focus special attention on rescue and recovery of those species that will suffer the most immediate effects.

A CLIMATE FOR LIFE

A pod of male narwhals gather to eat cod at the Arctic ice edge of Lancaster Sound in Nunavut, Canada. Many Arctic species rely heavily on cod as their primary food source, which, in turn, rely on plankton that are struggling to survive as water temperatures warm. PAUL NICKLEN

PREVIOUS PAGES:
Three baby African elephants follow their mother across a river toward a drinking hole. Though these elephants are most at risk from poachers, the drying effects of climate change and continuing encroachment by human settlements both pose serious threats. MICHAEL NICHOLS

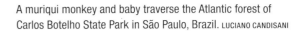

A muriqui monkey and baby traverse the Atlantic forest of Carlos Botelho State Park in São Paulo, Brazil. LUCIANO CANDISANI

CHAPTER SIX

Terrestrial Biodiversity

Lee Hannah, Miguel B. Araújo, Guy Midgley, Sandy Andelman,
Enrique Martínez-Meyer, Richard Pearson, Paul Williams, Thomas E. Lovejoy

The effects of climate change on species distributions and vegetation types across the globe are well-documented in the history of the Earth. However, the current rate at which human activity is imposing stress and potential impacts on biodiversity is unprecedented. To form proper conservation strategies for the future, it is imperative that we reflect upon the past and examine the ways in which human-induced climate change is creating a new ecological paradigm.

One of the most dramatic climatic changes in the last 100 million years was a period of rapid warming 55 million years ago in which entire orders of mammals appeared and disappeared in a small geological window. As climate warming released excess methane from sediments in the ocean, large numbers of species went extinct, while others, including horses, deer, and even the first primates made their appearance. While the warmth-extinction link is controversial, it is clear that extended periods of exceptional warming have severe consequences for biodiversity.

Climate change in the ice ages resulted in relatively few global extinctions, but many species experienced dramatic biological and habitat range shifts. Only when our current warm climate stabilized did today's communities of species become established. This climate stability is unusual for the past 2 million years, and it is feared that some current species may have lost some of their natural mechanisms to cope with climate change. Human-induced climate change now threatens to add heat to an already warm climate, and extinctions and biological changes are already taking place.

Species extinctions are the irreversible impacts of climate change on biodiversity, and the extinction of a number of species of frogs and toads throughout central and South America may be the result of a fungus that is thriving in the new conditions brought on by climate change. Many other species, while not necessarily threatened with extinction, are currently under severe stress due to changes in climate. Corals are bleaching (i.e., losing the algae that live within their cells as water temperatures rise) as well as having difficulty constructing their skeletons as seawater becomes more acidic from rising levels of CO_2. Meanwhile, many species of butterflies, birds, and plants are shifting their ranges towards the cooler poles and up slopes to

A northern spotted owl perches on a forest branch on the Pacific Northwest coast of North America. To survive and reproduce, these owls require large tracts of old-growth coniferous forest, much of which has been cut down through commercial logging. GERRY ELLIS

Researcher Piotr Naskrecki collects katydids at night in the rain forest of La Selva, Costa Rica. Even the most diverse animal groups, such as insects, are suffering as a result of climate change. FRANS LANTING

follow preferred breeding and feeding conditions as climates warm. These same changes are forcing flowers to bloom earlier and insects to complete more life cycles in each calendar year, which are having profound impacts on ecosystems across the globe.

Many of the species at risk are well-known, even to the general public. As Arctic sea ice melts, polar bears have less time to hunt and fatten before winter and less area in which to den and raise their pups. Whale populations are threatened as rising water temperatures destroy krill, the tiny organisms at the base of their food chain. Coral reef fish are experiencing high mortality as coral bleaching depletes their food supply. Trout and other Alpine plants and animals are struggling to reach higher altitudes to maintain their cool habitats. Seabirds are vulnerable to the rising sea levels brought on by climate change as their nests are subject to flooding. Meanwhile, sea turtles also nest on beaches but are also threatened because their gender is determined by nest temperature prior to hatching. Increased warming means that only female turtles may be produced.

Reducing the impact of climate change on biodiversity requires a two-pronged approach of mitigation (reducing greenhouse gases) and adaptation (strengthening conservation efforts). First, it is imperative that human-induced greenhouse gas emissions be stopped to avoid the worst-case climate-warming scenarios and their consequences for biodiversity, including species extinction. Next, our conservation efforts must take species movement and adaptation into account and incorporate a combination of new protected areas/parks, crucial connectivity through natural corridors, and rescue and recovery of threatened species. This dual approach of mitigation and adaptation is critical for the preservation of biodiversity in the face of climate change.

Biotic Response to Past Climate Changes

Climate change has altered species distributions and vegetation types across the entire planet many times in the history of the Earth (Overpeck et al., 2003). Global-change biology includes the study of these changes and the possible consequences of future climate change on the Earth's ecosystems. To understand the future, we must look at the past, examine changes already underway due to human-induced climate change, and use theory and models to explore possible future scenarios, especially those that have no analog in the past (Hannah et al., 2002).

Our understanding of the past improves as we get closer to the present (Broecker, 2001). Fossil records are sketchy on scales of millions of years, but improve greatly in the past two million years of the ice ages (the Pleistocene). The deep-time record therefore catches more dramatic events, while the recent past provides higher resolution insights into the rate of climate change and corresponding biological responses (Bartlein and Prentice, 1989). Though known in less detail, the record over hundreds of millions of years provides evidence of startling changes driven by climate changes in the past, so we start here with those.

Climate Change in the Deep Past

Perhaps the most provocative climate change event in the past 100 million years was a period of scorchingly rapid warming 55 million years ago (Zachos et al., 2001). This event took place during a period of relatively high temperatures, much warmer than today's climate, with rain forests extending well into what is now Canada, and provided a peak on top of these already warm climates.

The biological changes at that time were profound and lightning quick. Whole orders of mammals appeared and disappeared in a geological instant—less than 100,000 years (Gingerich, 2006). Horses and deer appeared for the first time during this rapid warming, as did the first primates—the ancestors of humans. Large numbers of species also went extinct in a virtual instant in geologic time. The biological changes at this time were so profound that geologists use them to mark the boundary between two geological epochs—the Paleocene and the Eocene. The full name of this rapid, large, climatic and biological change is therefore the rather intimidating Paleocene-Eocene Thermal Maximum, or PETM for short.

The cause of the PETM was climate warming past a threshold that mobilized the release of methane from sediments in the ocean (Kennett and Stott, 1991). Methane is a potent greenhouse gas, so its release led to a runaway greenhouse effect. In a few thousand years, global temperatures rose 4–7 degrees Celsius,

Climate Change in the Ice Ages

Surprisingly, there have been relatively few global extinctions associated with the rapid climate changes in the ice ages of the past 2 million years. Entry and exit from ice ages has been extraordinarily rapid, often taking place in a few tens of thousands of years, yet large extinction or speciation events such as the PETM are absent (Bennett, 1990).

It may be that the major loss of species occurred at the onset of the ice ages, as relatively warm-adapted species were lost. This may have left a pool of relatively cool-adapted species that were well-suited to glacial conditions and were able to survive the relatively short interglacials that have punctuated the past 2 million years (Coope, 1995). There is a well-documented wave of marine extinctions at the beginning of the ice ages, but few later marine extinctions (Roy et al., 2001). On land, there have been regional losses of substantial numbers of species (such as decreases in tree diversity in Europe) during the ice ages, but these were not global events and did not result in large numbers of global extinctions (e.g., many of the trees lost from Europe survived in other parts of the world). Whatever the reason for the low global loss of species during the ice ages, the extinction picture changed dramatically in the transition from the last ice age to the current, warm climate.

about as much as is projected this century due to today's human-induced climate change.

The PETM followed the extinction of the dinosaurs 65 million years ago, which itself was caused by an asteroid impact and its climatic consequences (Alvarez et al., 1980). The dinosaur extinction event set the stage for the rise of mammals, but it was the PETM that actually triggered evolution of many of today's best-known mammal groups, such as deer, horses, and primates.

If climate change can result in the extinction and evolution of large numbers of species in the PETM, could it be an analogy for the biological consequences of human-induced climate change? Recent research has revealed a correlation between major warm periods and mass extinction events (Mayhew et al., 2008). Some experts argue that these warm-associated mass extinctions may be triggered when ocean conditions change, causing the formation and release of hydrogen sulfide (Ward, 2006). The warmth-extinction link is controversial, but suggests that severe consequences may have accompanied past periods of exceptional warming.

Other past events suggest major biological impacts of climate change. Going back 440 million years, rapid cooling led to the extinction of a large number of species on Earth (the Ordivician-Silurian extinction event). Significant extinctions also accompanied the formation of modern land ice 30 million to 2 million years ago.

The clear difference in the transition to the current climate is the dominance of humans. Especially in North and South America, large numbers of extinctions accompanied the retreat of the ice age (Barnosky et al., 2004). The animals that went extinct at this time were diverse and large. Mammoths, saber-tooth cats, giant ground sloths, and more than 200 other vertebrate species disappeared between 20,000 years and 10,000 years ago, just as the last ice age ended (ibid.).

Earlier extinctions in other regions coincided with the arrival of humans, so it has been suggested that most extinctions at the end of the last ice age were human-induced (Alroy, 2001). However, it seems more likely that a combination of factors, including climate change and human arrivals, led to the extinctions.

While the cause of the end ice age extinctions remains uncertain, it is clear that many other biological changes accompanied climate change in the ice ages. These changes included species range shifts and the rearrangement of entire communities of plants and animals (Bartlein and Prentice, 1989). Some species shifted ranges many times, sometimes very rapidly in response to climate change in the ice ages (Markgraf and Kenny, 1995). These changes did not happen to whole plant and animal communities (Davis et al., 1998). Instead, each species moved in response to its own climatic tolerances, resulting in new and ever-changing combinations of species during the transition. Since entry to and exit from ice ages was typically abrupt, many of these range shifts happened very quickly as well. For example, trees in North America were all pushed well south of the huge Laurentide ice sheet, only to rebound far to the north as the ice sheet receded (M.B. Davis and Shaw, 2001). Oaks that existed as far south as Florida moved steadily northward into what is now the northern United States and Canada. Other species followed suit.

As the transition took place, forests likely looked little like those that we know today (Webb, 1995). When our current warm climate was fully established, climatic stability increased. Forests and other vegetation took on compositions similar to those that we know today. Animal communities changed as well. Just as with forest trees, mammals that co-occurred in the past do not exist together today, and the mix of species changed as climate evolved. Eventually, the relatively warm and stable climate of the current interglacial period led to relatively consistent communities of mammals and other animal species.

The stability of our present climate is unusual in the past 2 million years, which may have important biological consequences (Broecker, 1999). In this period, even climate changes that we consider relatively large, such as the Medieval Warm Period (c900-1300) and the Little Ice Age (c1600-1800), were small relative to the changes that occurred in the previous 10,000

years (Broecker, 2001). Have current species therefore lost some of their mechanisms to deal with change due to stability? This is an active area of research, but it seems clear that the combination of recent climatic stability and human domination of landscapes is a combination of factors that makes biological systems especially vulnerable to impacts of rapid climate change.

Since that time, the Earth has been in an unusually warm and stable climate (Hannah et al., 2005) in which all of human civilization has developed. Species extinctions have faded to background rates. Now human-induced climate change is adding additional heat to this already warm climate and may very well be destabilizing it. Extinctions and biological changes are already being seen. Unlike the previous changes to biodiversity due to climate change, the tale of these recent changes has been recorded by humans.

Recent Observations: Species Extinctions

Extinctions are among the irreversible recent impacts of climate change on biodiversity (Walther et al., 2002). Throughout Central and South America, a series of extinctions that may be linked to climate change have occurred in toads and frogs (Pounds et al., 2006). These extinctions are the result of a series of impacts ranging from habitat loss to ozone depletion to environmental changes to disease. Many of these impacts have a direct link to, or are compounded by, climate change.

Many of the extinct frog and toad species were colorful—both in pigmentation and in life history. Species of the genus *Atelopus* are striking multicolored combinations of black, orange, and green. The golden toad, one of the many species to disappear, was seen frequently in unmistakable breeding aggregations of hundreds of individuals until 1988 and 1989, when only one individual was recorded (Pounds et al., 1999). It has not been seen since. Vanishing suddenly is typical of these toad and frog extinctions. The cause seems to be linked to a skin fungus and the climatic conditions it prefers (Pounds et al., 2006).

Climate change may alter conditions favored by the fungus, which ordinarily occupies the skin of the amphibians with no known ill effect. It is hypothesized that changes in the presence of high clouds in mountainous areas decrease the amount of rain and mist usually associated with many amphibian breeding habitats. This change also influences nightly temperatures in both the rainy and dry seasons, creating an environment more favorable to the fungus. Most of the extinct toads and frogs were last seen in years of unusual dry and warm weather. This has led researcher Alan Pounds to claim, "the fungus killed the toads, but climate change pulled the trigger."

Other Impacts on Biodiversity

Other biological changes due to climate change include range shifts, changes in abundance, and changes in timing of biological events (Parmesan and Yohe, 2003; Root et al., 2003). These effects of climate change have been observed in both terrestrial and marine environments.

Coral bleaching is perhaps the most dramatic effect of recent climate change (Hoegh-Guldberg, 1999). Corals bleach when they lose the algae that live within their cells, providing photosynthesis in return for the structure provided by the coral (Pockley, 1999). Coral bleaching occurs when water temperatures rise above long-term local averages and has affected reefs all around the world. Many corals die following bleaching, while some recover. The fate of coral reefs is in significant doubt as the Earth continues to warm, both because of the effects of bleaching and because rising CO_2 levels make seawater more acidic, destroying the coral skeletons that ultimately form the structure typical of tropical reefs.

Range shifts in terrestrial species have been observed in butterflies, birds, and plants (Parmesan and Yohe 2003, Root et al., 2003). The quiver tree, a tree-sized aloe from southern Africa, is a good example. Quiver trees are dying in the northern part of their range as it gets too warm and dry (Foden et al., 2007), while the southern part of their range is moving upslope. Such range shifts towards the cooler poles help species track their preferred conditions as climates warm. These same types of shifts have now been observed in hundreds of birds and butterflies in Europe and the United States.

In the oceans, fisheries are impacted by changes in abundance of target species as climate changes. Salmon in the Pacific Northwest, mackerel in the North Sea, and numerous species off the coast of South America go through dramatic population changes with climate swings (Francis, 1990). Fish catches decline in downturns and rebound during climate-associated peaks. Such peaks are often driven by El Niño events, which may become more frequent as climate changes.

On land, another dramatic observation is the change in timing of biological events. Flowers bloom earlier, lakes become biologically active earlier as ice melts earlier, and insect pests complete more life cycles in earlier, warmer summers (Root, 2003). These and other changes in biological timing are having profound effects on ecosystems around the world.

In western North America, bark beetles have devastated millions of trees (Logan et al., 2003). Beetles that used to be limited to one life cycle per year now can complete two life cycles per year, allowing them to explode in huge synchronized outbreaks. At the same time, cool zones along the continental divide that used to prevent the beetles from spreading east are now warm enough for the beetles to penetrate. Beetle species formerly confined to the west may now invade millions of hectares of pines in central Canada and the eastern United States.

Lakes are also feeling the effects of earlier heat. Temperate lakes experience spring turnover earlier as climate warms, giving some species (such as undesirable algae) more time to thrive (Allan et al., 2005). As a result, algal blooms and anoxic conditions may become more common in many lakes. In addition, cold-water fish such as trout will find their habitat reduced as climate warms.

Species at Risk

Among the species at risk due to climate change are some of the best-known and most charismatic species on the planet. These species are only the tip of the iceberg, however. Working to stop climate change and strengthen conservation efforts (such as expanding protected areas) will help reduce the impacts on millions of other species.

Polar Bears. Sea ice is melting at both poles, but nowhere faster than in the Arctic, where it is now thinner than at any time since records have been

A trumpeter swan is colored by the peat of a glacial kettle pond in Canada's Yukon. YVA MOMATIUK & JOHN EASTCOTT

kept. The North Pole is frequently observed to be ice-free. Breakup of the ice is occurring on average two days earlier per decade, which is putting ice-dependent species such as polar bears at high risk.

Polar bears den in ice and hunt on ice, so many parts of their life cycle are disrupted when the ice disappears. Polar bears store fat by hunting seals on sea ice (Stirling and Parkinson, 2006). When ice melts, the bears make their way to land and survive the summer living off their fat stores. Earlier ice melt means longer fasting periods and longer swims to shore. Rapidly disappearing Arctic sea ice is also leading to reduced habitat for the seals that are the bears' preferred prey, reduction in available area for denning and raising pups (since dens are most often dug into snow and ice), and reduction of the time available to hunt and fatten on sea ice. Polar bears have also been observed to hybridize with grizzly bears, which may undermine the genetic identity of the species. In 2006, polar bears were placed on the IUCN Red List for the first time, with a status of Vulnerable.

Great Whales. The southern oceans are the feeding grounds for many species of great whales, all of which feed on krill, tiny organisms that form the base of the Antarctic food chain (Moline et al., 2004). Krill are sensitive to water temperature, and their populations have declined dramatically. Declining krill populations threaten populations of great whales, as well and other species in the region, such as penguins and seals.

Coral Reef Fish. Due to coral bleaching, coral reefs throughout the tropics are suffering damage and high mortality (Hoegh-Guldberg, 1999). With declining corals come declines in coral reef fish species. Parrotfish and other obligate coral feeders disappear when reefs are destroyed by bleaching. They are replaced by algae-eating fish, but the rich assemblages of fish life that make coral reefs famous do not return unless the area is recolonized by coral.

Salmonids. Salmon are sensitive to variations in sea-surface temperatures, while their cousins the trout are sensitive to temperatures in upper watersheds in freshwater streams (Anderson, 1998). Both trout and salmon are salmonids,

members of a diverse family of fish that include fresh and saltwater fishes, as well as anadromous fish such as salmon that spend part of their life in freshwater and part in saltwater.

Trout habitat is cold freshwater in high-country streams. Since the water in these streams is not deep, its temperature closely follows air temperature. As climate warms, the temperature of streams warms. To track the water temperatures they prefer, trout would have to move upslope to cooler waters. However, since they are already in upper-elevation streams, there is often little above them. Climate change is projected to dramatically reduce trout habitat in the western United States for this reason (Allan et al., 2005). Similar fates await trout habitat around the world if global warming remains unchecked.

The story of the salmon is different. Salmon are sensitive to freshwater and ocean temperatures, but ocean temperatures seem more important. Some groups of salmon are favored in cooler years, producing more adults, while other groups do better in warm years. If these trends hold across time, some groups of salmon may suffer major declines due to climate change, while others may benefit.

Alpine Plants and Animals. Like trout, Alpine plants and animals have little upward room to move in response to climate change. A broad range of species, from plants in the Alps to Boyd's forest dragon (*Hypsilurus boydii*) in Australia are threatened by warming (Williams et al., 2004). For example, a recent study predicted that up to 60% of plants in southern European mountains could lose adequate climate conditions for their persistence (Thuiller et al., 2005). In addition, evidence of a 200 m altitudinal shift of butterflies has been recorded in the past thirty years in the Guadarrama Mountain of Madrid (Wilson et al., 2005).

Some new Alpine habitats are opening up as glaciers retreat. These new habitats are colonized amazingly rapidly, often within a few years of glacier retreat (Seimon et al., 2007). Icy ponds in the Andes that were covered with ice less than a decade ago now harbor thriving populations of frogs. Other strange creatures eke out livings in these new high habitats. Certain spiders live on glacial shoulders and subsist on insects blown up from the lowlands

rise when it melts). As sea levels rise, low-lying islands are subject to inundation. Seabirds may require sandy soil for nesting, so moving inland may not be an immediate option for them even where islands are large enough to escape complete immersion. They may also face human development inland on larger islands.

As a result, a number of species on the international IUCN Red List of Threatened Species due to climate change are seabirds. Specialists studying the status of these birds are also finding declines due to fishing practices and other stressors, but climate change may prove to be the albatross around the neck of a number of seabirds.

on persistent updrafts.

Unfortunately, these new habitats are tiny compared to the habitats that are being lost due to climate change. Since mountains are pointed, the area vacated by glaciers is necessarily smaller than the Alpine habitats lower down the mountain that is being lost. They also lack soil suitable for many plants, and, therefore, may not provide habitat for these or the animals that depend on them once the ice recedes.

Amphibians in the Iberian Peninsula. The Iberian Peninsula holds as much as 62% of all amphibious species in Europe, and several are endemic to the area. For many of these species, reductions in water availability could lead to massive population losses. Indeed, in desert and semi-desert conditions in the north of Africa, there are almost no species of amphibians. Computer models developed for Europe predict that all amphibian species in the Iberian Peninsula could face massive reductions in their potential range sizes with projected twenty-first-century climate changes (Araújo et al., 2006).

Seabirds. Most seabirds nest on low-lying islands vulnerable to another manifestation of climate change—rising sea levels. Sea-level rise is caused by the expansion of seawater as it warms and by the melting of land ice (sea ice already displaces seawater and, thus, does not contribute to sea-level

Sea Turtles. Rising sea levels are a challenge for sea turtles as well. Like many seabirds, sea turtles are beach nesters. They bury their eggs in the sand where rising waters can literally drown young sea turtles before they can hatch.

Warming poses a second challenge to sea turtles because it is a gender-bender for hatchlings (Glen and Mrosovsky, 2004). The sex of sea turtles is determined by nest temperature prior to hatching. Warm temperatures produce predominantly female young, while cooler temperatures result in more males. Global warming means that more female turtles may be produced, creating a biased sex ratio within populations. Gender mismatch can reduce the production of young, jeopardizing populations. In the long term, selective pressure would likely correct the gender imbalance, and might not be a major concern in species facing few other threats. However, all seven species are impacted by hunting, fishing practices, and other threats, so climate change is a complicating threat that causes major problems for these animals.

Proteas of Southern Africa. Species at the tips of continents are at risk for the same reason as species near the tops of mountains. When there is little cooler space to move to, species may literally run out of room as the world warms. The

proteas of South Africa's Cape Floristic Province are one such set of species. The family Proteaceae includes more than 300 species of spectacularly flowering shrubs (Rebelo, 2001). The King protea is the national flower of South Africa, and this species and the intricately flowered pincushion proteas are prominent in the world commercial flower trade. Some are grown outside of South Africa, but many are grown in and exported from the Cape.

Computer modeling has shown many of the proteas to be at risk due to climate change (Midgley et al., 2002). Several species lose range altogether as suitable climate literally moves out to sea south of Cape Point. Other proteas move to much smaller ranges in the mountains to escape the warming. Some move out of protected areas, requiring new parks or reserves to be created if they are to be saved.

The proteas are a showy and well-known example of the Cape Flora, but many other species unique to this region of the world face an uncertain future as climate changes. Species at the tip of South America, Australia, and New Zealand may also struggle as warming pushes them toward the sea. Species at the top of North America and Europe may face fewer problems because snow and ice cover may recede, opening new habitats.

Queensland Rain Forests. Of the world's many rain forests, those of North Queensland in Australia may be the most threatened by climate change (Williams et al., 2004). These forests harbor many unique endemic species at mid and upper elevations. Genetic studies have shown that these forests survived the ice ages, but may have little capacity to weather warming above present levels (Schneider and Moritz, 1999).

As in the Cape, computer models have been used to gauge the fate of these species. One of the most spectacular is Boyd's forest dragon (*Hypsilurus boydii*), and it is also one of the most vulnerable. But it does not stand alone. While other rainforest species may be able to cope with warmer and wetter

conditions, it looks as if climate change may mean that time is running out for these unique Australian forest species.

Challenges for Conservation

As species ranges move, they may expand or contract relative to protected areas, such as parks. Since parks cannot move, the species they protect may have to be reassessed. Recent work has shown that not only will many species will move out of protected areas, but also that species moving out are likely to outnumber species moving in (Araújo et al., 2004). This is because species may not be able to keep up with climate change. Their suitable climatic range may shift faster than they are able to disperse, or it may move through urban or agricultural areas in which the species cannot survive.

Climate change will require more protected areas as a result. The amount needed varies greatly by region and also depends on the adequacy of current protected areas, since many don't adequately or uniformly protect all of the species in the region. To balance species moving out of reserves, additional protected areas can be situated in places where species movements will be limited, or may be captured in a limited space. In addition, conservation efforts may be required to assist the movement of species between sites (Hannah et al., 2007).

Completing species coverage of current protected areas provides an

Galapagos tortoises wallow in a seasonal pond on the rim of
the caldera of Alcedo Volcano on Isabela Island in Ecuador.
TUI DE ROY

opportunity to incorporate climate change at less cost. If current protection is completed first and then the area needed for climate change is added in a separate second step, the amount of area needed increases (Hannah et al., 2007). Conversely, if new areas to complete coverage of existing species ranges are planned to coincide with areas that will capture shifts due to climate change, the overall area required can be greatly reduced.

New connectivity will be needed in addition to new protected areas (P. Williams et al., 2005). Connectivity for climate change is the provision of areas of natural or semi-natural land between protected areas necessary for species range shifts or other responses to climatic alteration. Corridors of largely natural landscapes linking protected areas are one type of connectivity important for climate change. Corridors can serve multiple purposes, including habitat connections for wide-ranging mammals such as jaguar or wolves and migratory connections for mammals, butterflies, or birds. Each of these multiple uses will require different corridor attributes, and individual corridors can be tailored in different ways to maximize effectiveness for each purpose.

For instance, corridor connections for climate change may be designed using computer programs that simulate species movements. A model can indicate present and future range, as well as intermediate steps, allowing connections to be visualized and planned between protected areas. Long-range connectivity may be expensive and difficult, so curbing climate change before species range shifts become too pronounced is critical.

Finally, we also need to develop strategies to deal with impacts of climate change that protection or corridors alone cannot address, such as emerging diseases. In the case of amphibians, this means the establishment of captive breeding facilities to ensure the survival of species in danger of extinction until the technology of disease control can be developed to "cleanse" natural environments and rid them of the chytrid fungus that kills them. Once that is done, captive animals can be reintroduced to their previous natural habitats.

Conclusion

Concerted action on multiple fronts is needed to lessen the impact of climate change on biodiversity. New protected areas, enhanced connectivity, multiple-use corridors, and proactive modeling and management all will be required to ensure that biodiversity endures as the Earth warms.

These responses can help ensure that climate change that is already inevitable will not cause irreparable harm to natural systems. The Earth's mean temperature is already rising, emissions already in the atmosphere will cause it to rise further, and energy consumption patterns and other factors that will take time to change will lead to further inevitable change. Conservation responses have been identified that can make our conservation efforts responsive. The challenge now is to get these responses funded and in place before change takes place.

At the same time, runaway climate change will clearly lead to biological alterations that will be beyond our capacity to cope. Communities will be torn apart, mountaintop species will lose all range, and some species will see their suitable climate move far outside their dispersal range if the extreme climate changes projected for the end of the century come to pass. These extremes can be avoided if we take action to stop climate change.

Protecting biodiversity and our gains in nature conservation therefore requires a two-pronged solution. First, human greenhouse gas emissions must be stopped. This minimizes human-driven climatic changes, thus avoiding the most extreme warming scenarios and their likely biological consequences. Second, we must improve our conservation efforts to cope with the human-induced climate change that will take place even with strong action to stop greenhouse gas emissions. These strengthened conservation efforts will include new parks, corridors, connectivity, and some rescue and recovery.

Pursuing both of these paths, known as "mitigation" (stopping greenhouse gas emissions) and "adaptation" (strengthening conservation efforts to cope with climate change) provide the best hope of avoiding extinctions due to climate change. Fortunately, world policy leaders are moving forward on both of these fronts. Communities, policymakers, and conservationists can have a large impact on the future of biodiversity by supporting these efforts, both through local actions and in lending voices to the growing cry for international cooperation to avoid runaway climate change.

Gemsbok cast long shadows on the Namib Desert, home to the highest sand dunes in the world. The expansion of deserts worldwide is one projected consequence of climate change.
ROBERT B. HAAS

South Africa's Quiver Trees: Nowhere to Go

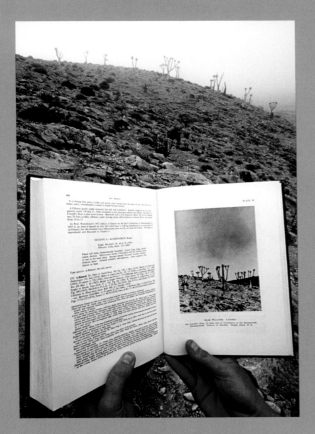

A botanist revisits the site of an old survey to document the extinction of tree aloes in Richtersveld National Park, South Africa.

LEFT: Giant quiver trees struggle to survive in South Africa.

Photographs by Frans Lanting

IN THREE DECADES OF NATURE photography around the globe Frans Lanting has often been a witness to environmental change.

"I'm very aware of the changes that are happening everywhere because of a warming climate," he said, "but I'm rarely in the position to document so precisely the specific changes that have happened in one particular location, and the effect on one particular species."

The place was South Africa, and the species was aloe trees, giant succulents that thrive in the dry climate at the edge of the Namib Desert. The larger of them are called "quiver trees" because generations of African bushmen have hollowed out sections of their branches to create quivers for their arrows. The bark is hard but the interior pith is light and spongy. Large trunks of dead trees are sometimes hollowed out and used as food refrigerators because the fibrous trunk has a cooling effect as air passes through it.

All aloes are threatened by a warming climate, but the most fragile is also one of the largest, *Aloe pillansii*, found mostly in the northern part of the Cape. Lanting's introduction to the plight of these trees came about while photographing the Cape Flora, smallest of the world's unique plant biomes and a place of extraordinary diversity.

"As you go south from Cape Town toward the Namibian border you see great changes in microclimates and that corresponds to botanical diversity," he said. "Aloe trees occur in the drier parts of South Africa, having adapted to desert. I was particularly keen to photograph *Aloe pillansii* because the distribution is now limited to one stand consisting of a handful of these giant succulents in Richtersveld National Park."

Like many other plant species on this arid peninsula, *Aloe pillansii*, whose stocky trunk and forked branches can stretch to more than 10 meters, gets its moisture from fog that sweeps in daily from the South Atlantic Coast. Modeling exercises done by scientists indicate that this ephemeral moisture source is being affected by global warming, and the Cape Flora will change dramatically as a result.

Confronted with climate change, a species has only three choices: migrate, adapt, or die. "We may end up losing *Aloe pillansii* because there's nowhere for the plants to migrate to find suitable conditions," Lanting said.

LEFT: A thunderstorm rolls over the Karoo landscape in Nieuwoudtville, South Africa.

Quiver trees line the horizon at dusk. These trees are at home in the arid desert and are probably the best-known aloe found in South Africa and Namibia.

Some of the aloe tree species can be transplanted to similar climates, and have already appeared as novelty shrubs in the Southwestern U.S. But the quiver tree *Aloe pallensii*, specifically adapted to tenuous circumstances in an area bounded by ocean water, has nowhere to go and is in imminent danger of disappearing altogether.

"I photographed pictures taken 100 years ago in the same place in the park, against a background of the trees that now exist," said Lanting. "You can see that some of these same trees are still there because they live a very long time, centuries and centuries. But it's also clear when you look at the site today that half of them have disappeared, and there are no young plants to speak of. It's one of those rare instances where you can see extinction in progress before your eyes."

Threatened by poachers and periodic outbreaks of Ebola, this silverback western lowland gorilla from Odzala National Park in the Republic of Congo must now also contend with climate change. MICHAEL NICHOLS

A male snowy owl stretches his wings and flares his talons in
pursuit of a mouse under the snow in Canada. VINCENT MUNIER

Migrating pronghorn antelope bound through snow in
Wyoming's upper Green River Basin. As climate conditions
shift, many species may be forced to respond by changing
their migration patterns. JOEL BERGER

A CLIMATE FOR LIFE

An Indian tiger leaps across a chasm in India's Bandhavgarh National Park. Even small changes in climate could accelerate the extinction of this critically endangered species.
MICHAEL NICHOLS

Freshwater Biodiversity

Although changing climate will affect all types of biodiversity, freshwater species may well experience the greatest extinction rates unless solutions are identified and implemented quickly. Policies and regulations to promote conservation and efficiency will not only protect this resource for our use, they will ensure the survival of critical habitats.

217

Water lilies mottle the surface of the Okavango Delta in Botswana. They represent one of the oldest evolutionary branches of flowering plants. FRANS LANTING

PREVIOUS PAGES:
With the 108-meter drop of Zambia's Victoria Falls just centimeters away, a swimmer stands at a hidden pool— a 2.5-meter-deep divot in the riverbed rock—accessible only when the Zambezi River runs low. ANNIE GRIFFITHS BELT

Pirapitanga fish school together in a clear-water stream in the Cerrado region of Brazil. LUCIANO CANDISANI

Freshwater Biodiversity

Michael Leonard Smith, Tracy A. Farrell, L.J. Gorenflo

The biological diversity on Earth faces enormous challenges in the next few decades due to climate change and the modified habitats that will accompany it. Although changing climate will affect all types of biodiversity, freshwater species may well experience the greatest extinction rates unless solutions are identified and implemented quickly. Anticipated impacts of climate change that will affect freshwater resources include increased temperature, increased climate variability (including storm intensity and drought frequency), and altered effects of extreme events such as El Niño. Rising water temperatures and the drying out of existing habitats may lead to catastrophic losses for freshwater ecosystems.

Freshwater biodiversity is particularly threatened under most climate-change scenarios for two principal reasons. First, large numbers of species and exceptionally high species density suggest that the freshwater biodiversity biome has the most to lose. Second, the geographic nature of most freshwater ecosystems (e.g., frequent small size and constraining boundaries) renders the species within those habitats incapable of absorbing sizeable changes. It is indeed this intense localization of species that accounts for the high level of extinction of freshwater invertebrate species. Some research indicates that 10,000 freshwater invertebrates may already be extinct (Strayer, 2006).

The impacts of climate change on freshwater systems will also present a set of new challenges to which humans and other species must adapt. The picture that emerges in a world of climate change, altered habitats, and growing human demand is a dynamic one of quick adjustments and geographic movements of myriad species, in many cases placing humans and non-human species in direct competition for resources. Geographic shifts in water availability and demand will require better management of water resources. In response to climate change and associated shifts in habitat, the ranges of many plant and animal species will change, likely having an enormous impact on biodiversity (Thomas et al., 2004). Further adding to the problem is that freshwater is already heavily over-exploited by an enormous and growing global human population, placing considerable stress on this essential resource before climate change of any consequence has even occurred.

The red-legged frog is a threatened species under close watch in British Columbia's Clayoquot Sound in Canada. JOEL SARTORE

A female sockeye salmon guards her nest in the Kennedy River on Vancouver Island in British Columbia. JOEL SARTORE

As humans continue to modify their environment to meet new demands, the future of freshwater biodiversity may well rest in the ways we improve the efficiency with which we use freshwater and the ways in which we become better stewards of this irreplaceable resource. Policies and regulations to promote efficiency will not only protect this resource for our use, it will ensure the existence of critical habitats. Meanwhile, dedicated conservation efforts will be essential not only for the protection of freshwater biodiversity, but also for the very survival of the human species.

Density of Diversity

The streams, lakes, and wetlands that comprise the world's freshwater eco-systems add up to a seemingly trivial portion of Earth's habitat for life, covering less than 1% of the Earth's surface compared to 28% of the surface that is land and 71% that is covered by the global ocean (McCallister, Hamilton, and Harvey, 1997). Measured by volume, the waters that contain freshwater biodiversity amount to only 0.02% of the Earth's total water in oceans, the atmosphere, glaciers, and groundwater (Gleick, 1996). Nevertheless, this small component of the biosphere contains a relatively large share of global biodiversity for many important taxa, rivaling that found in far larger terrestrial and marine biomes.

For example, the world's vertebrate species are about evenly divided among these three major biomes, despite their vast differences in area. As a result, the miniscule part of the surface that is covered by freshwater contains nearly one-third (31%) of the planet's vertebrate species. The best-studied group of aquatic organisms—the fishes—is particularly concentrated in freshwater. Calculations based on the Catalogue of Fishes Online (2007) show that freshwater fishes account for more than 45% of the world's total fish diversity. When the numbers of freshwater and marine fish species are normalized against the volume of their respective biomes, the density of species is 7,500 times greater in inland waters than in the ocean (Horn, 1972).

Although it is difficult to assess the numbers of freshwater species in groups such as invertebrates, plants, fungi, and micro-organisms that are less well known than fishes and the other vertebrate taxa, available evidence again suggests disproportionately high biodiversity. It is estimated that 12% of all animal species inhabit freshwater (Abramovitz, 1996). Attempts to assess total diversity at discrete freshwater sites indicate that the global estimates above may prove to be quite low. One of the few intensive assessments covering all invertebrate groups—a two-decade-long study of biodiversity in a small European creek about one meter wide and 4.5 km long—yielded an inventory of more than 1,000 invertebrate species (Allan and Flecker, 1993), dwarfing by far the better-known vertebrate and vascular plant components of the creek in a part of the world not known for high species richness.

Freshwater biodiversity embraces nearly the full range of the world's major groups of micro-organisms, algae, fungi, and invertebrate animals including freshwater sponges, flatworms, nematodes, mollusks, crustaceans, insects, and even jellyfish. Although the species in these groups tend to have relatively broad geographic ranges when they occur in terrestrial or marine settings, they exhibit an extraordinary degree of endemism when they occur in freshwater.

The Clinch River in Kentucky is home to a number of threatened freshwater mussels. Mussels are the most endangered groups of animals, with 50% now either endangered or extinct. JOEL SARTORE

Evolution

Although diversity is most easily measured in terms of numbers of species—the twigs at the tips of branches in the tree of life—it is also useful to consider diversity at deeper evolutionary levels, taking into account the major branches themselves. Freshwaters are truly exceptional, as they contain a disproportionate share of the most ancient lineages of vertebrates, including lampreys, sturgeons, paddlefishes, gars, the archaic bowfin of central North America, and the lungfishes that comprise the basal sister group to all vertebrates

This is particularly true in lakes. Siberia's Lake Baikal, which is known (so far) to contain more than a thousand species of animals and another thousand of algae, has levels of endemism reaching as high as 99% in some of its major invertebrate groups (Mackay, Flower, and Granina, 2002).

The reasons for such high freshwater biological diversity are not always entirely clear. For example, freshwater species occasionally occur in putative species flocks, or groups of closely related species, in certain ancient lakes. Although species flocks are common in freshwater, the existence of large numbers of sister species in a shared locality is unprecedented in marine or terrestrial settings, and the situation poses conceptual challenges to most models of species formation. Freshwater species flocks have therefore attracted intensive study of species limits and evolutionary processes. Even after 200 years of investigation, the world's ancient lakes continue to yield discoveries of more species.

Most spectacular are the well-known clusters of cichlid fishes in the East African rift lakes, where hundreds of closely related species co-occur, but smaller species flocks are known in ancient lakes in most parts of the world, from Lake Titicaca in the Andes to Lake Baikal in Siberia. The extraordinary diversity of crustaceans in Lake Baikal probably gives it the distinction of being the most speciose lake on Earth, despite its location at high latitude.

on land. Only six species of lungfishes survive—one in South America, four in Africa, and one in Australia. As is clear from their distribution on three separate continents, this small group of relics dates from an age when these continents were one. Some of the most intriguing vertebrates in freshwater are the ten species of bichirs (family Polypteridae), an ancient branch of African fishes that are more archaic than dinosaurs. First discovered in the Nile during Napoleon's ill-fated military (and scientific) campaigns in Egypt, a bichir specimen was brought to the great comparative anatomist, Georges Cuvier, who risked lèse-majesté by telling Napoleon that, for this discovery alone, the failed French invasion was worthwhile (Griffiths, 2006).

The flowering plants, like vertebrates, also underwent a significant evolutionary radiation in Earth's early freshwater habitats, and this left representatives of ancient plant lineages in freshwaters throughout the world. Recent phylogenetic reconstructions based on molecular data (Qiu et al., 1999, 2000) show that the water lilies and their relatives (about seventy species usually classified in the family Nymphaeaceae) occupy one of the two basal-most (or oldest-diverging) positions of all of the approximately 300,000 species of flowering plants that are extant today. Another worldwide plant family, the hornworts, diverged very early from the line leading to all other flowering plants (Les, 1988; Chase et al., 1993). The hornworts have the distinction of being pollinated by water itself. Although all but six species are now extinct,

A CLIMATE FOR LIFE

During an ancient courtship ritual, two sandhill cranes pursue each other across a secluded wet meadow slough near the Platte River in central Nebraska. MICHAEL FORSBERG

Portraits of a Shrinking Prairie Habitat

Photographs by Michael Forsberg

A LOVE OF PRAIRIE LED Midwesterner Michael Forsberg to the potholes of the Dakotas, "pearls of life," he says, that are rapidly disappearing.

"Most people don't realize the importance of this highly degraded, often-overlooked, misunderstood ecosystem," he said. "Its 300,000 square miles were once covered with grass and dotted with potholes, a biome brimming with waterfowl, shorebirds, land mammals, amphibians, and macro-invertebrates. Now two-thirds of it has been converted to cropland, which has vast implications not only for the life that exists there but also for the loading of greenhouse gases into the atmosphere."

Prairie potholes were shaped when the Wisconsin glaciers receded about 12,000 years ago, leaving northern prairies dotted with depressions. Filled with rainwater, they form verdant feeding and hatching grounds for thousands of waterfowl and shorebirds.

"Imagine the deepest part of a pothole as a bulls-eye, and the area surrounding it as separate zones, each one a niche for a diversity of flora and fauna," said Forsberg. "In the shallow water you have different species than in the deep, and at the shoreline you have wet marshes of sedge. Beyond the shoreline grows prairie grass that provides nesting sites for birds.

"Take the northern pintail, a prairie duck. You may find its nest a mile from the pothole, but when the eggs hatch, momma marches the ducklings to the water where they can escape predators such as coyotes, foxes, and raccoons. In the water they find a host of things to eat so they can grow to maturity. A friend of mine calls potholes 'duck soup.' When a pothole disappears, you break that chain of life."

A drying climate might be expected to imperil a water-based system, but the numbers supporting such a threat are not yet confirmed.

"It's not like watching an iceberg melt," said Forsberg. "In prairie it's hard to look at the landscape and say what is changing. The Great Plains have always been shaped by cycles of flood and drought, cold and hot. Nature has adapted itself to take advantage of those changes. We do know, however, that climate change is likely to make droughts longer and human demands for water greater for irrigation, so it's likely to have an effect."

An American white pelican forages for aquatic vegetation in a prairie pothole wetland in Stutsman County, North Dakota.

LEFT: Early fall evaporation in a prairie pothole reveals a salt pan in Lost Lake National Wildlife Refuge in North Dakota.

RIGHT: Potholes permeate the agricultural landscape in central North Dakota.

A northern harrier shields an egg and chick from the hot midday sun in Stutsman County, North Dakota.

The immediate concern is destroying this unique ecosystem for human needs. From 2002 through 2007 more than a half million acres of native grasslands have been converted to other uses in the Dakotas and Montana. Most have been plowed under and have had their wetlands drained for food croplands, but now the prospect of raising plants for ethanol imperils them even further.

"When you plow grasslands you release the carbon that has been stored there, plus you diminish the ability of the land to sequester the carbon that we produce," Forsberg said. "So destroying prairie adds to the greenhouse effect.

"This ecosystem has been chopped off at the knees over the past century, and it makes me wonder about its ability to survive. I worry that my kids will only read about prairie potholes in books or see them in museums. I care about what is happening to the prairies, and I'm trying to put a face on that before it's all gone."

Dark rings on the trees are historical markers of previous high-water levels in this shrinking pothole lake in Kidder Country, North Dakota.

LEFT: Western grebes perform their dancing courtship on a prairie-pothole lake in North Dakota.

A CLIMATE FOR LIFE

Cambodian children celebrate the first day that clean water flows from a well drilled in their village. ANNIE GRIFFITHS BELT

A CLIMATE FOR LIFE

In search of wild salmon, this fisherman casts into the healthy waters of the Hvita River in Iceland. PAUL NICKLEN

The Role of Oceans

Extensive warming, sea-ice retreat, changes in currents, sea-level rise, and acidification will have serious implications for marine biodiversity. Hope lies in first reducing the production of greenhouse gases and then establishing conservation strategies that accommodate changes in migration, breeding, and feeding patterns, thereby protecting key ecosystems that maintain species resilience.

A CLIMATE FOR LIFE

Baitfish form a ball near the islands of Raja Ampat. Powerful currents protect the area from ocean warming elsewhere in the region, making these marine habitats some of the most resilient in the Coral Triangle. MICHAEL AW

PREVIOUS PAGES:
A red pigfish and schools of blue maomao swim inside a cavern on the Poor Knights Islands in New Zealand. Protecting marine habitats that naturally withstand climate change often requires removing the human pressures that might destroy their natural resilience. BRIAN SKERRY

King penguins swim offshore from their breeding colony near Macquarie Island in sub-Antarctic Australia. The loss of Antarctic sea-ice has resulted in declining krill populations, which gravely threatens the survival of many species, including penguins, that rely on krill as their primary food source. TUI DE ROY

The Role of Oceans

Emily Pidgeon, Scott C. Doney

The ocean is immense, powerful and wild, immune to the actions of humanity. At least that is how the seas have been represented throughout history and even through mythology. New science findings belie that image, however. Whether it is through overfishing or pollution, our collective environmental footprint on the ocean is, in fact, pervasive and growing rapidly. And now there is strong and startling evidence that human-driven climate change is altering the fundamental nature of the oceans (IPCC, 2007).

Human-driven climate change is predicted to accelerate over the next several decades, leading to numerous impacts on ocean ecosystems. Extensive ocean warming, sea-ice retreat, changes in ocean currents, sea-level rise, and ocean acidification will all have serious implications for marine biodiversity. While biological responses will vary from region to region, broad trends can be identified, including poleward shifts in species, disruptions to existing ecosystems, and direct threats to the survival of some marine species. These changes are already beginning to unfold across the oceans. For marine turtles, warmer temperatures affect the ratio of male to female hatchlings with serious implications for future populations. In the Galapagos Islands, changes in ocean currents have severely impacted virtually all the species in the region, from green algae all the way up the food chain to the seabird and sea lion populations that rely on fish for their survival. In the Antarctic, declining sea-ice has resulted in the loss of krill populations, again the foundation of the ecosystem's food chain. Retreating sea ice in the Arctic has reduced the hunting season for polar bears and the time available for seals and walruses to birth and feed their pups. Ocean acidification is weakening a multitude of species that form shells from calcium carbonate, which includes everything from microscopic plants at the base of the food chain to familiar species such as coral, clams, crabs, and lobsters.

The principal solution to counter the impacts of climate change must be to address the causes of climate change itself, namely the production of greenhouse gases by humans. However, climate change is already changing the marine environment and impacting the diverse species of our oceans. There are additional actions we can take now to safeguard the resilience and ability of biodiversity to adapt to the changing environment. These solutions

A whitecoat (juvenile) harp seal swims gracefully in the icy waters of the Gulf of St. Lawrence in Canada. As sea ice diminishes, vital habitat for harp seals, ringed seals, and walruses will disappear. BRIAN SKERRY

include establishing conservation strategies that can accommodate changes in the migration, breeding, and feeding of species and protecting key ecosystems that maintain the resilience of species. Much as there is no one cause for the loss of biodiversity in our oceans, there is no one solution.

Changing How Our Oceans Work

On a global scale, the oceans act together as a giant heat engine, with a complex network of ocean currents moving heat from the tropics to temperate and polar oceans. These current systems, often called the global ocean conveyor belt, consist of two components, an upper limb with poleward movement of warm surface waters heated by the sun in the tropics and a deep return flow of cold waters formed near the poles. The movement of heat from the tropics to the poles by the ocean is critical to maintaining the planet's climate, and human-driven climate change will alter significantly ocean currents and heat transport, with large-scale consequences for ocean ecosystems and regional climate.

The largest ocean currents are thousands of kilometers in length and carry several hundred times the volume of the Amazon, the world's largest river. For example, the Gulf Stream is an arm of the ocean conveyer that originates in the tropics of the Atlantic Ocean and transports warm, salty water north along the east coast of North America, and out across the Atlantic. The Gulf Stream releases heat into the atmosphere in the northern Atlantic, particularly in winter. This effect combines with seasonal warming by the upper ocean to make the North Atlantic climate significantly warmer and milder than might otherwise be expected for such northern latitudes (Trenberth and Caron, 2001; Seager et al., 2002).

There are two main drivers of the currents that circulate water around the oceans. Atmospheric winds blow across the ocean, setting up the surface currents that include the Gulf Stream off the east coast of North America, the Kuroshio current in the northern Pacific, and the Antarctic Circumpolar current, which passes through the Drake Passage at the southern tip of the Americas and encircles the southern continent (Siedler, Church, and Gould, eds., 2001). Deep-ocean currents are driven by thermohaline (i.e.,

temperature and salt) circulation. Thermohaline circulation starts with the sinking of colder, saltier, and, hence, denser water at a few small locations in the polar North Atlantic and around Antarctica. Despite the limited number of starting points, this sinking is a primary force driving the ocean conveyor system. The sinking water forms cold, dense ocean currents that move slowly at great depths, winding a path through most of the world's oceans. The water of these deep currents eventually rises to the surface again to join the surface current system. Thus, the systems of wind and thermohaline circulation are intimately linked together, forming continuous conveyor belts of water.

There is evidence that climate change may be affecting this pattern of ocean circulation. The Arctic and northern Antarctic Peninsula are warming several times faster than the planetary average. Warming of surface ocean waters in these areas results in the melting of the polar sea-ice and glaciers. At the same time, high latitude rainfall rates are increasing. Together, the melting ice and more rain result in the surface of the polar oceans becoming less salty. This warmer, less salty ocean water is more buoyant and less able to sink into the deep sea. Thus climate change can slow the formation of the cold, deep currents that drive the conveyor system of ocean currents and, thus, the global system of circulation in the ocean. Some scenarios suggest the possibility for a complete shutdown in the formation of the deep current in the North Atlantic (Manabe and Stouffer, 1994), though other research findings argue for a less dramatic, but still important, slowdown in sinking near the poles (Bryan et al., 2006). This has significant implications for the climate across the globe. In the North Atlantic, slowing the ocean conveyor system will weaken the Gulf Stream and reduce its moderating influence on atmospheric temperatures.

Changing Ocean Temperatures

Consider the story of the tide gauge on the Honolulu shore that has been recording the continuous ebb and flow of the mid-Pacific ocean tides since 1872. Even today, this tireless instrument measures the height of the ocean every hour. The effect of the sun, moon, and planets that produce the tides dominate this long history of the ocean around the island of Oahu. Since ancient times, sailors have relied upon the tides to be unchanging and

the sinking of thermohaline cold water near the poles and the warming of ocean water as deeper currents rise to the surface. Ocean warming has also been concentrated near the ocean's surface, in the upper 700m of the average 3700m depth of the ocean.

The impacts of ocean warming on the myriad life in the oceans are as diverse as the multitude of marine species. Some species react immediately to higher water temperatures around them. For example, prolonged exposure to warmer water can have drastic impacts on corals, often causing them to lose the symbiotic algae living in their tissues that provides their color. As a consequence, the corals bleach white. Bleaching that lasts longer than one week can kill the coral and decimate the habitats they provide for extremely diverse coral reef ecosystems. In August 2005, the waters of the Caribbean Sea reached record-breaking high temperatures for weeks on end, greater than the summer warming in the Caribbean in all the previous twenty years. These conditions caused the worst coral bleaching event on record in the Caribbean, with as much as 90% of corals bleached and 40% mortality at many sites throughout the region (Eakin et al., in prep). On an even larger scale, mass bleaching and mortality of the world's corals accompanied unusually warm ocean temperatures in 1997 and 1998 that were linked to El Niño conditions in the tropical Pacific. Along the coral reefs of the Western Pacific, 50 to 70% of the corals died. In large areas of the East African coast and the Indian Ocean the coral mortality was almost 100%. The extent of coral mortality was unprecedented in the historical record (Sheppard, 2003).

continuous. However, a meticulous analysis of the Honolulu measurements has found that the tides around Hawaii, particularly the twice-per-day lunar tide, have changed over the last 100 years. The distance between high and low tide has grown, and the rhythm of the tides has drifted in time. The best explanation we have for this is that the ocean is changing. The ocean is warming, and, as a result, the water is expanding, raising the surface of the ocean and changing the tides (Colosi and Munk, 2006).

Observations from around the world make clear that every component of the Earth's climate system has warmed over the last fifty years. Our focus has naturally been on how increasing concentrations of greenhouse gases increase atmospheric temperatures over land. However, more than 80% of the heat added to the Earth system by climate change has been absorbed by the oceans; the oceans hold twenty times more of the extra heat than the atmosphere (Levitus, Antonov, and Boyer, 2005). The ocean has been by far the dominant sink for human-driven global warming, and not accounting for the heat absorbed by the oceans is to ignore the largest single physical impact of climate change on the Earth.

The warming of our oceans has not been uniform. The most rapid changes have occurred in the North Atlantic, the southern Indian and Pacific Oceans, and around the tip of Africa (Willis, Roemmich, and Cornuelle, 2004). This unevenness comes from the patterns of the ocean current systems, including

Changing atmospheric and ocean temperatures also directly threaten larger ocean species. Marine turtles are already some of the most threatened species in the oceans: three of the world's seven species of sea turtle are classified as critically endangered. Destructive fishing practices and poaching of turtle eggs are decimating populations across the globe. Further, turtle nesting beaches are being lost at alarming rates to development (Mast, 2006;

A spine-cheek anemonefish lives in a bulb-tipped sea anemone bleached by excessively warm El Niño waters in Papua New Guinea's Kimbe Bay. FRED BAVENDAM

Mast, 2007). The addition of climate-change pressures further threatens the long-term survival of nearly all marine turtles. For example, like all marine turtle species, the number of male and female loggerhead turtle hatchlings is determined by the incubation temperature of the eggs: warmer temperatures mean more female hatchlings. Currently along the beaches of Florida, less than 10% of the loggerhead hatchlings are male. This region is expected to experience increasing atmospheric temperatures, conservatively estimated to be 2°C or more (IPCC, 2007). Such a temperature change will likely result in a shift to all female hatchlings. With 3°C of warming, many loggerhead turtle nests in Southern Florida would experience temperatures that are lethal to loggerhead hatchlings (Hawkes et al., 2007).

Changing ocean temperatures will force many species to move so they can maintain the temperature conditions they need for feeding and reproduction. Ocean temperature can directly affect the development, age of sexual maturity, timing of spawning, growth, and survival of most fish and cephalopod (such as squid and octopus) species. The waters of the North Sea warmed by 0.6°C between 1962 and 2001. Although this seems like a small temperature increase, during this time nearly two-thirds of the regional fish species shifted either northward or deeper into cooler water. The blue whiting (*Micromesistius poutassou*), one of the largest fisheries in the Atlantic, moved its range 816 kilometers north. The temperatures in the North Sea are predicted to increase by a further 1.0–2.5°C by 2050. With such changes, important commercial fishes, such as blue whiting and redfishes (*Sebastes* spp.), may disappear completely from the region (Perry et al., 2005).

Changes in fish distribution will have dramatic repercussions on entire marine ecosystems. Many marine mammals such as blue and humpback whales require dense patches of prey: crustaceans (krill), squid, or schooling fish. These whales migrate vast distances between polar feeding and tropical breeding grounds on a calendar timed to maximize available prey. Temperature changes that shift the distribution of their prey will mean that food will not be available at the end of their poleward journey or that their annual migrations will need to be even longer, reducing the time available for feeding. A decrease in the threatened North Atlantic right whale calf survival has been related to such an effect of climate variability on the amount of available prey. Similarly, observations near the Galápagos Islands strongly indicate that female sperm whales have a lower rate of conception after periods of warmer ocean temperatures, during which squid—their main food source—is greatly reduced.

The Galápagos Islands are renowned for their biological diversity, both marine and terrestrial. Lying at the convergence of warm and cold ocean currents, the waters around the Galápagos Islands simultaneously provide habitat for tropical species such as corals and boobies, temperate species such as kelp and sea lions, and unusual endemic species found nowhere else on Earth, such as the marine iguana and the flightless cormorant. During normal years, upwelling of deep ocean water to the surface around the Galápagos Islands supplies nutrients to support the unique ecosystems found in the region. The possible effects of rising ocean temperatures, however, are demonstrated during an El Niño year. Occurring every two to seven years, El Niño conditions bring warm ocean water from across the Pacific to surround the Galápagos, blocking (putting a lid on) the upwelling of deep waters. Without this usual source of cold, nutrient-rich water, the whole marine ecosystem suffers, from

A Coleman's shrimp is camouflaged on a fire sea urchin off Komodo Island in Indonesia's Komodo National Park. The increase in ocean acidification due to warming temperatures affects shell-building sea life. TIM LAMAN

the green marine algal plants to the fish that feed on them.

In recent years, severe El Niño events have resulted in losses of more than 95 percent of the coral reefs; populations of Galápagos penguins decreased by almost 80 percent; and species of corals, algae, and the Galápagos damsel fish were so severely impacted that they have not been sighted since (Edgar et al., in press). During the 1997-98 El Niño, dead sea lions and marine iguanas became common sights throughout the islands. The Global Marine Species Assessment (GMSA) has recently determined that two of the Galápagos corals—Floreana coral (*Tubastraea floreana*) and Wellington's solitary coral (*Rhizopsammia wellingtoni*)—should be classified as Critically Endangered by the IUCN Red List, and a third—*Polycyathus isabela*—should be listed as Vulnerable. In addition, the GMSA also assessed ten Galápagos seaweeds to be Critically Endangered. Climate change is predicted to bring about stronger and more frequent El Niño-like conditions (Boer et al., 2004). So, although the Galápagos have felt the impacts of El Niño for many thousands of years, climate change will magnify its impacts beyond anything that the biodiversity of the region has seen before.

From California to Peru to the West coast of Africa, the world's most productive fishing grounds are found in upwelling zones where deep nutrient-rich waters rise from the deep to the surface of the ocean. In these regions, the supply of nutrients fuels the entire coastal marine food web. By changing wind patterns, ocean currents, and ocean temperatures, climate change will alter the intensity and timing of upwelling, with severe implications for entire ecosystems, including the important fisheries they support. For example, in 2005 the upwelling season along the coast of California was delayed by one month. That year the upwelling winds were the lowest in twenty years, the surface waters averaged 2°C warmer than normal, and nutrient levels were 30% less than normal. As a result, the amount of food available throughout the entire marine ecosystem was reduced. The density of mussels and barnacles was reduced by 83% and 66% respectively. The sea lions in Monterey Bay usually stay close to shore, but in 2005 they swam hundreds of kilometers offshore in search of fish. Widespread mortality and breeding failure occurred in coastal seabirds such as the Cassin's auklet (*Ptychoramphus aleuticus*). These changes in upwelling pattern match predictions of the influence of climate change on numerous coastal regions around the world (Barth et al., 2007).

Globally, seabirds have been affected already by changing ocean temperatures. Populations in North Scotland have experienced breeding failures approaching 100% in recent years. This appears to stem from warmer waters leading to a decline of plankton and fish. Migratory birds typically require very productive areas in which to fatten before migration. When these fail, catastrophic declines can take decades to rebound (Wormworth and Mallon, 2006). It is estimated that the threat of climate change to migratory birds (marine and terrestrial) is equal to the sum of all other human-caused threats combined, with more than 80% of migratory bird species facing some type of climate change threat (Robinson et al., 2006).

The Fragile Ecosystem of Sea Ice

The Arctic Ocean is almost solely known for the floating ice cap that covers it. Historically, that ice has ranged in size from about 16 million square km

sea level across the oceans is estimated to have been 17 cm (IPCC, 2007). However, the changes in sea level have been far from uniform across the oceans. In some regions, the rate of sea level rise has been several times the average; over the last ten years sea levels have been rising at up to five times the global average in the western Pacific. Elsewhere, in specific locations such as the eastern Pacific, sea levels have dropped during that period (IPCC, 2007).

Over the next century, global sea levels are projected to rise at even faster rates. At a minimum, an average sea-level rise of 38 cm above 1990 levels is expected by 2100, and a rise of over 100 cm or more is possible (Rahmstorf, 2007). Accurately predicting future changes in sea level is difficult because of the complex nature of its climate change-related causes: the expansion of sea water as it warms, the melting of glaciers and polar ice sheets, and changes in the water stored in lakes, groundwater, and other terrestrial reservoirs all contribute. The future melting of the Antarctic and Greenland ice sheets may have the largest single impact on sea level. Complete melting of the polar ice would result in a global sea-level rise of about 70 m (ibid.). However, the contribution of polar ice melting to sea-level rise was almost completely unknown until satellite observations became available. To date, these new measurements have not been fully incorporated into calculations of sea-level rise, and thus current estimates may be conservatively low (Nerem, Leuliette, and Cazenave, 2006).

Although only 2% of the world's land lies at 10 meters elevation or less, 10% of the world's population lives in these areas—634 million people who are directly threatened by sea-level rise. (McGranahan, Balk, and Anderson, 2007). The impacts of sea-level rise on coastal regions will be extensive. Increased coastal flooding, inundation of low-lying regions, salt water inundation of groundwater, and accelerated erosion are already being observed in numerous coastal locations around the world. The increased frequency of severe storm

events and changes in rainfall patterns also expected from climate change will act to further exacerbate the degradation resulting from sea-level rise.

The biodiversity of coastal and nearshore ecosystems is similarly threatened. The ability of coral reefs, mangroves, sea grasses, coastal marches, and other critical habitat-forming species to adapt to sea-level rise will hinge on their ability to move upward and shoreward. Slow-growing species are the most unlikely to be able to keep pace with the rising oceans. Natural and manmade barriers such as cliffs, sea walls, and coastal development will also stand in the way of the inland migration that might save many coastal ecosystems.

The small island nations of the Pacific Ocean are the most immediately vulnerable to the impacts of climate change, and particularly to sea-level rise. Typical of these is the Republic of Kiribati, a nation of thirty-three coral atolls that lies near the Equator, halfway between Hawaii and Australia, and stretches nearly 4,000 km from east to west and 2,000 km from north to south. The islands of Kiribati are on average less than 2 meters above sea level. The country has a population of approximately 100,000 people, nearly half of whom live in the urban area of South Tarawa, which is less than 3 meters above sea level. Sea-level rise has already taken its toll on Kiribati. Two of the nation's islands have disappeared into the ocean. Increasing erosion is destroying the coconut trees that line the nation's beaches and provide its single largest export. It is estimated that Kiribati will lose up to 30% of its

Fishermen in Senegal haul in nets loaded with fish. Climate change will deeply affect the fisheries upon which millions of people rely for their survival. RANDY OLSON

mangroves to sea-level rise by 2100. Unlike other coastal areas, island nations such as Kiribati have no hinterland to which people or species can migrate when coastal areas are lost. The communities of Kiribati are working to adapt to the impacts of climate change and are focusing on improving urban water supplies, replanting mangroves, strengthening laws that reduce coastal erosion, and assessing population settlement to reduce the risks of injury and loss of life. However, if predictions of sea-level rise are accurate, the island will be largely overcome by the surrounding ocean within the century, leaving a nation of people without a home.

Ocean Acidification

Global warming and the changing climate are not the only impacts of greenhouse gases threatening the seas. The same burning of fossil fuels and tropical forests that is driving the warming of the Earth is also altering the composition of seawater, making the oceans more acidic. The resulting ocean acidification threatens numerous types of sea life, and for some plants and animals, acidification of the oceans may be a more urgent threat than climate warming (Doney, 2006).

The basic story of ocean acidification is clear. The carbon dioxide that is released by cars and power plants initially goes into the air; but not all of it stays there. About one-third dissolves into the surface ocean—about 22 million tons of CO_2 per day (Sabine et al., 2004). Once in the sea, the carbon dioxide combines with water to form carbonic acid, which then undergoes a cascade of acid-base chemical reactions. Just as in a can of soda pop, the overall effect of adding carbonic acid is to make the seawater more acidic (Feely et al., 2004). The surface waters of the world's oceans have already changed by about 0.1 pH units, the basic measure of acidity. This may sound insignificant, but it translates into a 30% increase in acid-inducing hydrogen ion levels. And acidification will almost undoubtedly accelerate in the future.

Computer model forecasts predict that ocean pH levels may drop by another 0.3 to 0.4 units by the end of this century unless we sharply reduce fossil-fuel use (Orr et al., 2005). The ocean chemistry is changing at least 100 times more rapidly than it has changed over the past 650,000 years. If present

carbon dioxide emission trends continue, ocean acidification will increase to an extent and at rates that have not occurred for tens of millions of years (Feely et al., 2004). Most of the human-driven ocean acidification is concentrated near the ocean surface (Sabine et al., 2004) over the depths that are most densely populated with life.

Acidification directly harms the many ocean plants and animals that build shells out of calcium carbonate, the same material that makes up chalk and limestone. Some of the shell-forming organisms are familiar, such as the numerous corals that build large reefs in the tropics; the clams, scallops, and other mollusks that live in coastal sediments; and crustaceans like lobsters and crabs. There are also less familiar cold-water corals that grow deeper in the water along the continental shelf and slope and act as habitat for many fish. The largest populations of shell-forming species, however, are microscopic, floating in the upper layers of the open ocean. For example, coccolithophores are single-celled plants that form such large and dense populations that that they can be viewed from space. Coccolithophores are protected by an external layer of calcium carbonate scales a few thousandths of a millimeter in diameter and shaped like hubcaps. They provide the foundation of the food web in many marine ecosystems: these tiny plants are food for fish that support squid and, hence, marlin, swordfish, and sharks.

Ocean acidification directly threatens these shell-forming species as their calcium carbonate shells start to dissolve under more acidic conditions. Even small increases in ocean acidity impair the ability of many organisms to build their shells (Kleypas et al., 2006). To test this, researchers have grown many different types of shell-forming plants and animals in the laboratory under different levels of carbon dioxide. The organisms grown under higher carbon dioxide levels have difficulty building their shells. The shells are often malformed (Riebesell et al., 2000), and in some experiments the shells start to fall apart even while the creatures are alive (Orr et al., 2005). Further, the biological impacts of ocean acidification extend beyond shell formation to include lower growth and reproduction rates.

Many of the shell-forming organisms threatened by acidification provide critical habitat and food sources. Tropical corals support some of the richest

A CLIMATE FOR LIFE

Mackerel swim through the surf off the coast of Japan. Climate change may force many species to adapt in various ways, but unsustainable fishing practices threaten the survival of even the hardiest marine species. DAVID DOUBILET

The Phoenix Islands: Adapting to Sea-level Rises

Coconut crabs, overharvested elsewhere, thrive on the unspoiled Phoenix Islands of Kiribati, Micronesia.

LEFT: A diver looks for lobster in the surf zone of Orona Island in the Phoenix Islands of Kiribati, Micronesia. Conservation International's Global Conservation Fund and the New England Aquarium worked closely with the government of Kiribati to help create the world's largest marine protected area around these islands.

Photographs by Paul Nicklen

APPROACHING ONE OF THE PHOENIX ISLANDS on the diving boat *Naia* in 2001, Paul Nicklen saw what looked from a distance like swarms of mosquitoes hovering in the air. When the boat drew closer he saw that the swarms were hundreds of thousands of seabirds, whose calls made human conversation nearly impossible.

Between the birds in the air and the marine animals beneath the surface of the water, the wildlife photographer was astounded at the immensity of life in the remote coral ecosystem. The Phoenix Islands, located halfway between Hawaii and Fiji and part of the Micronesian nation of Kiribati, are one of the most isolated places on Earth. And yet, in a subsequent visit a year later he saw that even this Eden could be affected, maybe even devastated, by human activities.

"We sailed for days just to get there," he said. "The only people who live in the Phoenix Islands live on the main island of Kanton, and it's a thousand miles away from the ones we wanted to see.

"In that first visit we were looking at 150,000 spectacled and sooty terns, and 50,000 fairy terns," he said. "There were thousands of magnificent frigate birds, lesser frigate birds, and noddies. The bottom of the sea was covered with healthy coral, necessary for fish to hide in. Giant clams were everywhere. We were seeing black-tipped sharks constantly, and on the islands the ground was crawling with coconut crabs.

"It was like going back in time, before man left any kind of imprint."

When he re-visited the islands a year later, the change was obvious. "We saw far fewer species. A small, illegal fishing boat had literally wiped out the black-tipped sharks, taken 6,000-7,000 of them in a very short time. The coconut crabs, which are easy to catch, were mostly gone. There's a very nasty predatory fish called a bohar snapper, and without the sharks to keep them in check, the bohar population had increased and eaten many of the smaller fish. So the whole ecosystem was changing.

"Sailing around the islands we came across open ocean tuna trawlers, big ships with helicopters on board. They powered away from us, so they were probably illegal."

BELOW: Masked boobies roost and fly in Kiribati, Micronesia. Low-lying islands like these are at great risk of inundation as sea level rises.

RIGHT: Frigatebirds soar over Rawaki Island in Kiribati, Micronesia. The Phoenix Islands are a central Pacific atoll archipelago uninhabited by humans, but rich with biodiversity both above and below the deep water that surrounds them.

The islands face threats even greater than illegal fishermen. Global warming could raise the temperature of the water and by melting the great ice sheets at both poles, raise sea level until the Phoenix Islands could disappear altogether. The highest point on some of the islands is only seven feet above sea level.

"The marine biologists on board said a one-degree rise in temperature could be enough to make this whole ecosystem go away," said Nicklen. The scientists are conducting a baseline survey to see what is there and what would be lost.

"What we saw in that first visit was a perfect, balanced ecosystem, and it could be destroyed by global warming," he said. "It was sobering to realize that even areas like this, areas that few people ever visit, could be wiped out by human activities and global warming. You realize that no place in the world is safe."

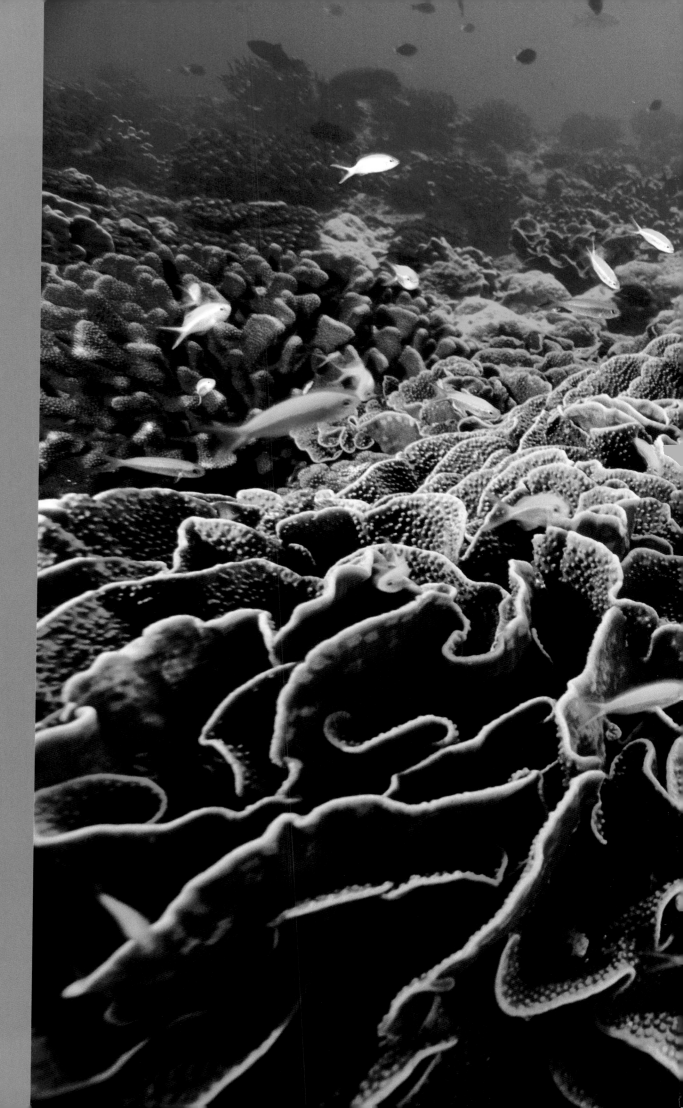

Fairy basslet fish dart among blooms of lettuce coral in the Phoenix Islands. PAUL NICKLEN

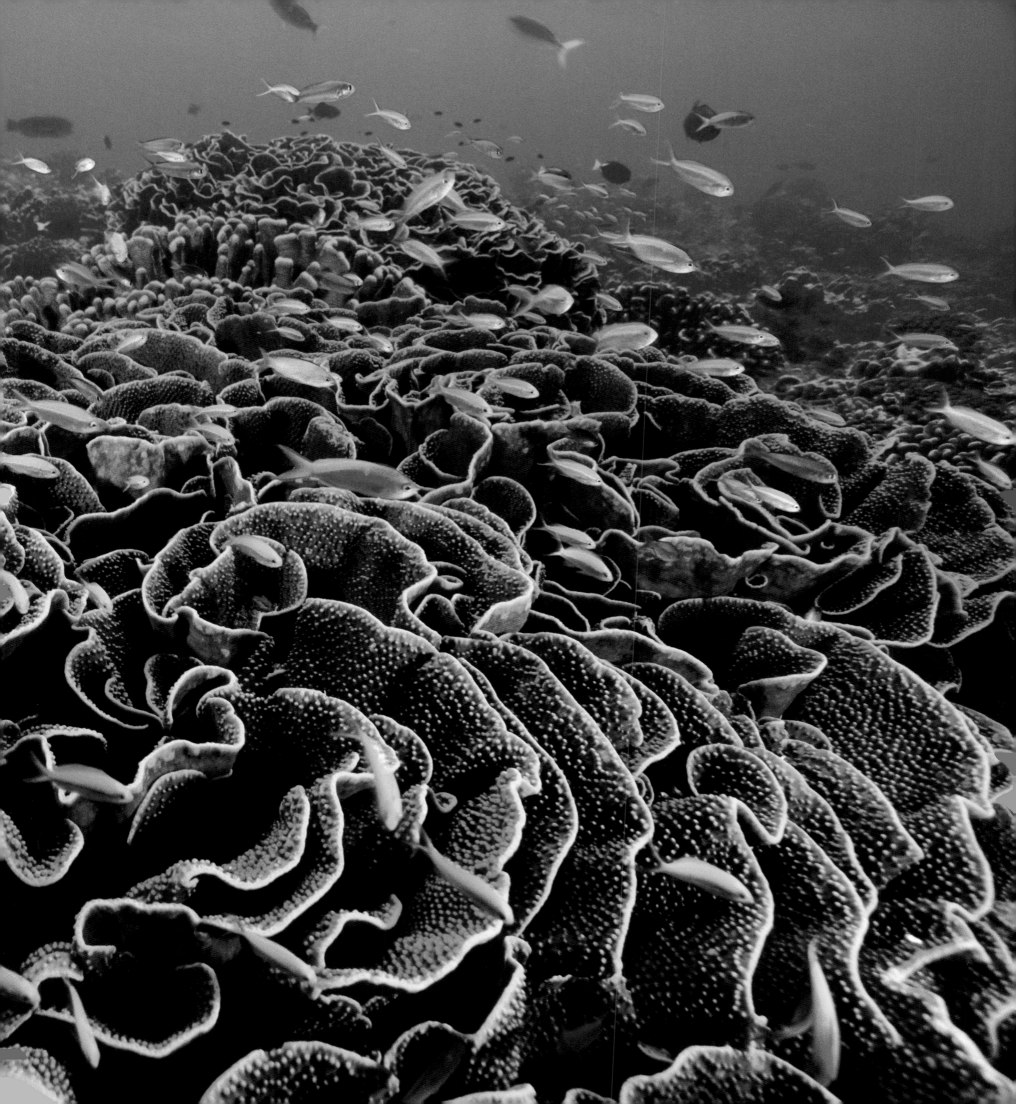

A long-beaked common dolphin swims with sardines. Warming ocean temperatures will force many species to shift their feeding ranges. THOMAS P. PESCHAK

Human Dimensions

Climate change will require agriculture to adapt to changing rainfall, industries to adapt to changing resource availability, governments to increase disaster prevention and relief, and vulnerable peoples to adapt to more frequent outbreaks of disease. It is critical that we begin mitigating impacts immediately and adapting to changes already underway.

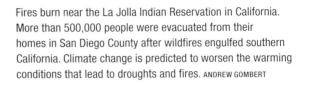

Fires burn near the La Jolla Indian Reservation in California.
More than 500,000 people were evacuated from their
homes in San Diego County after wildfires engulfed southern
California. Climate change is predicted to worsen the warming
conditions that lead to droughts and fires. ANDREW GOMBERT

Human Dimensions

Katrina Brandon

Climate-change impacts are already evident and are rapidly intensifying, affecting biodiversity and global ecosystems, as well as human health and welfare.

Severe weather events are likely to become more frequent and more severe. Sea levels will rise, leading to the catastrophic inundation of coastal areas. Atypical weather patterns will intensify, resulting in droughts for many parts of the world and flooding in others, threatening the availability of freshwater. Regions suitable for agriculture will shift, with many unforeseeable consequences for food production, distribution, and availability. Disease shifts, with the threat of global pandemics, represent a threat as warming increases. All of these impacts will have major socio-economic impacts, whether through direct threats to human life, the increased spread of pestilence and disease, or the projected economic and political implications of an altered environment in the future. Actions for mitigating these impacts through technological innovations, improved governance and land-use planning, economic policy reforms, and protection and restoration of carbon-rich ecosystems are essential to reduce the consequences of climate change on human society. Yet, adaptation action also is vitally needed and is viewed as a priority for the international development community (UNDP, 2007).

Climate-change impacts will not be distributed evenly. The magnitude of economic impacts—the total cost—will likely be greatest in developed countries simply because the volume and value of commodities and property is so high. But the impacts will be strongest, affecting the greatest number of people, in the tropics—and will be especially damaging to Africa and small island nations. They will make already vulnerable people and ecosystems even more vulnerable, and the worst impacts will affect countries and people who can least afford to adapt. The irony is that the people least responsible for producing the greenhouse-gas emissions causing climate change will bear the brunt of its impacts. Yet even rich people in wealthy countries may be unable to insulate themselves adequately from the different types of impacts that are likely to occur.

We know enough to be able to say with certainty that there are many climate-change impacts that we have yet to anticipate that will surprise us.

More and more housing developments are encroaching on diminishing wetlands near Naples, Florida. As with mangrove forests in other places, wetlands help buffer storm surges and mitigate the effects of hurricanes. JOEL SARTORE

But there are others that we are certain are already happening or will happen in the near future that will place enormous stress on human societies. Climate change will require agriculture to adapt to changing rainfall; industries to adapt to changing water and energy availability; governments to increase disaster prevention, relief and aid; and vulnerable indigenous and traditional peoples to adapt to increases in the frequency of disease outbreaks. We need to reconcile the development desires of countries like China and India, while also reforming the highly consumptive and energy-intensive demands that characterize most developed countries. Dealing with climate-change impacts rapidly and equitably is clearly the greatest challenge that human society has ever faced. We have to begin mitigating impacts immediately, while also adapting to the changes that are already taking place.

Complicating Factors

Several issues complicate discussions of climate change. Impacts are often interconnected, there are feedbacks and unpredictability in both natural and human systems, tipping points are unknown, and there are differences in risk and vulnerability. An example of interconnection of systems, for example, is that flooding can ruin houses and agricultural crops, contaminate freshwater supplies, and bring diseases such as cholera. While specialists attempt to study climate change and its likely impacts within sectors, it is important to remember that any particular impact will have ripple effects. The best way to understand climate-change impacts is to look at one specific place and then trace possible linkages as they cross different sectors.

There is also a great deal of unpredictability due to feedback loops and tipping points that may change the rate and magnitude of impacts and that occur in both natural and human systems. A classic example of a feedback loop that happens in urban areas across North America is the relationship between hot days, air conditioning, and electric utilities. On very hot days, people turn on their air conditioners. While they stay cool, the overall impact of all those individual air-conditioner units working increases the level of heat in the city, requiring air conditioners to work even harder to make things cooler, which in turn makes the city even warmer and uses more electricity. The demand for electricity can increase dramatically, causing power shortages in the form of brownouts or blackouts. Similar feedback loops occur in nature as well and may increase the magnitude and severity of climate-change impacts. Tipping points, the threshold of impacts that can be tolerated, are unknown for many natural and human systems. But there is evidence that some natural systems, such as coral reefs, may have already reached a tipping point from which they cannot recover. Such impacts on natural systems are linked to broad impacts for humans that can affect tourism, fisheries, storm buffers, and even potential pharmaceutical discoveries.

Many impacts are related to risk and vulnerability, which are not the same thing. Risk is the chance that an impact will occur in a given place—the likelihood that a hurricane will hit an island, for instance. In many cases, there is little that we can do to lower the risk from many undesirable events (e.g., flooding or hurricanes). Poorer people and countries have fewer resources and options to minimize the negative impacts that climate change brings. Even within countries, there may be groups that are especially disadvantaged,

Residents could only watch as damaging winds from Hurricane Allen reached more than 160 kilometers per hour in Corpus Christi, Texas. Scientists predict that climate change will result in a higher frequency of hurricanes with greater intensity.
ANNIE GRIFFITHS BELT

such as indigenous and traditional peoples. Globally, there are certain groups (e.g., babies and young children, the elderly, the infirm and malnourished) that are especially vulnerable. But we can take action to reduce peoples' vulnerability, the coping mechanisms and actions that people can take to reduce how (and how much) they will be affected by different components of climate change (Confalonieri et al., 2007).

Weather and Disasters

Climate change will increase the frequency and severity of weather events and will lead to increased natural hazards. Most models of human-induced climate change show that climate-change impacts will increase extreme weather events across the globe (Poverty-Environment Partnership, 2003). If current trends continue, disasters could have a global cost of $300 billion per year by 2050 (UNDP, 2004).

Notable changes are already evident. In all regions, the climate has warmed and, more importantly, the variability in the amount of rain from year to year has increased significantly (Giorgi and Bi, 2005). During the 1990s, an estimated two billion people globally were affected by disasters, triple the number impacted in the 1970s, while economic losses increased by a factor of five, from $138 billion to $629 billion, between 1970 and 1990 (IFRC, 2003). While 90% of people exposed to disasters live in developing countries, the direct economic impacts are often higher in developed countries because of the higher value of real estate, goods, etc. For this reason, insurance companies have been at the forefront of understanding and modeling the risks from climate change (e.g. Höppe and Pielke Jr., 2006). They have documented the following:

- Between 1970 and 1990, there were three years with more than twenty weather events that counted as significant natural catastrophes. Since 1990, each year has had at least twenty such events.
- Four hurricanes that hit the U.S. in 2004 cost a record $56 billion in total losses over a few weeks, setting a record.
- In 2004, ten typhoons hit Japan, four more than the previous record,

making it the costliest year ever for typhoon damage there.
- In 2003, the European summer was the hottest in the past 500 years, causing 22,000 premature heat-related deaths accompanied by wildfires causing $15 billion in losses.
- The number of severe winter storms in Britain has doubled over the last fifty years (Association of British Insurers, 2005).

2007 was a record-setting year. In the words of Sir John Holmes, who heads the United Nations Office for the Coordination of Humanitarian Affairs (OCHA), one branch of the UN that deals with international disasters, 2007 amounted to a climate-change "mega disaster" with record numbers of floods, droughts, and storms around the world. OCHA has made the highest-ever number of climate-related emergency appeals. Estimates are that in South Asia, flooding made 66 million people homeless or seriously affected them. Flooding has affected millions of people across Africa, especially in Sudan, Mozambique, Madagascar, Zambia, and Uganda. Ghana, Burkina Faso, and Togo may soon join them. In contrast, severe drought reduced harvests by half in Swaziland and Lesotho.

In assessing the impacts of natural hazards, it is important to think about exposure and vulnerability. Some countries may have high physical exposure (e.g., Japan to earthquakes, tsunamis, and typhoons), but they have taken actions to lower their vulnerability. Some places are less lucky than others— and they can be subject to multiple hazards. For example, the Philippines are at risk from volcanic activity, typhoons, and related landslides and flooding. As an island chain, they will be heavily impacted by climate change. Other places may have only one hazard, but the probable intensity of the event could be huge (e.g., a potential large-scale volcanic eruption). Still other places are affected by some type of hazard, over and over—the Caribbean and Madagascar are barraged with cyclones year after year.

Countries with higher income, democracies, and nations with higher-quality institutions suffer less death from natural disasters (Kahn, 2005). For example, countries that ranked high on human development indices represent 15% of the global population exposed to hazards, but they represented only

1.8% of the deaths (UNDP, 2004). Therefore, their exposure and risk is much greater than their vulnerability, which depends on the risk of physical exposure, the number of people likely to be exposed, the ecological conditions to serve as catalysts or buffers for disasters, and the organization and response capacity. The figures for the number of deaths do not necessarily correspond to impact from hazards, although in developing countries they tend to overlap. For example, developed countries may sometimes bear high economic losses, simply because what is lost or destroyed has a higher economic value (e.g., property [real estate and personal] in New Orleans has a higher value than a comparable area in Honduras). But the impact of a disaster can be greater and long-lasting in poorer countries, where there are few buffers to help people cope with devastation. Impacts also vary with preparedness. Evacuating people, boarding windows, and building houses on stilts are all appropriate actions to prepare for some hazards, and can also reduce vulnerability.

Environmental degradation worsens the impact of many hazards. A study in Science found that villages with intact mangroves or coastal forests were spared from the impacts of the 2004 Asian tsunami, while neighboring villages without mangroves or forests were completely destroyed (Danielsen et al., 2005). Significant impacts are felt in coastal cities in areas where coral reefs, mangroves, barrier islands, and wetlands have been degraded or removed and are more prone to disasters from hurricanes, tsunamis, and flooding. The confluence of deforestation and climate change in the tropics puts human settlements in the path of future flooding disasters.

There remains debate in the scientific community on the relationship climate change exerts over the frequency and strength of tropical cyclones (Emanuel, Sundararajan, and Williams, 2008). Yet many climate-change models predict fiercer cyclones in some parts of the world, or slower-moving cyclones that would lead to higher damages since the wind and rain last longer. One study found that Atlantic-basin hurricanes have grown more than twice as powerful in the past three decades, with a notably sharp upswing since 1995. The study proposed that storm intensity is greater when ocean-surface temperatures rise. If this research is correct, then hurricanes reaching the United States with wind speeds that are 5 or 10% more powerful would double the cost of the damage (Stern, 2006).

One way to predict what will happen in the future is to look at the impacts of events similar to what we would expect in the future, such as the last strong cycle of El Niño that began in mid-1997 and continued through 1998 (Simms, 2006). A large number of countries in Central and South America and the Asia-Pacific region were severely affected by El Niño-related floods and droughts, and huge areas of some countries such as Indonesia and Brazil had enormous fires. The global economic losses for this 18-month event were estimated to be between US$32 billion to US$96 billion. Using El Niño as a basis, the projected impacts from climate change (UNDP, 2004) are as follows:

Asia. Asia is likely to suffer from the worst natural disasters in the future. In more populated central and southern Asia, sea-level surges and increased intensity of tropical cyclones will affect heavily populated areas of low-lying land such as southern Bangladesh, the Nile delta, parts of eastern China, and

Water surrounds homes just east of downtown New Orleans in this aerial view of the damage wrought by Hurricane Katrina in late August 2005. SMILEY N. POOL

many atoll islands of the South Pacific and Indian Oceans. They will also damage the coastlines of Indonesia and Pakistan. Ice melt will affect Tibet, changing the timing and volume of surges in major rivers such as the Yellow, Yangtze, Mekong, Irrawaddy, Ganges, and Indus.

Africa. Water will be the main problem for Africa, with droughts affecting most inland areas and sea-level surges affecting most of Africa's largest cities, especially stretches of low-lying coasts in western Africa from Senegal to Angola. Crop failures, famine, and disease will dramatically increase.

Latin America. Flooding, droughts, and tropical cyclones will all pose problems in different areas, with sea-level rise especially affecting Caribbean coastal areas of Central America and the coastline from Venezuela to Recife in Brazil.

Small Island States. These will have the most serious problems, suffering from the impacts of increased cyclones and sea-level rise and surges, loss of land, salinization of freshwater aquifers, and damage to highly productive coastal mangrove and coral ecosystems. The nation of Kiribati in the Pacific, where the highest point is only 5 m above sea level, is already losing land area.

Floods cause more damage than any other natural disaster largely because they have other ripple effects (e.g., damage to agriculture and infrastructure) and can lead to outbreaks of waterborne diseases. Huge annual losses result from the disruption to economic livelihoods, businesses, infrastructure, services, and public health. In developing countries where infrastructure is often weak, the impact of flooding can cause particular difficulties. In the ten years from 1993 to 2002 flood disasters "affected more people across the globe (140 million per year on average) than all the other natural or technological disasters put together" (IFRC, 2003). So far, 2007 is confirming the projections about serious impacts from floods.

Coasts and the Sea. We know that sea-level rise is already happening, which should be cause for tremendous concern. Sea levels have already risen by 9

to 20 cm in the last century (Bindoff, et al., 2007). What we don't know is how high, and how fast, sea-level rise will occur in the coming decades, although it is projected to increase dramatically this century. The most conservative estimates are for a one-meter rise, while other estimates go as high as five meters (Rahmstorf, 2007; Hansen, 2007). The 2007 opening of the Northwest Passage through the Arctic and cracks in the West Antarctic ice sheet give cause for serious concern. The key factors in the speed and level of sea-level rise depend primarily on what happens in Greenland and the polar ice caps and on potential feedback loops. Because the international community has been trying to reach consensus through mechanisms such as the IPCC, only climate models that represent scenarios within scientific certainty have been included. Such consensus may be important for forging international agreements, but it limits policy-makers from knowing the spectrum of scientific opinion (Oppenheimer et al., 2007).

As stated in the chapter on oceans, coastal areas only account for about 2% of the world's land area, yet 10% of the world's urban population (634 million people) lives in these low-lying coastal areas (McGranahan, Balk, and Anderson, 2007). Even with a one-meter rise, coastal cities, agriculture, livelihoods, and infrastructure will be affected. The impacts will be greatest in Asia, where 75% of people live in vulnerable zones. Other regions with high relative impacts are East Asia and Middle East/North Africa (Dasgupta et al., 2007).

The ten countries with the largest number of vulnerable people are China, India, Bangladesh, Vietnam, Indonesia, Japan, Egypt, the United States, Thailand, and the Philippines. These top-ten countries have more than 70% of their total population living in susceptible coastal areas. Yet these numbers hide countries with lower populations, where rising oceans will affect almost everyone. All small island nations (e.g., the Netherlands, Guyana, and Suriname) are highly vulnerable. Other countries, such as China, will also bear large impacts simply because they have large coastal areas with high numbers of people.

There are more than 180 countries with people living in susceptible coastal areas. Within many of these countries, the area where the impacts are

As water supplies diminish during drought, more and more use is made of less and less water, leading to the likelihood of diseases spreading. KAREN KASMAUSKI

concentrated may be small. But if major cities are located in these areas there will be serious problems. The IPPC 2007 Fourth Assessment Report noted that twenty-one major cities are highly vulnerable to rising sea levels. The most vulnerable cities are New York, Los Angeles, Tokyo, Bangkok, Jakarta, Buenos Aires, Rio de Janeiro, Shanghai, Cairo, Mumbai, and Karachi (Nicholls et al., 2007; Worldwatch, 2007). Yet there are another twenty-three cities with more than eight million people each that are also at risk.

Buenos Aires is a good example of the scale of the problem. It lies within a susceptible coastal area, putting thirteen million people, one-third of the population of Argentina, in a risk zone. People, businesses, sewage, subway, and school systems will all be affected. The tremendous economic costs involved in adapting to impacts could easily put this middle-income country into a downward spiral. Unfortunately, many of the countries with the largest cities are developing countries with a low capacity to respond. Hurricanes, cyclones, and other storm surges will compound the direct problems of sea-level rise, as will degraded environments. Places where wetlands, coastal forests, and barrier islands have been destroyed are at higher risk. Ironically, coastal real estate with beautiful views overlooking the ocean still command the highest real-estate prices, but that will begin changing.

Other important climate-change impacts relate to the life within the oceans and the lives of the people who depend on these resources. Just as impacts on land are closely linked to one another, so are impacts in the oceans. Coral reefs already have been bleaching, the result of warming water that kills the algae that live within them. When reefs die, many of the species that depend on them suffer, tourism disappears, fish catches decline, and their value as a storm buffer is lost. Combined, human activities have already destroyed more than 25% of the world's coral reefs, and nearly 60% of the remaining areas are threatened.

Climate change is also leading to chemical reactions in the ocean, as carbon dioxide is absorbed and converted to carbonic acid. This acid is reducing the levels of calcium carbonate and increasing ocean acidification, leading to the decline of many species—a problem for communities that depend on fish for their survival. In addition, as traditional habitats for fish get warmer, many fish are migrating to cooler and less-accessible areas. Increased warming also increases the diseases fish get. Combined, these impacts are serious for the survival of marine species, as well as for the huge number of people who depend on the oceans for their food. Worldwide, both marine and freshwater fish support more than 20% of the protein for 2.6 billion people, generating more than $130 billion annually (Combes, 2005).

Freshwater

Lack of clean and available freshwater is the greatest environmental contributor to human illness and death, and the quantity of freshwater is declining while contamination is increasing. The World Health Organization says that one billion people already lack access to potable water—about one out of every six people. At current trends, by 2025 two out of every three people will live in water-stressed conditions. The really bad news is that those projections don't even include the impacts of climate change.

There are many different ways that climate change will affect water quality, quantity, and availability. Models show that the hydrological cycle

A man inspects a corn field damaged during floods in Yuanqu county in north China's Shanxi Province. Experts warn that global warming will fuel more violent weather and greater impacts on agriculture in China. REUTERS/STR /LANDOV

and lakes, rivers, and aquifers are not recharged. Changed weather patterns have already radically altered the size of Lake Chad's surface area from 22,902 km in 1963 to 304 km in 2001—a drop that has had huge implications for the countries surrounding it. Droughts can quickly become a problem, especially when major cities have few alternative sources of water.

There are a few places where water stress will be particularly severe, such as in the Sahel and northern Africa, northeastern Brazil, and northern China. Projections show that by 2025, up to 65% of Africa's population will be at risk of water stress and scarcity. The Yangtze River provides water for hundreds of millions of people and is considered to be at risk. However, even wealthier areas are not immune from serious droughts. Southern Europe, North Africa, southern Australia, Patagonia, and the southwestern United States are all expected to have devastating and long-term droughts, according to experts at Columbia University and the IPCC (IPCC, 2007).

Farming and Food

As global climate change alters the face of the world's ecosystems, it will also change agricultural production, practices, and food availability. Direct impacts that will change yields are hotter temperatures, changes in rainfall patterns and timing, and the effects of extreme weather events such as floods and droughts. Warmer and wetter conditions will increase the number of crop pests, diseases, and weeds. Such conditions will be ideal for increased fungal infestations, and milder winters mean that crop pests won't be killed off. Agricultural yields will also decline as the numbers, types, and patterns of pollinators change and many decline. This is significant because wild bees, flies, bats, and birds are responsible for pollination resulting in up to 30% of global agricultural food production (Daily and Ellison, 2002). In both the United States and Europe, the honeybee population has collapsed by

will change with the air becoming warmer and wetter in most of the world, although some areas will have much drier conditions. This will affect weather patterns, causing some areas to get much more rainfall than normal and using it up for other areas that will be gripped by drought. Ironically, rainfall at the wrong time can decrease the overall water supply since it reduces how much water is stored.

Many parts of the world depend on glaciers for much of their water supply. The precipitation that feeds glaciers comes as snow, and the glaciers grow and store water. During summer months, glaciers melt and release more water, precisely when agriculture needs it most. But changing weather patterns and warming have directly caused glaciers to shrink. When rain falls instead of snow, glaciers melt even faster, leading to lowland flooding. Glaciers are especially important as a water source in the Himalayas and the Andes. Studies throughout the world show that glaciers are rapidly melting. The Quelccaya Glacier in Peru feeds irrigation systems built by the Incas that are still used by their descendents. It has been shrinking at nearly 1% per year for the last thirty-three years (Struck, 2006). The Swiss Academy of Sciences has reported that eighty-four out of ninety-one glaciers retreated between 2004 and 2005.

Coastal areas will be dealing with too much seawater and its impacts on shallow aquifers or lakes that could be contaminated because of salt-water infiltration. Inland areas will face dramatic problems if they receive less rainfall

half—especially troubling in Europe, where 80% of crops are insect-pollinated (Teagasc, 2007).

While warmer temperatures and more CO_2 may be good for some crops, climate change will certainly lead to shifts in what crops are suitable for a given place. This means that farmers in many parts of the world will bear much higher risks as they try to adapt to growing crops that may be new to them. In contrast, yields in many industrialized countries could increase up to nearly 9% from longer growing seasons, warmer weather, and what is known as "carbon fertilization," which is increased plant productivity that results from more carbon in the air. However, there is also growing evidence that some assumptions about the effects of carbon fertilization may be missing important differences in the way that tropical and temperate plants react to more carbon, diminishing potential benefits. Finally, while there may be some regional gains in productivity, all farmers will face higher risk and uncertainty—uncertainty of how climate changes will affect agriculture.

Global estimates of future agricultural production vary, since they are built on different assumptions and models about rainfall, drought, and direct CO_2 effects on plants. Yet the best estimates suggest that by 2080, worldwide agricultural productivity will decline between 3–16% if guesses about carbon fertilization are correct, but by 10–25% if they are wrong (Cline, 2007). These numbers mask huge differences in projected yields between temperate and tropical countries and even within different regions of those countries. Adding to the complexity is that these changes will happen amid more frequent and bigger weather extremes and hazardous events, growing human populations, greater demands to use land for energy crops (biofuels), and worsening land degradation.

Clearly, the agricultural implications of global climate vary geographically: Farmers in drier, more marginal climates will suffer the most, while cold-weather peoples may see a jump in farm yields. Citizens in the United States may see little cause for alarm, particularly in the first half of the century when yields are expected to increase a bit. But in many tropical, developing countries, climate change is already altering yields. Sahelian Africa and Southern Africa are already witnessing changing weather patterns, with warmer, drier, and shorter growing seasons while drought and erratic rainfall are affecting yields in Southern Africa. Cacao farmers in West Africa are watching their tree crops become stressed and cacao yields fall.

As with so many other impacts from climate change, Africa is the region that will likely be hit hardest. Changes in rainfall patterns are such that by 2020, yields from rain-fed agriculture in some countries could be cut in half. Yet projected consequences for India will be equally dire, especially considering that India has more poor people than all of sub-Saharan Africa and yields are projected to decline a staggering 30–40% (Cline, 2007). China, further from the Equator than most developing countries, could escape major damage on average, although its south-central region will be in jeopardy. The picture is similar in the United States, with projected reductions of 25–35% in the southeast and the southwestern plains but significant increases in the northern states.

Health Problems and Spread of Disease

Climate change is projected to worsen human health in several key ways,

Families struggle to gather their belongings after Cyclone Nargis destroyed their houses in Myanmar's Konegyangone township on the outskirts of Yangon. The survivors of the May 2008 cyclone will also face outbreaks of disease as they search for clean water, food, and shelter. KHIN MAUNG WIN

with increased illness and death directly resulting from many of the impacts described in earlier sections (Epstein and Mills, 2005). For example, extreme weather events such as intense heat waves or more deadly hurricanes will directly lead to more deaths. Yet such events often have secondary impacts, such as waterborne diseases that typically accompany flooding. The crowding of displaced people following such events facilitates the spread of diseases such as typhoid and cholera, especially with people who may be malnourished or have weakened immune systems. WHO estimates that by 2030, climate change will increase the estimated risk of diarrhea by 10%.

Even where there aren't extreme events, a slow decline in water quality and quantity will lead to drought, hunger, and increases in dysenteric and water-borne diseases affecting hundreds of millions of people. Temperate countries, such as Europe and the United States, will have powerful and long-lasting heat waves, which will directly affect vulnerable populations such as the elderly. When combined with drought, these create the conditions for wildfires, such as those seen in southern California and Greece in 2007. Such fires directly affect people but also worsen particulate matter and can worsen air quality in surrounding areas for hundreds of miles.

The El Niño Southern Oscillation (ENSO) events trigger conditions similar to climate change, so we can already see likely changes in the form of droughts and floods and the risks of waterborne diseases. Likewise, by modeling the dynamic interactions of climate change, land-cover change, ecology, epidemiology, and human behavior, we can understand better how rates of infectious diseases such as malaria or dengue might change over time. For example, warmer temperatures improve the conditions for the spread of many diseases. Climate has had a proven role in outbreaks of Hantavirus Pulmonary Syndrome, cholera, and dengue, as well as in malaria transmission where warmer temperatures allow mosquitoes to inhabit new areas and increase reproduction and infection rates. Flood and drought cycles create conditions to amplify the spread of leishmaniasis and viral hemorrhagic fevers. There are many other impacts that will be related to climate change, such as increased allergens, more respiratory problems, and worsening air pollution.

There is strong evidence that healthy ecosystems are linked to better human health (Pattanayak et al., 2005). A carefully controlled study has recently found that malarial mosquito biting rates are 278 times greater in deforested areas than in areas of intact forest (Vittor et al., 2006). Small changes in temperature may have huge disease impacts; one study found that a temperature increase of only 0.5°C increased the number of mosquitoes by 30–100% (Pascual et al., 2006). The intertwined effects mean that newly deforested areas set the conditions for diseases like malaria to have huge increases. Another example of how these effects can be magnified is a recent finding that babies born of HIV-positive women who also have malaria have three times the risk of being born with AIDS than those born of a mother who doesn't have malaria (Brahmbhatt et al., 2003).

Health effects are not likely to be "center stage" in the future. More dramatic and extreme events—floods, hurricanes, droughts, fires—will get more attention that the spread of diseases to new areas or the emergence of new diseases or increased numbers of people affected by diseases. Yet the mental-health impacts of devastation are likely to be significant in many parts of the globe. Across the globe, disease puts a strain on economies, diminishing economic activity and serving as a drag on development.

Social and Economic Consequences

The impacts of climate change will crosscut all sectors of society—economics, health, education, employment, sports, recreation, and leisure. It will be impossible for anyone on the planet to escape from climate-change impacts. What is unknown is when, where, and how forcefully impacts will occur. The countries responsible until now for most greenhouse gas emissions that cause climate change are largely the same places where impacts will be less serious, where economies are big enough to absorb losses, and where governments generally have the capacity to respond. In contrast, the regions, countries, and people responsible for the lowest percentage of emissions are those that will suffer the most.

Given this inequitable context, it is hard to imagine a peaceful or prosperous world in the future. Instead, a majority of the world's people

will likely see the wealthy and consumptive lifestyles of residents in developed countries as responsible for their misery. Within countries, both rich and poor, climate-change impacts will highlight inequities. For example, Hurricane Katrina affected poor areas of New Orleans worse than rich areas, and the lingering effects have been hardest on the poor, who have few resources on which to fall back. How we cope with global inequities, within countries and within cities and towns, will be highly variable, but it is certain that climate change impacts will highlight inequities, and cause both social and economic disruption.

On many different levels, climate change is viewed as a threat to global security, a concern that is being increasingly expressed by national security experts (WBGU, 2008; CNA Corporation, 2007). Poorer countries tend to have weak governance and greater civil conflict, which will be magnified when there is resource scarcity (e.g., food, water), which is projected to intensify under climate change. Some social scientists think that in the future we will see increasing conflicts and wars over resources, especially energy and water, and that these could pose a dramatic threat to global security, further destabilizing certain regions. Already, even without drought, there is evidence that countries that share rivers or other water resources have more disputes over them (Gleditsch et al., 2004; Klare, 2002). Another problem that can influence stability is the prospect of massive migration caused by a flow of environmental refugees into nearby areas, and the Stern report envisions that there could be up to 300 million climate-change refugees in the future. Greater violence is also likely in cities when serious disruptions or shortages occur, such as looting following hurricanes.

While there are numerous grim scenarios of the conflicts that may accompany climate change, problems are most likely in places where environmental degradation is high and the adaptive capacity of governments is low. Also, for any given country, there are strong links between the severity and size of different impacts, how well a country can reduce its vulnerability, and the cost of the disaster or impact relative to the size of its economy. Even poor countries can do an exceptional job of minimizing the impacts of hazards. For example, Cuba has one of the best systems in the world to safeguard its residents when hurricanes approach. However, already poor countries, with high environmental degradation and weak governance, lack the conditions to do much to mitigate or adapt to impacts. Research over the past several decades indicates that some developing countries are losing 4–8% of their gross domestic product (GDP) due to environmental and resource degradation (World Bank, 2004; World Bank, 1997; Repetto et al., 1989). Gains in economic development and poverty reduction can quickly be wiped out, as shown in the example below.

Case Study: Honduras

Honduras is one of the poorest countries in Latin America and suffers from severe income inequality. More than 62% of the rural poor live in extreme poverty, and their lives are precarious in many ways—92% of people who live on steep slopes live on US$1 per person per day. Before Hurricane Mitch in 1998, Honduras was steadily reducing poverty. But Mitch caused US$3.8 billion in losses, US$2.2 billion of that in direct damage to property. After the hurricane, it became clear that high rates of forest clearing had combined

Refugees from Myanmar wait for a delivery of fish meal at a camp on the border with Thailand. One of the devastating side effects of climate change is the displacement of people who are forced to migrate to survive. ANNIE GRIFFITHS BELT

with Mitch to create a disaster. Between 1990 and 2005, Honduras lost 37% of its forest cover—around 2.74 million hectares (Telford et al., 2004). Upland deforestation led to soil erosion and faster water runoff, exacerbating downstream infrastructure destruction and flooding.

Despite this knowledge and the massive investment in Honduras after Mitch, deforestation has increased by nearly 9% since 1998—making the conditions that would bring about future destruction even worse and increasing the potential of hurricanes even smaller than Mitch to have devastating impacts on the poor. Scientists predict that climate change will bring more hurricanes of higher intensity. This is particularly troubling for Honduras and other Central American countries where poverty, deforested and eroded slopes, and high water runoff coincide. Yet we know that relatively small investments, compared with the costs of the impacts, could reduce much of the risk.

Unfortunately, few countries are paying serious attention to climate-change impacts and really engaging in the broad scale reforms needed to mitigate and adapt. Yet the cost of mitigation is estimated to be a fraction of that of inaction, costing 1% of global GDP if we take action now, but up to 20% of global GDP if action is substantially delayed (Stern, 2006). Economists debate the exactness of these estimates, sparring over the right discount rate to estimate future economic losses, ways to treat risk and uncertainty, and the methodologies for calculating and comparing costs and benefits (Ackerman, 2007; Weitzman, 2007; Sterner and Persson, 2007; Cline, 1992). Sir Nicolas Stern himself, in April 2008, said "We underestimated the risks…we underestimated the damage associated with the temperature increases…and we underestimated the probability of temperature increases," (Harvey and Pickard, 2008). Yet the majority of economists agree that a failure to take action soon will hamper economic growth. Keeping current policies, subsidies, incentives, and regulations that reward inefficient and destructive uses of energy, biological, and natural resources is an absurd waste that could be channeled to protect what remains and restore what is lost, while improving the lives and livelihoods of billions of the world's residents.

Other chapters in this book provide greater details on the innovative technology, policy, and financing options that could be pursued. Obvious actions are removing perverse subsidies that drive investment into energy sources that are costly, risky, and polluting or that reward other sectors or actors to destroy biological and natural resources for short-term profits, such as subsidies to agriculture, logging, and fisheries. Removal of these subsidies would help developing countries compete and would encourage sustainable investments and management. Other actions, such as enabling carbon-rich and biodiversity-rich, but cash-poor developing nations to market reductions of emissions from deforestation as creditable and tradeable mitigation options (See chapter on REDD) would have a huge and rapid payoff. Such highly effective ways of simultaneously supporting economic development while reducing greenhouse gas emissions rebuts those critics who contend that climate-change mitigation and adaptation measures will harm poor countries. Policy reforms and programs channeling support for mitigation and adaptation to developing countries, if funded and implemented at the levels required, could represent substantial contributions to the development of impoverished nations. Many of the policy reforms at national and international scales needed to support and finance mitigation and adaptation are well known. Still unknown is how long it will take those in positions of global power across all sectors to demonstrate leadership on the most important challenge humankind has ever faced.

A CLIMATE FOR LIFE

Fog surrounds loaf-shaped mountains at sunrise in the Valle de Vinales in Cuba. Like most Caribbean nations, Cuba is hit by several violent storms each season. To protect itself from the ocean, Cuba has one of the best hurricane-preparedness systems in the world. STEVE WINTER

Climate Change Linked With Increases In Malaria

Photographs by John Stanmeyer

Thousands of *Diptera* mosquitoes swarm around the low heat of smoldering trees that were clear cut along the highway outside of Iquitos, Peru. At night, the harmless *Diptera* will be replaced by *Anopheles* mosquitoes, which carry malaria.

LEFT: Peter Anthony Guza is nearly buried behind a mountain of nets he has sewn at a Tanzanian textile factory in Dar es Salaam. Tanzania is the largest manufacturer of mosquito nets in Africa.

WHILE PHOTOGRAPHING an international story about malaria, John Stanmeyer noticed a connection between deforestation, climate change, and the world's deadliest disease. Malaria kills more people annually than any malady on earth.

"While focusing on malaria in Peru, I noticed that deforestation in the Amazon region outside Iquitos is accelerating like crazy," he said. "The reasons are well-known— humans encroaching into jungles and forested areas, companies harvesting timber, settlers planting food crops and farming fish in ponds.

"Cutting down trees creates a perfect breeding ground for the mosquito-borne disease by creating stagnant pools of water that are heated by being exposed to the sun. Fish farming ponds also become breeding places for the *anopheles* mosquito, which carries malaria in tropical areas. Malaria cases in Peru have shot up almost 300 percent in the past 10 years.

"And, of course, cutting down trees also contributes to global warming by diminishing the oxygen that is produced, and reducing the sink for carbon dioxide. So a link exists between the deforestation that is going on around the world in tropical areas, which causes climate change and also creates a higher incidence of malaria. Despite modern medicines and the use of DDT to kill mosquitoes, malaria cases are not diminishing worldwide."

In a more direct way, climate change is now suspected of being the culprit in malaria cases that have sprung up recently in southern Italy and Sicily. "The evidence is not yet conclusive," Stanmeyer said, "but some scientists are trying to connect it to global warming because of the temperature increases, which allow the anopheles mosquito to move farther north."

Since malaria and climate change are linked, incidences of Acquired Immune Deficiency Syndrome (AIDS) must also be brought into the mix, he pointed out. "I began to notice that every time I went to a hospital to photograph malaria victims I was directed to the AIDS ward. I realized that when you get AIDS your immune system is knocked down, so it's almost a death sentence to get malaria. Your system just can't handle fighting the malaria parasite. So malaria and AIDS have a tragic tango going on that deeply affects people in the tropics."

Stanmeyer has seen many changes in the 12 years he has made his home in Asia and focused on the human condition with emphasis on conflict, poverty, and health. Changes include the incredible increase in human rubbish.

Rubbish in urban areas may have an oblique connection to climate change. If, as suspected, a warming climate changes wind patterns and increases rainfall in some tropical areas, manmade containers create more receptacles for stagnant water. Poor drainage systems in urban areas also create stagnant pools and rubbish contributes by clogging the drains. Increased rainfall and stagnant pools offer breeding grounds for malaria-bearing mosquitoes.

"If wealthier nations do not have malaria, often the idea of being proactive to eradicate malaria has been weak," he said. "There could never be a better time than now to reduce malaria on our planet."

Egypt's Nile Delta is twice as populated as Bangladesh. By 2050, nearly one-fifth of Egypt's arable land, where 16% of the population live, could disappear as a result of sea-level rise.
STUART FRANKLIN

Tipping Points

The global average temperature is increasing many times faster than the natural rate experienced since before the rise of civilization. The Arctic provides early indicators of impending changes that may pass a tipping point— the critical threshold at which tiny disturbances may thrust us into a new climatic regime.

A CLIMATE FOR LIFE

Its image mirrored in icy water, a polar bear swims submerged in Lancaster Sound in the Northwest Territories of Canada. The continuous loss of the sea-ice platform on which polar bears forage has led to shorter hunting seasons, which increasingly threatens their survival. PAUL NICKLEN

PREVIOUS PAGES:
Meltwater lakes and streams crisscross the Greenland ice sheet east of Kangerlussuaq. The combined effect of future melts in Antarctica and Greenland may have the largest impact on sea level. Complete melting of the polar ice would result in a global sea-level rise of about 70 meters. JAMES BALOG

Tipping Points

M. Torre Jorgenson, Guy Midgley, Michael Totten

A group of climate scientists recently cautioned that "society may be lulled into a false sense of security by smooth projections of global change." Writing in the Proceedings of the National Academy of Sciences, they warned that current knowledge points to a myriad of "tipping elements" that human-induced climate change could push to their critical point some time this century (Lenton et al., 2008). Earth history is replete with episodes of climate change occurring over geological time spans, with many periods that dramatically, sometimes catastrophically, impacted life worldwide. The crux of concern over climate change in our time is the extraordinarily rapid rate of global average temperature increase, which is occurring fifteen to sixty times faster than the natural rate experienced by the human species since long before the rise of civilization.

Research indicates that the collective impact of carbon-intensive activities by the world's nearly seven billion people may have the potential to "push components of the Earth system past critical states into qualitatively different modes of operation, implying large-scale impacts on human and ecological systems" (Lenton et al., 2008). Climate-triggered release of carbon from soil is one among a number of possible tipping elements, a term scientists use for describing large-scale components of the Earth system that may pass a tipping point—the critical threshold at which a tiny disturbance can qualitatively alter a system. From time to time, the media has reported on some of these potential tipping elements, such as the rapid disappearance of Arctic sea ice, melting of the Greenland ice sheet, collapse of the West Antarctic Ice Shelf (WAIS), burning of the boreal forest, thawing of permafrost, release of methane hydrates from ocean sediments, dieback of the Amazon rainforest, Indian and West African monsoons, and the shutdown of the Atlantic Ocean thermohaline circulation (Rahmstorf, 2006; Gregory, Huybrechts, and Raper, 2004; Oppenheimer and Alley, 2004; Cox et al., 2000).

Many of these elements relate to the frozen state of a substantial portion of the Earth, where the transition from ice to water is highly sensitive to climate warming and is relatively easy to measure in many ecosystems. The Arctic is a key area to focus on because it also is an integral part of the Earth system that provides important feedbacks that may tip the world past a threshold

Ibyuk is a pingo that rises nearly 50 meters above the surrounding coastal plain on Canada's Tuktoyaktuk Peninsula. Pingos are cone-shaped mounds of ice formed when cold temperatures free subsurface water and force frozen ground upward. BERNARD EDMAIER

307

Synthetic blankets reflect the sun off a Pitztal Glacier ski slope in Austria in an attempt to stave off glacial melting and preserve the area's ski industry. MELISSA FARLOW

Epochal Change, Happening Within A Human Lifetime

Summer sun melts the terminus of Matanuska Glacier in Alaska.

LEFT: The Jakobshavns Isbrae (Jakobshaven Ice Stream) has calved these icebergs that will melt into the North Atlantic Ocean. The Jakobshavn Glacier puts more ice into the ocean than any other in the northern hemisphere. The iceberg that sank the *Titanic* probably originated here.

Photographs by James Balog

A JOLT OF RECOGNITION hit James Balog when he began photographing melting ice at many locations around the world for a project called the Extreme Ice Survey (www.extremeicesurvey.org).

"I realized that I was seeing monumental geologic change, and it was happening right in front of my eyes," he said. "We usually think that these kinds of events occur in the distant past, or will happen so slowly that their effects will be seen far in the future. But the melting of the world's glaciers is taking place now, in a fraction of a person's lifetime. It's all because of atmospheric conditions, and those conditions are manmade."

No stranger to mountain dynamics, Balog was trained in alpine geomorphology, the study of earth's relief features and how they are shaped. A mountaineer since the 1970s, he has a master's degree in geography from the institute of Arctic and Alpine Research at the University of Colorado. "I've done technical climbing in mountains and ice fields for decades," he said, "and I know what to expect when I see glaciers and mountainscapes."

Mountains may be built by continental collision, but they are often shaped by the ice that forms on them from compacted snow. Creeping glaciers carve valleys, sharpen spires, and bulldoze moraines of jumbled rock along their periphery. For centuries glaciers have been fed by snowfall at high altitudes, but with global warming the heights are starved of snow. When glaciers and snowfields are dried up by global warming—which is now occurring in mountain ranges like the Himalaya, Tibetan Plateau, Karakoram, Rockies, Andes and Alps—people downstream have less water supply and the water released raises sea levels.

"I was shocked to see how fast glaciers are disappearing," said Balog. "It was faster than anything my science training or mountaineering experience prepared me for."

In the Alps alone, the area covered by glaciers has shrunk by 35 percent in a little over a hundred years, and most moving ice will completely disappear by the end of this century. Glacier National Park in Montana (U.S.A.) may have to change its name by 2040 because it will be all but devoid of ice. Besides the Alps and Glacier National Park, Balog's Extreme Ice Survey supplies visual evidence of shrinking glaciers in Alaska, British Columbia, Iceland, Greenland, and Bolivia.

"Much of the visual evidence of glacial change is based on aerial photographs or pairs of pictures shot many, many decades—perhaps even a century—apart.

The Columbia Glacier west of Valdez, Alaska, has retreated 16 kilometers since 1984. When tidewater glaciers like this one reach an unstable phase, vast amounts of ice can be dumped very rapidly into the sea, with ice deposited centuries ago turning into seawater in a matter of years.

This approach is too abstract for the average viewer," he said. "I wanted to show how fast glaciers were changing right now, in the time frame that we're living through and remembering. This action is happening really quickly, so quickly that the old expression "glacial pace" has become an oxymoron.

"My idea was to put out time-lapse cameras that would take pictures every hour of the day during the warmer parts of the year, March through October. In the winter months we take just two photographs per day. Currently we've got 27 time-lapse cameras on 15 glaciers in every location but the Alps and Bolivia, where for financial reasons we take repeat photographs from the same spot, once a year."

Although active in mountaineering and always interested in glaciers, Balog spent much of his early career in photography recording endangered species. Since the 1990s he'd had an interest in photographing some aspect of global warming, but wasn't sure how. Magazine assignments to document melting ice convinced him he'd found his calling.

"Documenting changing ice has brought together most of the major currents of my professional life—the mountaineering, the earth science, and the photography. Bearing witness to this changing moment in earth history, I realized, is exactly what I am supposed to be doing with my existence.

"When I shoot an iceberg floating out to sea I know that I may be recording the extinction of something that existed on land for thousands of years. Glaciers won't reconstitute themselves, not with the current changing climate. This project is a memorial to them. And it is, above all, a call to take positive action on global warming."

Surrounded by open sea, a mother walrus and calf (obscured by shadow) float on an ice floe in the Foxe Basin of the central Canadian Arctic on a summer's midnight. NORBERT ROSING

The scientific evidence is clear. There is a direct relationship between human activity, the rising levels of greenhouse gases in the atmosphere, and climate change. More than at any point in our history, the global community requires rapid deployment of innovative policies and incentives to combat climate change.

A Call to Action

Laura Ledwith Pennypacker, Michael Totten, Carlos Manuel Rodríguez, Guy Midgley, Yasu Hibi, Frederick Boltz, Benjamín Vitale, Russell A. Mittermeier, Glenn Prickett, Cyril Kormos, Joanna Durbin

As noted in preceding chapters, the scientific evidence is clear. There is a direct relationship between human activity, the rising levels of greenhouse gases in the atmosphere, and climate change. We are already seeing the effects of climate change around the world, and every day we understand more clearly the very serious and growing threat human-induced climate change presents to our environment and our social, political, and economic systems. Compounding this threat is the considerable delay in implementing an effective global response.

In the six-year period of 2000 to 2006, global carbon dioxide (CO_2) emissions grew at a staggering rate of 3.3%, more than 2.5 times greater than the growth rate of the preceding ten years (1.3%) (Canadell et al., 2007). The global community allowed this high growth rate even while the Intergovernmental Panel on Climate Change's (IPCC) scientists were telling the world that there was strong evidence that human-induced greenhouse gas (GHG) emissions were influencing the global climate (IPCC, 2001).

Climate change will have impacts on our lives, and our children's and grandchildren's lives, even if we achieve the most optimistic GHG emissions reductions targets currently under consideration. Significant impacts will occur well beyond our great-grandchildren's lives if we do not scale up efforts to reduce GHG emissions and help vulnerable people, species, and ecosystems cope with the impacts of irreversible change.

Scientists warn that to keep the global mean temperature from increasing more than 2°C above pre-industrial levels and avoid catastrophic climate change, we must stabilize the atmospheric concentration of greenhouse gases at 350 to 400 parts per million (ppm) CO_2e (Hansen et al., 2008; Meinshausen, 2005). This is an imperative in order to ensure irreplaceable biodiversity and valuable ecosystems are not lost; and some systems may be severely damaged even at 400 ppm. Given the current level of 386 ppm, and an increase of 2 ppm per year, humanity must reduce and cap GHG emissions as rapidly as possible over the next forty years to 60% below 1990 levels.

Compare this with the Kyoto Protocol's modest requirement that only industrialized countries cut their emissions by an aggregate of 5.2% percent of 1990 emissions by 2012, which is less than 1% of the total global emissions

A polar bear settles in the grass in Canada's Wapusk National Park near Manitoba. THOMAS D. MANGELSEN

PREVIOUS PAGES: Frost covers a peat bog landscape on a winter morning in the Vosges Mountains of France. VINCENT MUNIER

	2005 Market Value (million $)	2005 Volume* (MtCO₂)	2006 Market Value (million $)	2006 Volume (MtCO₂)	Eligible Forestry Options
Regulatory					
CDM Kyoto Protocol	$2,638	351	$5,257	475	Afforestation/ Reforestation (very limited)
EU Emissions Trading Scheme	$7,908	321	$24,357	1101	All forestry excluded until at least 2008 (likely longer)
Australia (New South Wales Abatement Scheme)	$59	6	$225	22	Australian forest restoration only
Voluntary					
Voluntary Retail Carbon Market	$44	6	$100	10+	Tropical forest conservation and restoration
Chicago Climate Exchange	$3	1	$38	10	Tropical forest conservation and restoration

* Regulatory Volume data includes transactions published from various trading platforms as well as volume known to be exchanged over-the-counter. Voluntary Volume data includes project-based transactions supplied by Evolution Markets and Natsource. Transactions include only signed contracts (i.e., those resulting in Emissions Reductions Purchase Agreements [ERPAs]). Data: (Capoor and Ambrosi, 2007)

largest GHG emissions source—deforestation, degradation, and other land use. Carbon emissions from tropical deforestation, if left unchecked, could increase atmospheric CO_2 concentration by as much as 129 ppm this century, much more than previously estimated (IPCC, 2007).

Fortunately, however, the regulated market is not the only trading venue that exists. An active and somewhat innovative voluntary and retail carbon market has developed over the past few years in parallel with the regulated market. Unlike the regulated carbon markets, the voluntary and retail carbon markets have evolved primarily through demand by companies, organizations, and individuals for credible carbon-mitigation actions that enable them to reduce the climate impact of their operations. The voluntary and retail carbon market, while significantly smaller than the regulated market in the volume of CO_2 traded and value generated, holds considerable promise as a mechanism from which to test and innovate CO_2-reducing strategies and technologies for the regulated sector. In particular, the voluntary and retail carbon market has led the way in the production

and trading of land-use emissions offsets.

A large portion of the voluntary and retail carbon markets offer forestry offsets, with recent estimates indicating that approximately 36% of total voluntary carbon offset transactions (based on volume) were from forestry activities (Hamilton et al., 2007). An especially important innovation pioneered in the voluntary forest carbon offset markets is the pursuit of activities that result in multiple benefits (e.g., forestry activities that deliver cost-effective carbon sequestration or storage benefits for climate, but also additional benefits, most notably promoting local sustainable livelihoods, protection of threatened biodiversity, and myriad ecosystem services that often secure valuable indirect climate benefits as well. High-quality projects pursue independent validation and verification and are designed to capture these multiple benefits. Standards have been developed in the retail markets to validate that forestry carbon projects provide these multiple benefits. Preeminent in this regard are the Climate, Community & Biodiversity Standards (CCBA, 2008).

The Climate, Community & Biodiversity Alliance

Well-designed, land-based activities are an essential component of strategies to mitigate climate change, expanding effective GHG emissions reductions by avoiding deforestation and sequestering carbon through reforestation and agroforestry. Land-based climate-change mitigation activities also have exceptional potential to deliver additional social and environmental benefits. Designed comprehensively, they can help local people by generating sustainable livelihoods through diversification of agriculture, soil and water protection, direct employment, use and sale of forest products, and ecotourism, while also strengthening capacity to adapt to the effects of climate change. They can also contribute substantially to conserving biodiversity by restoring and protecting natural ecosystems around the world, saving threatened animal and plant species from extinction, and maintaining resilient and productive natural life-support for humankind.

To realize this potential, Conservation International convened the Climate, Community & Biodiversity Alliance (CCBA), a partnership between thirteen of the world's leading companies and NGOs. CCBA members include six companies—BP, Intel, SC Johnson, Sustainable Forestry Management, Weyerhaeuser, and GFA (Germany)—and seven NGOs—Conservation International, CARE, the Hamburg Institute of International Economics, Pelangi Indonesia, Rainforest Alliance, The Nature Conservancy, and the Wildlife Conservation Society. The CCBA aims to foster the creation of a robust, global market for multiple-benefit land-based activities and their associated carbon offsets, in particular by developing and promoting the Climate, Community & Biodiversity Standards.

The Climate, Community & Biodiversity (CCB) Standards provide investors and project managers with a practical tool to evaluate land-based carbon mitigation projects from the early stages of development. The CCB Standards work like other product certification schemes, such as "fair-trade" and "organic" labeling. They enable investors who seek to offset their residual GHG emissions (after reducing emissions as far as possible) to choose forest carbon initiatives that will make meaningful reductions to global GHGs, ensuring that gains are truly additional, that they will be permanent, and that they will not result in leakage of deforestation to other sites. The CCB Standards not only give assurance on the GHG claims of the project, but also ensure that projects generate positive social and environmental benefits. CCB Standards help investors to screen out projects that could cause negative impacts like monoculture plantations of non-native trees or projects that displace indigenous or other local communities from their land.

The Climate, Community & Biodiversity (CCB) Standards evaluate agriculture, forestry, and other land-based carbon-mitigation activities, including reducing emissions from deforestation and degradation and reforestation. Once designed, a third-party evaluator assesses a project against a series of required and optional "point-scoring" criteria. Only projects that use best practices and deliver significant and measurable climate, community, and biodiversity benefits will earn CCB approval.

The standards were created through a rigorous two-year development process and are based on international best practices for project design regarding climate, community, and biodiversity impacts. Input from development and environmental groups, companies, academics, project developers, and others contributed to the development of the standards. The standards were then field-tested on projects in Asia, Africa, Europe, and the Americas, and peer reviewed by the world's leading tropical forestry research institutes: the Center for International Forestry Research (CIFOR), the Tropical Agricultural Research and Higher Education Center (CATIE), and the World Agroforestry Centre (ICRAF).

Since their release in May 2005, the CCB Standards have become the most widely used and respected international quality standard for land-based carbon projects. The majority of forest carbon projects around the world are now using the CCB Standards to improve project design and generate compelling multiple benefits. The Chinese government is using them, and the world's pre-eminent investors (e.g., the World Bank) are applying the standards to their extensive portfolios. CCB-certified projects are restoring native forests for local use that also serve as a buffer to protect habitat for endangered species such as pandas and tigers in the mountains of southwest China. They are also restoring productive native forests on abandoned cattle ranches, providing jobs for indigenous people in Panama. New projects in the pipeline are helping local peoples in India to build sustainable livelihoods by planting native trees to diversify their incomes and strengthen land tenure; protecting the last major intact tracts of rainforest in Sumatra; and connecting forest fragments to restore habitats for endangered lemurs, frogs, and birds, while also providing local farmers with alternatives to unsustainable slash-and-burn cultivation in Eastern Madagascar.

—*Joanna Durbin*

financial incentives necessary to harness these natural benefits, we may further burden ourselves with a cycle of complicated, highly expensive, human-constructed technical efforts to address the challenge of losing and rebuilding nature's own solution to climate change.

Developing-country social and economic pursuits, and associated emissions and environmental degradation, are projected to grow rapidly in the coming decades. Temperatures and natural disturbances are expected to increase in severity and frequency as the planet experiences the effects of climatic changes resulting from our current committed future emissions. Providing support and economic incentives for the protection and restoration of the natural capital to address climate change effectively is one immediate and cost-effective way to bring these countries into the climate solution while simultaneously enhancing their economic development.

Fortunately, several key actions can be taken over the next few years to ensure that we effectively harness the immense opportunities that nature, particularly the biologically richest ecosystems, can provide to help us address climate change. These include the following:

Accelerate investments in scientific and technical research efforts.
The IPCC Fourth Assessment Report identified a number of knowledge gaps that are critical for effectively harnessing nature, including the relationship between biodiversity and the resilience of ecosystem services; the role and impacts of increased frequency and intensity of disturbances (drought, floods, fire, wind-storms, insect outbreaks, and diseases) on alien species invasion and subsequent interactions with ecosystem responses to climate change; and the impacts of rising CO_2 emissions on ocean acidification and warming of coral reefs and other marine systems, to name just a few (IPCC, 2007). The longer we delay in filling these gaps in knowledge and technology, the more challenging it will be for us to implement climate responses with appropriate precision and effectiveness.

Demonstrate how ecosystem-based solutions can work for addressing climate change, while simultaneously providing additional livelihood and biodiversity co-benefits.
Immediate investments in forest protection and restoration activities can provide critical practical insights into how nature-based mitigation solutions can work at a sufficient scale and rigor to produce real, verifiable, and measurable emissions reductions, as well as additional benefits to local communities and threatened biodiversity. Perhaps even more critical and most often overlooked, investments in multi-faceted, large-scale adaptation activities are needed to

help increase terrestrial, marine, and freshwater ecosystem resilience to climate change and demonstrate the long-term potential of ecosystem restoration and protection as effective climate-coping solutions.

Build on existing tools and strategies that have already proven to be effective, and transfer these to the developing world.
Considerable knowledge and a variety of tools already exist in sectors beyond climate change, especially biodiversity conservation, where nature-based solutions have been underway for decades. To avoid unnecessary financial cost and lost time, every effort should be made to build upon lessons learned and successful strategies developed for ecosystem protection. Sharing and utilizing the wealth of information already available will allow rapid scaling-up of activities and replication by others. Of particular relevance is the role that marine and terrestrial protected areas can play in ensuring long-term provision of ecosystem services, including carbon sequestration.

Ensure that policies and markets are comprehensive in order to avoid perverse incentives and minimize negative externalities.
For the world to adequately address climate change in the short time frame necessary (forty to fifty years), broad and aggressive emissions reductions and adaptation actions will be required from all nations, both developed and developing. Inclusion of nature-based solutions will be a critical addition to climate policies if we are to reach these targets. Special care must be taken to ensure that mitigation and adaptation activities incorporating ecosystems do not create perverse incentives or negative externalities. For example, if a deforestation prevention policy is developed that only provides incentives to those countries that have been historically high CO_2 emitters due to deforestation (e.g., Indonesia and Brazil), we may create perverse incentives in other tropical-forest rich countries to begin accelerating rates of deforestation, either because demand for timber and agricultural land has shifted to these countries or because they hope to tap into these climate incentives in the future (da Fonseca et al., 2007). This is a very significant point, as much of the remaining tropical forest occurs in these so-called High Forest Cover—Low Deforestation Rate (HFLD) countries.

Promote participatory and rights-based policy design and market access.
Success for all climate solutions, particularly those that are nature-based, will require the involvement, participation, and consent of civil society, particularly those most dependent on the natural resources being used to abate climate or the natural resources that may be negatively impacted by

climate change. Indigenous and other local communities, which are highly resource-dependent, may be disproportionately impacted. However, if effective policies are pursued, these highly vulnerable communities may also realize major opportunities to improve governance and management and to secure financial benefits from the climate-regulating services their areas provide to the global community.

Developing countries will require considerable up-front investment to implement scientific research, policy reform, governance and financial structures, technical capacity, enforcement mechanisms, and stakeholder participation and outreach necessary to achieve mitigation and adaptation results worthy of regulatory markets. These investments will need to come from a variety of sources, including the financial sector, overseas development assistance, and private philanthropists. Failure to harness sufficient resources toward nature-based climate solutions will likely result in continued ecosystem destruction and GHG emissions and will accelerate the need for humans and other species to adapt to climate-induced disturbances.

However, incorporating ecosystem services into climate policies, markets, and funding mechanisms will not be enough. A new international climate treaty will likely be needed with the ambition and scope required to achieve significant emissions reductions over the next forty years. Such a treaty must include full participation and aggressive commitments by all major GHG emitters (the United States, the EU, China, Indonesia, Brazil, Australia, and others) and all major GHG sources. The industrialized world will need to set an example and significantly reduce its own emissions, to share its technological innovations with the developing world, and to provide incentives for ecosystem protection and restoration if we are to safeguard the future for our children, grandchildren, and many generations to come.

While many of the actions needed to reduce greenhouse gas emissions make economic sense, many societies are unlikely to undertake them voluntarily in sufficient quantity or with the necessary speed without well-focused incentives, removal of barriers to action, innovative regulations, and far more ambitious research, development, and demonstration initiatives. And to keep climate change to safe levels, many early actions will be needed that currently may not be economically justified in their own right, but offer multiple benefits (e.g., climate mitigation and adaptation, poverty alleviation, biodiversity protection, and ecosystem services). Public policies are clearly needed to spur action on climate change. Tackling a global problem like climate change will require an economy-wide response by all sectors of global society.

A Time for Climate Action

World-renowned biologist and evolutionary scientist Edward O. Wilson makes the compelling case for why saving "The Creation"—nature and the millions of species that inhabit it—is of paramount importance to humans and our future generations. "The worst thing that can happen, will happen," he emphasizes, "is not energy depletion, economic collapse, limited nuclear war, or conquest by a totalitarian government. As terrible as these catastrophes would be for us, they can be repaired within a few generations. The one process ongoing [since] the 1980s that will take millions of years to correct is the loss of genetic and species diversity by the destruction of natural habitats. This is the folly our descendants are least likely to forgive us" (Wilson, 2006).

This book's signature theme—A Climate for Life—is that preventing the destruction of the world's biodiversity is inextricably interwoven with preventing the other unparalleled threat demanding human action—climate change. Fortunately, we can envision and pursue "a climate for life." Humans have the scientific capacity, technological ingenuity, financial wizardry, and policy innovations essential for reversing a climate meltdown and mass extinction. In the process, society can avoid more human and financial suffering than the two world wars and the Great Depression put together (Stern, 2006).

But time is of the essence. Scientists first issued warnings and the need for concerted actions a quarter century ago. We do not have the luxury to squander another quarter century. Nor do we have unlimited wealth to waste. We must not delay action and investment in what we know we can do immediately, cost-effectively, and with multiple benefits: protect nature; drive continuous efficiency improvements in delivering energy, water, and resource services; and accelerate commercialization of the most benign, long-term global energy supply option—solar power.

We must do this while at the same time investing in additional multiple-benefit solutions we know will be required to achieve deep emissions reductions at the global scale this century. We cannot be distracted or deterred. We must find the personal and public determination and political will to act boldly and swiftly, so that our grandchildren and their grandchildren look upon our generation as one of the most courageous, conscientious, and visionary in the history of human civilization.

A CALL TO ACTION

The Varanger Peninsula in Norway is where tundra meets the ocean. Temperatures plummet and winter wraps thick ice around the ebb and flow zone of the sea. Here the sea is breaking through the ice just as a heavy cloud of snow rolls in and the sun sets. ORSOLYA HAARBERG

References

Introduction

BBC World Service. 2007. All countries need to take major steps on climate change: Global poll. Prepared jointly by GlobeScan with the Program on International Policy Attitudes (PIPA) at the University of Maryland, www.worldpublicopinion.org/pipa/pdf/sep07/BBCClimate_Sep07_rpt.pdf

Canadell, Joséph G., C. Field, C. Lequere, N. Nebojsa, M. Raupach. 2006. *Vulnerabilities of the global carbon cycle in the 21st century, Global carbon project activity—Overview and progress*, August 23, 2006, www.globalcarbonproject.org/global/doc/VulnerabilityActivityReport2006-07.doc

Cline, William. 2007. *Global warming and agriculture*, Peterson Institute for International Economics, www.petersoninstitute.org

da Fonseca, Gustavo A.B., C.M. Rodríguez, G. Midgley, J. Busch, L. Hannah, R.A. Mittermeier. 2007. No forest left behind. *PLoS Biology*. 5: issue 8, www.plosbiology.org

Friedman, Thomas L. 2007a. In the Age of Noah. *The New York Times*, December 23, 2007.

Friedman, Thomas L. 2007b. What Was That All About. *The New York Times*, December 19, 2007.

Friedman, Thomas L. 2007c. It's Too Late for Later. *The New York Times*, December 16, 2007.

Friedman, Thomas L. 2007d. Lead, Follow or Move Aside. *The New York Times*, September 26, 2007.

Gallup. 2007. American opinions on global warming. Gallup, Yale University, and ClearVision Institute poll, Fall 2007, http://www.environment.yale.edu/doc/5305/american-opinions-on-global-warming/

Gilman, Nils, D. Randall, P. Schwartz. 2007. *A system vulnerability approach to consider the potential impacts to 2050 of a mid-upper GHG emissions scenario*. Global Business Network, March 2007, http://www.gbn.com/ArticleDisplayServlet.srv?aid=39932

Google. 2007. Google's goal: Renewable energy cheaper than coal. Google Press release, November 27, 2007, http://www.google.com/intl/en/press/pressrel/20071127_green.html

Grieg-Gran, Maryanne. 2006. *The cost of avoiding deforestation*. Report prepared for the Stern Review of the economics of climate change. October 2006. International Institute for Environment and Development, www.hm-treasury.gov.uk/media/1/4/stern_review_supporting_technical_m_greiggran_261006a.pdf

Hansen, J., M. Sato, P. Kharecha, D. Beerling, V. Masson-Delmotte, M. Pagani, M. Raymo, D. Royer, J. Zachos. 2008. Target atmospheric CO_2: Where should humanity aim? Goddard Institute of Space Studies, NASA. Main paper is at http://arxiv.org/abs/0804.1126 and the supporting material is at http://arxiv.org/abs/0804.1135

Hansen J., M. Sato, P. Kharecha, G. Russell, D.W. Lea, M. Siddall. 2007a. Climate change and trace gases, *Philosophical Transactions of the Royal Society* A. 365: 1925–1954, May 18, 2007, www.planetwork.net/climate/Hansen2007.pdf

Hansen J., M. Sato, R. Ruedy. 2007b, Dangerous human-made interference with climate: A GISS modelE study, *Atmospheric Chemistry and Physics*. 7:2287–2312, May 7, 2007, www.atmos-chem-phys.org/7/2287/2007/acp-7-2287-2007.pdf

Hansen J., M. Sato, R. Ruedy, K. Lo, D.W. Lea, M. Medina-Elizade. 2006. Global temperature change, *Proceedings of the National Academy of Sciences*.103: No. 39, pp. 14288–93, September 25, 2006, www.pnas.org/cgi/reprint/103/39/14288

Hansen, J.E. 2007. Scientific reticence and sea level rise, *Environmental Research Letters*. 2:024002, May 24, 2007, online at http://stacks.iop.org/ERL/2/024002

Hoegh-Guldberg, O., P.J. Mumby, A.J. Hooten, R.S. Steneck, P. Greenfield, E. Gomez, C.D. Harvell, P.F. Sale, A.J. Edwards, K. Caldeira, N. Knowlton, C.M. Eakin, R. Iglesias-Prieto, N. Muthiga, R.H. Bradbury, A. Dubi, M.E. Hatziolos. 2007. Coral reefs under rapid climate change and ocean acidification, *Science*. 318: 1737-42, December 14, 2007.

Houghton, R.A. 2007. Reducing emissions from deforestation. The role of forests in the global carbon cycle. October 18-19, 2007, The Kathryn Fuller Science for Nature Symposium. World Wildlife Fund, Washington, DC, www.panda.org/.

IFAD. 2001. *Rural poverty report 2001—The challenge of ending rural poverty*. International Fund for Agriculture Development, Oxford University Press, http://www.ifad.org/poverty/

IPCC. 2007. *Climate change 2007*. Working Group II contribution to the Fourth Assessment Report of the Intergovernmental panel on Climate Change. Multiple volumes. Cambridge University Press, available online at http://www.ipcc.ch/

Killeen, Timothy A., L. Hannah, L.A. Solórzano. 2007. How can conservation strategies mitigate impacts of climate change in Amazonia? Center for Applied Biodiversity Sciences and Gordon and Betty Moore Foundation.

Killeen, T.J., V. Calderon, L. Soriana, B. Quezeda, M.K. Steininger, G. Harper, L.A. Solorzano, T.J. Tucker. 2006. Thirty years of land-cover change in Bolivia: Exponential growth and no end in sight. Submitted to *Ambio*.

Koelle, Katia, X. Rodó, M. Pascual, Y & G Mostafa. 2005. Refractory periods and climate forcing in cholera dynamics, *Nature*. 436, August 4, 2005, doi:10.1038/nature03820.

Lovins, Amory B., K. Datta, O-E Bustnes, J.G. Koomey, N.J. Glasgow. 2004. *Winning the oil endgame: Innovation for profits, jobs, and security*. Rocky Mountain Institute, www.oilendgame.org/

Machado, R.B., M.B. Ramos Neto, P.G.P. Pereira, E.F. Caldas, D.A. Gonçalves, N.S. Santos, K. Tabor e M. Steininger. 2004. Estimativas de perda da área do Cerrado brasileiro. Relatório técnico não publicado. Conservação Internacional, Brasília, DF.

Moutinho, Paulo and Stephan Schwartzman, eds. 2005. *Tropical deforestation and climate change*. Belém, Para, Brazil and Washington, DC: Amazon Institute for Environmental Research. Available at www.environmentaldefense.org/go/CR

NASA. 2002. Breakup of the Larsen ice shelf, Antarctica, Earth Observatory, NASA, http://earthobservatory.nasa.gov/Newsroom/NewImages/images.php3?img_id=8257

Nghiem, S.V., K. Steffen, G. Neumann, R. Huff. 2007. Snow accumulation and snowmelt monitoring in Greenland and Antarctica—Monitoring and understanding a dynamic planet with geodetic and oceanographic tools: Proc. IAG Symp. (Cairns, August 2005) Intl. Assoc. Geodesy Symposia vol. 130, C. Rizos and P. Tregoning, eds. New York: Springer.

Nobel Prize Committee. 2007. The Nobel Peace Prize for 2007, http://nobelprize.org/nobel_prizes/peace/laureates/2007/

NSIDC. 2008. Antarctic ice shelf disintegration underscores a warming world. March 25, 2008, National Snow and Ice Data Center, http://nsidc.org/news/press/20080325_Wilkins.html

Page, Susan E., F. Siegert, J.O. Rieley, H.D.V. Boehm, A. Jaya, S. Limin. 2002. The amount of carbon released from peat and forest fires in Indonesia during 1997. *Nature*. 420:61.

Pascual, M., J.A. Ahumada, L.F. Chaves, X. Rodó, M. Bouma. 2006. Malaria resurgence in the East African highlands: Temperature trends revisited. *Proceedings of the National Academy of Sciences USA*. 3: 5829–5834, April 11, 2006, http://www.pnas.org/cgi/content/short/103/15/5829

Patz, Jonathan A., S.H. Olson. 2006. Malaria risk and temperature: Influences from global climate change and local land use practice. *Proceedings of the National Academy of Sciences USA*. 103: 5635-5636, April 11, 2006, www.pnas.org/cgi/reprint/103/15/5635

Pogge, Thomas. 2008. *World poverty and human rights*, 2nd edition. Cambridge, UK: Polity Press.

Rahmstorf, Stefan. 2007. A semi-empirical approach to projecting future sea-level rise, *Science*. 315:368.

Raupach, Michael R., G. Marland, P. Ciais, C. Le Quere, J.G. Canadell, G. Klepper, C.B. Field. 2007. Global and regional drivers of accelerating CO_2 emissions. *Proceedings of the National Academy of Sciences USA*, May 22, 2007, www.pnas.org/cgi/content/abstract/0700609104v1

Schimel, David and David Baker. 2002. The wildfire factor. *Nature*. 420:29.

Steininger, M.K., C.J. Tucker, J.R.G. Townshend, T.J. Killeen, A. Desch, V. Bell, P. Ersts. 2001. Tropical deforestation in the Bolivian Amazon. *Environmental Conservation*. 28:127-134.

Stern, Nicholas. 2006. *The Economics of Climate Change: The Stern report*. Cambridge University Press. Available online at http://www.hm-treasury.gov.uk/independent_reviews/stern_review_economics_climate_change/stern_review_report.cfm

Stott, Peter, D.A. Stone, M.R. Allen. 2004. Human contribution to the European heat wave of 2003. *Nature*. 432:7017, pp. 610-14.

UNFCCC. 2002. Text of the UN framework convention on climate change, http://unfccc.int/resource/docs/convkp/conveng.pdf

United Nations. 2007. Actions on climate change will define global legacy left for future generations, says Secretary-General, as high-level event convenes, September 24, 2007, United Nations Press Release, http://www.un.org/News/Press/docs/2007/ga10618.doc.htm

Viña, Andrés, F.R. Echavarria, D.C. Rundquist. 2004. Satellite change detection analysis of deforestation rates and patterns along the Colombia-Ecuador border. *Ambio*. 33: No. 3, May 2004, Swedish Royal Academy of Sciences, http://www.ambio.kva.se

Vittor, Amy Yomiko, R.H. Gilman, J. Tielsch, G. Glass, T. Shields, W.S. Lozano, V. Pinedo-Cancino, J.A. Patz. 2006. The effect of deforestation on the human-biting rate of *Anopheles darlingi*, the primary vector of *Falciparum* malaria in the Peruvian Amazon, *Am. J. Trop. Med. Hyg*. 74(1): 3–11.

Ward, Peter D. 2007. *Under a green sky: Global warming, the mass extinctions of the past, and what they can tell us about our future*. New York: HarperCollins.

Ward, Peter D. 2006. Impact from the deep. *Scientific American*. October: 65-71, www.sciam.com/

Wei, Wenxia, T. Zhang, S.Li, D.Wang, M. Steininger. 2005. Remote sensing analysis to forest changes of the biodiversity hotspots in Southwest China. Geoscience and Remote Sensing Symposium, 2005. IGARSS apos;05. Proceedings. 2005 IEEE International. 7:5019 – 5022.

Westerling, A.L., H.G. Hidalgo, D.R. Cayan, T.W. Swetnam. 2006. Warming and earlier spring increase western U.S. forest wildfire activity. *Science*. 313: 940-943.

Mitigation

Association of British Insurers (AIB). 2005. Financial risks of climate change.

FAO. 2007. *State of the world's forests 2007*. Food and Agriculture Organization of the United Nations, Rome.

Koplow, Doug. 2007. Biofuels at what cost? Government support for ethanol and biodiesel in the United States: 2007 update. Geneva: Global Subsidies Initiative, p. 54. Available at http://www.earthtrack.net/earthtrack/library/BiofuelsUSupdate2007.pdf

Lynas, Mark. 2008. *Six degrees: Our future on a hotter planet*. Washington, DC: National Geographic Books.

MacDonald-Smith, A. 2007. Climate change to boost insured losses, Allianz says. Bloomberg, September 18, http://www.bloomberg.com/apps/news?pid=newsarchive&sid=ag6mOBlfHCqk

Meinshausen, Malte. 2005. On the risk of overshooting 2 degrees C: Avoiding dangerous climate change. International Symposium on the Stabilisation of greenhouse gas concentrations, Hadley Centre, Met Office, Exeter, UK, February 1-3, 2005, www.stabilisation2005.com/programme.html

Mills, Evan and Eugene Lecomte. 2006. From risk to opportunity: Insurer responses to climate change. Prepared for CERES, August 2006, www.ceres.org/

St. Louis, V.L, C.A. Kelly, E. Duchemin, J.W.M. Rudd, D.M. Rosenberg. 2000. Reservoir surfaces as sources of greenhouse gases to the atmosphere: A global estimate. *BioScience*. 50: 766–75

Swiss Re. 2006. The effects of climate change: Storm damage in Europe on the rise. Report 6/06, 2500en.

Energy Efficiency

Appalachian voices. End mountaintop removal. www.ilovemountains.org, accessed September 7, 2007.

Bettencourt, L.M.A., J. Lobo, D. Helbing, C. Kuhnert, and G.B. West. 2007. Growth, innovation, scaling, and the pace of life in cities. *Proceedings of the National Academy of Sciences* 104(17):7301-7306, April 24, http://www.pnas.org

Carbon Dioxide Information Analysis Center, http://cdiac.ornl.gov/pns/faq.html, accessed September 7, 2006.

DOE. 2007. Solid-state lighting portfolio, U.S. Department of Energy, Energy Efficiency and Renewable Energy, www.netl.doe.gov/ssl

European Commission, Directorate-General XII, Science, Research and Development, JOULE. 1998. ExternE project: Externalities of energy, methodology report, www.externe.info/reportex/vol2.pdf

Ford, K., ed. 1975. *Efficient use of energy: A physics perspective*. American Physical Society, American Institute of Physics, APS/AIP conference proceedings.

Goldemberg, J., T.B. Johansson, A.K.N. Reddy, and R.H. Williams. 1988. *Energy for a sustainable world*. New York: Wiley.

Hansen, J., M. Sato, P. Kharecha, D. Beerling, V. Masson-Delmotte, M. Pagani, M. Raymo, D. Royer, J. Zachos. 2008. Target atmospheric CO_2: Where should humanity aim? Goddard Institute of Space Studies, NASA, www.columbia.edu/~jeh1/2008/TargetCO2_20080317.pdf

Hawkins, D. 2002. Passing gas: Policy implications of leakage from geologic carbon storage sites. Presented at the Sixth International Conference on Greenhouse Gas Control Technologies (GHGT-6), Kyoto, Japan.

Hawkins, D. 2001. Stick it where? Public attitudes towards carbon storage. Presented at the First National Conference on Carbon Sequestration, Washington, DC, www.netl.doe.gov/publications/proceedings/01/carbon_seq/1c2.pdf

Holdren, J. 2007. "Threat of climate change." Presidential address. American Association for the Advancement of Science. February 16, Washington, DC, www.aaas.org/climate

IEA. 2007. *World energy outlook 2007*. International Energy Agency/OECD, http://www.iea.org

Kats, G., L. Alevantis, A. Beman, E. Mills, and J. Perlman. 2003. *The costs and financial benefits of green buildings: A report to California's sustainable building task force*, October, www.ciwmb.ca.gov/GreenBuilding/Design/CostIssues.htm#Cost&Benefit

Keystone Center. 2007. Nuclear power joint fact finding dialogue. June 14, www.keystone.org/spp/energy07_nuclear.html

Kintner-Meyer, M., K. Schneider, and R. Pratt. 2007. Impacts assessment of plug-in hybrid vehicles on electric utilities and regional U.S. power grids, part 1: Technical analysis. Pacific Northwest National Laboratory. January, www.pnl.gov

Koplow, D. 2005. Nuclear power in the U.S.: Still not viable without subsidy. Nuclear Power and Global Warming Symposium, Nuclear Policy Research Institute. November 7-8, Warrenton, VA, www.earthtrack.net/earthtrack/library/NuclearSubsidies2005.pdf

Koplow, D. 2006. Subsidies in the U.S. energy sector: Magnitude, causes, and options for reform, November http://www.earthtrack.net/earthtrack/library/SubsidyReformOptions.pdf

Krause, F., J. Koomey, and D. Olivier. 2000. *Cutting carbon emissions while making money: Climate saving energy strategies for the European Union, Vol. II, part 2, Energy policy in the greenhouse,* February, International Project for Sustainable Energy Paths, http://stephenschneider.stanford.edu/Publications/PDF_Papers/Krause2000.pdf

Lovins, A.B. 2007. Gala speech, Rocky Mountain Institute (RMI) 25th anniversary, "Imagine a world," Aspen, CO, Aug 10, www.rmi.org

Lovins, A.B. 2004. Energy efficiency, taxonomic overview. In *Encyclopedia of energy,* Cutler J. Cleveland, ed. in chief. 2:383-401, 6 vols. Elsevier, San Diego and Oxford (U.K.), www.elsevier.com and www.rmi.org/sitepages/pid171.php#E04-02

Lovins, A.B., E.K. Datta, O.-E. Bustnes, J.G. Koomey, and N.J. Glasgow. 2004. *Winning the oil endgame: Innovation for profits, jobs, and security.* Snowmass, CO: Rocky Mountain Institute, www.oilendgame.org

Lovins, A.B., K. Datta, T. Feiler, K. Rábago, J. Swisher, A. Lehmann, and K. Wicker. 2002. *Small is profitable: The hidden economic benefits of making electrical resources the right size.* Aspen, CO: Rocky Mountain Institute, www.rmi.org

Lovins, A.B. and R. Sardinsky. 1988. *The state of the art: Lighting.* Snowmass, CO: Rocky Mountain Institute, www.rmi.org

Lovins, A.B., L.H. Lovins, F. Krause, and W. Bach. 1982. *Least-cost energy: Solving the CO_2 problem.* Andover, MA: Brick House Pub. Co.

Meinshausen, M. 2005. On the risk of overshooting 2 degrees C. *Scientific Symposium, "Avoiding Dangerous Climate Change"* February 2. MetOffice, Exeter, U.K.:DEFRA, http://www.simcap.org or www.stabilisation2005.com/day2/Meinshausen.pdf

MGI (McKinsey Global Institute) 2007. *Curbing global energy demand growth: The energy productivity opportunity.* May, www.fypower.org/pdf/Curbing_Global_Energy_FR.pdf

MIT (2007), *MIT Future of Coal Study,* http://webmit.edu/coal

Nadel, S., A. Shipley, and R.N. Elliott. 2004. *The technical, economic, and achievable potential for energy-efficiency in the U.S.: A meta-analysis of recent studies.* Aug. American Council for an Energy-Efficient Economy, http://aceee.org/energy/eemra/eeassess.htm

NDCF (National Defense Council Foundation). 2007. The hidden cost of imported oil. January 8, www.ndcf.org

RAP (Regulatory Assistance Project). 2005. Regulatory reform: Removing the disincentives to utility investment in energy efficiency. *Issues Letter.* September, www.raponline.org

Rosenfeld, A. 2006. Presentation to Google, Aug. 13, http://www.energy.ca.gov/commission/commissioners/rosenfeld.html

Schubert, E.F. and J.K. Kim. 2005. Solid-state light sources getting smart. *Science* 308:1274-1278. May 27, www.sciencemag.org

SEEEM (Standards for Energy Efficiency of Electric Motor Systems Initiative) 2006. www.seeem.org, accessed September 7, 2007.

Totten, M. 2007. Annotated bibliography of sustainable energy assessments. April, unpublished, Center for Environmental Leadership in Business. Conservation International.

Tsao, J., ed. 2002. *Light emitting diodes for general illumination, OIDA technology roadmap update.* November Washington, DC: Optoelectronics Industry Development Assoc., http://www.net.doe.gov/ssl/workshop/Report%20led%20November%202002a_1.pdf

Ward, P.D. 2007. *Under a green sky: Global warming, the mass extinctions of the past, and what they mean for our future.* New York: Smithsonian Books/Collins.

Wellinghoff, J. 2007. Presentation on Demand Response: "From water heaters to cashback hybrids," March 16. Washington, DC, http://www.ferc.gov/EventCalendar/Files/20070402144423-SVEUPres03-16-07.pdf

West, G. 2007. "Power laws and social organization," TechTalk. August 1. Mountainview: Google Corporation headquarters.

Williams, R. 2001. Nuclear and alternative energy supply options for an environmentally constrained world: A long-term perspective. Nuclear Control Institute Conference on Nuclear Power and the Spread of Nuclear Weapons: Can We Have One Without the Other? April. Washington, DC, http://www.princeton.edu/~energy/publications/pdf/2001/Williams_01_Nuclear_and_Alternative_Energy.pdf

World Bank. 2005. *Potential for biofuels for transport in developing countries.* October, http://wbln0018.worldbank.org/esmap/site.nsf/files/312-05+Biofuels+for_Web.pdf/$FILE/312-05+Biofuels+for_Web.pdf

WRI (World Resources Institute). 2000. *The weight of nations: Material outflows from industrial economies.* Washington, DC, http://pdf.wri.org/weight_of_nations.pdf

Renewable Energy

Archer, C. L. and M.Z. Jacobson. 2005. Evaluation of global wind power. *Journal of Geophysical Research,* Vol. 110, www.stanford.edu/group/efmh/winds/2004jd005462.pdf

ASES (American Solar Energy Society). 2007. *Tackling climate change,* www.ases.org

Bräutigam, A. 1999. The freshwater biodiversity crisis. *World Conservation* 30(2):4-5.

CARD (Center for Agricultural and Rural Development). 2007. Emerging biofuels: Outlook of effects on U.S. grain, oilseed, and livestock markets. S. Tokgoz, A. Elobeid, J. Fabiosa, D. Hayes, B. Babcock, T-H. Yu, F. Dong, C. Hart, J. Beghin. Staff Report 07-SR 101, Iowa State University, May, http://www.card.iastate.edu

DeCanio, S. 2003. *Economic models of climate change: A critique.* New York: Palgrave MacMillan.

EREC (European Renewable Energy Council). 2007. *Energy [r]evolution, A sustainable world energy outlook,* EREC and Greenpeace, www.energyblueprint.info/fileadmin/media/documents/energy_revolution.pdf

Fargione, Joséph, J. Hill, D. Tilman, S. Polasky, P. Hawthorne. 2008. Land clearing and the biofuel carbon debt. *Science Express,* February 7, 2008, 10.1126/science.1152747, www.sciencexpress.org/

Fearnside, P.M. 2002. Greenhouse gas emissions from a hydroelectric reservoir (Brazil's Tucuruí Dam) and the energy policy implications. *Journal of Water, Air, and Soil Pollution,* 133:69-96.

GWEC (Global Wind Energy Council). 2006. *Global Wind Energy Outlook 2006.* GWEC and Greenpeace, http://www.gwec.net/index.php?id=65

Hamrin, J., H. Hummel, and R. Canapa. 2007. *Review of the role of renewable energy in global energy scenarios.* June. Center for Resource Solutions, San Francisco, CA, www.resource-solutions.org/lib/librarypdfs/Executive_Summary-Review_of_RE_in_Global_Energy_Scenarios.pdf

Hansen, J. 2005. Is there still time to avoid "dangerous anthropogenic interference" with global climate? Presentation at the American Geophysical Union, December 6, http://www.columbia.edu/~jeh1/keeling_talk_and_slides.pdf

Hansen, J., M. Sato, P. Kharecha, D. Beerling, V. Masson-Delmotte, M. Pagani, M. Raymo, D. Royer, J. Zachos. 2008. Target atmospheric CO_2: Where should humanity aim? Goddard Institute of Space Studies, NASA, www.columbia.edu/~jeh1/2008/TargetCO2_20080317.pdf

Jacobson, M.Z. 2007. Wind versus biofuels for addressing climate, health, and energy. Atmosphere/Energy Program, Department of Civil and Environmental Engineering, Stanford University. Palo Alto, CA, March 5, http://www.stanford.edu/group/efmh/jacobson/0703Energy.pdf

Kazmerski, L.L. 2002. Photovoltaic myths–The seven deadly sins. *Solar Today,* July/August 16(4):40-43.

Kempton, W. and J. Tomić. 2005. Vehicle to grid implementation: From stabilizing the grid to supporting large-scale renewable energy. *Journal of Power Sources* 144(1):280-294, June 10, www.udel.edu/V2G

Killeen, T.J. 2007. A perfect storm in the Amazon wilderness: Development and conservation in the context of the "Initiative for the Integration of the Regional Infrastructure of South America (IIRSA)" Center for Applied Biodiversity Sciences, Conservation International, Arlington, VA.

Komanoff, C. 2006. Whither wind? Wind, windpower, and open space. *Orion Magazine,* Sept.-Oct., www.orionmagazine.org/index.php/articles/article/178

Koplow, D. and J. Dernbach. 2001. Federal fossil fuel subsidies and greenhouse gas emissions: A case study of increasing transparency for fiscal policy. *Annual Review of Energy and Environment* 26:361-389, November, http://www.mindfully.org/Energy/Fossil-Fuel-Subsidies.htm

Lovins, A.B., E.K. Datta, O.-E. Bustnes, J.G. Koomey, and N.J. Glasgow. 2004. *Winning the oil endgame: Innovation for profits, jobs, and security.* Snowmass, CO: Rocky Mountain Institute, www.oilendgame.org

Lovins, A.B. and L.H. Lovins. 1982. *Brittle power: Energy strategy for national security,* funded by the Civil Defense Preparedness Agency, U.S. Department of Defense. Andover, MA: Brickhouse Pub. Co., www.natcapsolutions.org/publications_files/BrittlePower/Brittle Power_Parts 123.pdf or http://www.reactor-core.org/brittle-power.html

Martinot, E., C. Dienst, L. Weiliang, and C. Qimin. 2007. Renewable energy futures: Targets, scenarios, and pathways. *Annual Review of Environment and Resources* 32:205-239, http://www.martinot.info/futures.htm

Morton, D., R.S. DeFries, Y.E. Shimabukuro, L.O. Anderson, E. Arai, F. del Bon Espirito-Santo, R. Freitas, and J. Morisette. 2006. Cropland expansion changes deforestation dynamics in the southern Brazilian Amazon. *Proceedings of the National Academy of Sciences,* September 26, 2006, 103(39): 14637-14641, www.pnas.org

NRDC (Natural Resources Defense Council) and Pacific Institute. 2004. *Energy down the drain: The hidden costs of California's water supply,* www.nrdc.org/water/conservation/edrain/contents.asp

NREL (National Renewable Energy Laboratory). 2006. *China wind energy resource mapping activity.* Prepared as part of the United Nations' Solar and Wind Energy Resource Assessment, http://swera.unep.net/typo3conf/ext/metadata_tool/archive/download/chinawindreport_ch_244.pdf

PNNL (Pacific Northwest National Laboratory). 2007. Impacts assessment of plug-in hybrid vehicles on electric utilities and regional U.S. power grids. Part 1: Technical analysis. Prepared by M. Kintner-Meyer, K. Schneider, and R. Pratt, November, www.pnl.gov/energy/eed/etd/pdfs/phev_feasibility_analysis_combined.pdf

Romm, J. 2007. *Hell and high Water: Global warming–the solution and the politics–and what we should do.* New York: William Morrow.

Searchinger, T., R. Heimlich, R.A. Houghton, F. Dong, A. Elobeid, J. Fabiosa, S. Tokgoz, D. Hayes, T. Yu. 2008. Use of U.S. croplands for biofuels increases greenhouse gases through emissions from land use change. *ScienceExpress.* February 7, www.sciencexpress.org

Smil, V. 2003. *Energy at the crossroads: Global perspectives and uncertainties,* MIT Press.

St. Louis, V.L., C.A. Kelly, E. Duchemin, J.W.M. Rudd, and D.M. Rosenberg. 2000. Reservoir surfaces as sources of greenhouse gases to the atmosphere: A global estimate. *BioScience* 50(19): 766-775, www.biology.ualberta.ca/faculty//vincent_stlouis/uploads/pdfs/BioScience%20 paper.pdf

Totten, M. 2007. China's bold initiative. *Solar Today.* American Solar Energy Society, http://www.solartoday.org/2007/mar_apr07/china.htm

WADE (World Alliance for Decentralized Energy). 2004. *The WADE economic model: China,* www.localpower.org

WCD (World Commission on Dams). 2000. *Dams and development: A new framework for decision-making,* www.dams.org

Williams, R.H. 2001. Nuclear and alternative energy supply options for an environmentally constrained world: A long-term perspective. Paper presented at the Nuclear Control Institute Conference. Nuclear Power and the spread of nuclear weapons: Can we have one without the other? Washington, DC www.nci.org/conf/williams/williams.pdf

Zhi, L., M. Totten, and P. Chou. 2006. Spurring innovations for clean energy and water protection in China: An opportunity to advance security and harmonious development. China Environment Series, No 8, December. Woodrow Wilson International Center, www.wilsoncenter.org/index.cfm?topic_id=1421&fuseaction=topics.publications&group_id=216701

Zhou, Y. and R.S.J. Tol. 2003. Implications of desalination for water resources in China: An economic perspective. Working paper FNU-22, Research Unit Sustainability and Global Change, Center for Marine and Climate Research, Hamburg University, www.uni-hamburg.de/Wiss/FB/15/Sustainability/desaltchina.pdf

Zweibel, K. 2004. 2nd Generation (2G) PV: CdTe, CIS, and a-Si thin films, and some reflections on the Federal R&D Program. Presentation at Rice University, www.nrel.gov/pv/thin_film/docs/zweibel_rice_2004_2g_thin_films.ppt

Biofuels

Blum, J. 2006. Fuel for growth. *Washington Post,* February 18, p. D01, http://www.washingtonpost.com/wp-dyn/content/article/2006/02/17/AR2006021702109.html

Buckland, H. 2005. The oil for ape scandal: How palm oil is threatening orang-utan survival. Friends of the Earth, The Ape Alliance, The Borneo Orangutan Survival Foundation, The Orangutan Foundation (UK), The Sumatran Orangutan Society. September, www.foe.co.uk/resource/reports/oil_for_ape_full.pdf

Clay, J.W. 2006. Biofuels–Are they renewable? Presentation at COCERAL (Comité du Commerce des céréales, aliments du bétail, oléagineux, huile d'olive, huiles et graisses et agrofournitures). May 11-12, Budapest, Hungary.

Colchester, M., N. Jiwan, Andiko, M. Sirait, A.Y. Firdaus, A. Surambo, and H. Pane. 2006. Promised land: Palm oil and land acquisition in Indonesia, implications for local communities and indigenous peoples. Joint report by Forest Peoples Programme, Perkumpulan Sawit Watch, HuMA and the World Agroforestry Centre, http://www.forestpeoples.org/documents/prv_sector/oil_palm/promised_land_eng.pdf

Colchester, M. and N. Jiwan. 2006. Ghosts on our own land: Indonesian oil palm smallholders and the roundtable on sustainable palm oil. Forest Peoples Programme and Perkumpulan Sawit Watch, http://www.forestpeoples.org/documents/prv_sector/oil_palm/ghosts_on_our_own_land_txt_06_eng.pdf

Dros, J.M. 2003. Accommodating growth: Two scenarios for oil palm production growth. AIDEnvironment. September, http://assets.panda.org/downloads/accommodatinggrowth.pdf

Inovação Unicamp. 2006. Novas variedades de cana, melhores técnicas agrícolas, mais eficácia na fermentação e destilação: pesquisas por mais etanol. April, http://www.inovacao.unicamp.br/etanol/report/le-pesquisaetanol.php

Khorana, L. and P. Bhattacharya. 2007. New feedstock for biofuels. *The Wall Street Journal.* October 19, p. 19.

Killeen, T.J. 2007. *A perfect storm in the Amazon wilderness— Development and conservation in the context of the initiative for the integration of the regional infrastructure of South America (IIRSA).* Arlington, VA: Center for Applied Biodiversity Sciences, Conservation International, http://www.

conservation.org/publications/Documents/AABS.7_Perfect_Storm_English.low.res.pdf

Koh, L.P. 2007. The oil palm conundrum: How oil palm agriculture affects tropical biodiversity, and what we can do about it. Presentation to Conservation International, December 7.

Koplow, D. 2007. *Biofuels: At what cost? Government support for ethanol and biodiesel in the United States: 2007 update.* Global Subsidies Initiative, Geneva, http://www.earthtrack.net/earthtrack/library/BiofuelsUSupdate2007.pdf

Kutas, G., C. Lindberg, and R. Steenblik. 2007. *Biofuels: At what cost? Government support for ethanol and biodiesel in the European Union,* Global Subsidies Initiative, Geneva, http://www.globalsubsidies.org/IMG/pdf/Global_Subsidies_Initiative_European_Report_on_support_to_Biofuels.pdf

Malhi, Y., J.T. Roberts, R.A. Betts, T.J. Killeen, W. Li, and C.A. Nobre. 2007. Climate change, deforestation, and the fate of the Amazon. *Science Express,* November 29, and *Science* 319(5860):169-172, www.sciencexpress.org

Morton, D.C., R.S. DeFries, Y.E. Shimabukuro, L.O. Anderson, E. Arai, F. del Bon Espirito-Santo, R. Freitas, and J. Morisette. 2006. Cropland expansion changes deforestation dynamics in the Southern Brazilian Amazon. *Proceedings of the National Academy of Sciences* 103(39):14637-14641, September 26.

National Academy of Sciences (NAS). 2007. *Water implications of biofuels production in the United States,* prepublication. National Research Council, October, http://www.nap.edu/catalog/12039.html

Nellemann, C., L. Miles, B.P. Kaltenborn, M. Virtue, and H. Ahlenius, eds. 2007. *The last stand of the orangutan – State of emergency: Illegal logging, fire, and palm oil in Indonesia's national parks.* GRID-Arendal, Norway: United Nations Environment Programme, http://www.unep-wcmc.org/resources/PDFs/LastStand/orangutanreport_1to11.pdf

New, P. 2007. World demand for biofuels. Paper presented at the conference: A Expansão da Agroenergia e Seus Impactos Sobre os Ecossistemas Brasileiros. Rio de Janeiro, March 26-27.

Peh, K.S.-H., J. de Jong, N.S. Sodhi, S.L.-H. Lim, and C.A.-M. Yap. 2005. Lowland rainforest avifauna and human disturbance: Persistence of primary forest birds in selectively logged forests and mixed-rural habitats of southern peninsular Malaysia. *Biological Conservation* 123(4):489-505.

Peh, K.S.-H., N.S. Sodhi, J. de Jong, C.H. Sekercioglu, C.A.-M. Yap, and S.L.-H. Lim. 2006. Conservation value of degraded habitats for forest birds in southern peninsular Malaysia. *Diversity and Distributions* 12(5):572-581, September, http://www.stanford.edu/~cagan/PehDivDist2006.pdf

Renewable Energy Policy Network for the 21st Century. 2006. Renewables global status report update, http://www.ren21.net/globalstatusreport/download/RE_GSR_2006_Update.pdf

Reuters. 2007. FACTBOX: Selected national biofuels targets. February 25, http://www.reuters.com/article/gc07/idUSL2112847820070225

Righelato, R. and D.V. Spracklen. 2007. Carbon mitigation by biofuels or by saving and restoring forests? *Science* 317(5840):902, August 17, www.sciencemag.org/cgi/content/short/317/5840/902

Roach, J. 2005. 9,000-year-old beer re-created from Chinese recipe. *National Geographic News,* July 18, http://news.nationalgeographic.com/news/2005/07/0718_050718_ancientbeer.html

Rosenthal, E. 2007. Once a dream fuel, palm oil may be an eco-nightmare. *New York Times,* January 31, http://www.nytimes.com/2007/01/31/business/worldbusiness/31biofuel.html?_r=1&oref=slogin

Runge, C.F. and B. Senauer. 2007. How biofuels could starve the poor. *Foreign Affairs,* May/June, http://www.foreignaffairs.org/20070501faessay86305/c-ford-runge-benjamin-senauer/how-biofuels-could-starve-the-poor.html

Searchinger, T. 2007. Biofuels, land conversion, and greenhouse gases. Presentation to Conservation International, July 12.

Singleton, I., S. Wich, S. Husson, S. Stephens, S. Utami Atmoko, M. Leighton, N. Rosen, K. Traylor-Holzer, R. Lacy, and O. Byers, eds. 2004. *Orangutan Population and Habitat Viability Assessment: Final Report,* IUCN/SSC Conservation Breeding Specialist Group, Apple Valley, MN, http://www.cbsg.org/cbsg/content/files/REPORTS/PHVA_Reports/Mammals/OrangutanPHVA04_Final%20Report.pdf

United States Department of Energy. 2006. *Annual energy outlook 2006 with projections to 2030,* February, http://www.scag.ca.gov.rcp/pdf/publications/1_2006AnnualEnergyOutlook.pdf

World Business Council for Sustainable Development. 2007. EU cuts back on biofuel crop subsidies. October 18, http://www.wbcsd.org/plugins/DocSearch/details.asp?type=DocDet&ObjectId=MjY3ODA

Forest Conservation

Achard, F., H.D. Eva, P. Mayaux, H.J. Stibig, and A. Belward. 2004. Improved estimates of net carbon emissions from land cover change in the tropics for the 1990s. *Global Biogeochemical Cycles.* 18: GB2008, doi 10.1029/2003GB002142.

Balmford, A., K.J. Gaston, S. Blyth, A. James, and V. Kapos. 2003. Global variation in terrestrial conservation costs, conservation benefits, and unmet conservation needs. *Proceedings of the National Academy of Sciences of the U.S.A.* 100:1046–1050.

Boltz, F., T.P. Holmes, and D.R. Carter. 2003. Economic and environmental impacts of conventional and reduced impact logging in tropical South America: A comparative review. *Forest Policy and Economics* 5:69-81.

Bruner, A., R.E. Gullison, and A. Balmford. 2004. Financial costs and shortfalls of managing and expanding protected-area systems in developing countries. *BioScience.* 54:1119–1126.

Bruner, A., R.E. Gullison, R. Rice, and G.A.B. da Fonseca. 2001. Effectiveness of parks in protecting tropical biodiversity. *Science.* 291:125–28.

Cairns, M.A., S. Brown, E.H. Helmer, and G.A. Baumgarder. 1997. Root biomass allocation in the world's upland forests. *Oecologia.* 111:1–11.

Canadell, J.G., C. Field, C. Lequere, N. Nakicenovic, and M. Raupach. 2006. *Vulnerabilities of the global carbon cycle in the 21st century: Global carbon project activity - Overview and progress.* August 23, 2006, www.globalcarbonproject.org/global/doc/VulnerabilityActivityReport2006-07.doc

Capoor, K. and P. Ambrosi. 2007. *Status and trends of the carbon market 2007.* Washington, DC: The World Bank.

Chape, S., J. Harrison, M. Spalding, and I. Lysenko. 2005. Measuring the extent and effectiveness of protected areas as an indicator for meeting global biodiversity targets. *Philosophical Transactions of the Royal Society.* B 360: 443-455.

Chomitz, K.M., P. Buys, G. De Luca, T.S. Thomas, and S. Wertz-Kanaounnikoff. 2007. *At loggerheads? Agricultural expansion, poverty reduction, and environment in the tropical forests.* Washington, DC: The World Bank.

Curran, L.M., S.N. Trigg, A.K. McDonald, D. Astiani, Y.M. Hardiono, P. Siregar, I. Caniago, and E. Kasischke. 2004. Lowland forest loss in protected areas of Indonesian Borneo. *Science.* 303:1000–1003.

Dixon, R.K., S. Brown, R.A. Houghton, A.M. Solomon, M.C. Trexler, and J. Wisniewski. 1994. Carbon pools and flux of global forest ecosystems. *Science.* 263:185-190.

Dudley, N., A. Belukurov, O. Borodin, L. Higgins-Zogib, M. Hockings, L. Lacerda, and S. Stolton. 2004. *Are protected areas working? An analysis of forest protected areas by WWF.* Gland, Switzerland: WWF.

Emerton, L., J. Bishop, and L. Thomas. 2006. *Sustainable financing of protected areas: A global review of challenges and options.* Gland, Switzerland: IUCN.

FAO. 2007. *State of the world's forests 2007.* Rome: Food and Agriculture Organization of the United Nations.

Fearnside, P.M. 2001. Land-tenure issues as factors in environmental destruction in Brazilian Amazonia: The case of southern Pará. *World Development.* 29: 1361-1372.

Field, C.B., M.J. Behrenfeld, J.T. Randerson, and P. Falkowski. 1998. Primary production of the biosphere: Integrating terrestrial and oceanic components. *Science.* 281(5374), 237.

da Fonseca, G.A.B., C.M. Rodríguez, G. Midgely, J. Busch, L. Hannah, and R.A. Mittermeier. 2007. No forest left behind. *PLoS Biology* 5(8): e216. doi10.1371/journal.pbio.0050216.

Grieg-Gran, M. 2006. *The cost of avoiding deforestation.* Report prepared for the Stern Review. London: International Institute for Environment and Development.

Hamilton, K., R. Bayon, G. Turner, and D. Higgins. 2007. *State of the voluntary carbon market 2007: Picking up steam.* London: New Carbon Finance, and Washington, DC: Ecosystem Marketplace.

Holmes, T.P., G.M. Blate, J.C. Zweede, R. Perreira Jr., P. Barreto, F. Boltz, and R. Bauch. 2002. Financial and ecological indicators of reduced impact logging performance in the eastern Amazon. *Forest Ecology and Management.* 163: 93-110.

Houghton, R.A. 2000. A new estimate of global sources and sinks of carbon from land use change. *EOS.* 81 (19, Supplement), S281.

Houghton, R.A. 2003. Revised estimates of the annual net flux of carbon to the atmosphere from changes in land use and land management. *Tellus.* 55B:378-390.

Houghton, R.A. 2005. Tropical deforestation as a source of greenhouse gas emissions. Pp. 13-21. In *Tropical deforestation and climate change.* P. Moutinho and S. Schwartzman, eds. Belem, Brazil: Instituto da Pesquisa Ambiental da Amazonia.

Houghton, R.A. 2007. Balancing the global carbon budget. *Annual review of Earth and planetary science.* 35:313-47.

Houghton, R.A. and J.L. Hackler. 1999. Emissions of carbon from forestry and land use change in tropical Asia. *Global Change Biology.* 5:481.

IPCC. 2007. *Climate change 2007.* Working Group II contribution to the Fourth Assessment Report of the Intergovernmental panel on Climate Change. Geneva, Switzerland: Intergovernmental Panel on Climate Change (IPCC).

James, A., K. Gaston, and A. Balmford. 2001. Can we afford to conserve biodiversity? *BioScience.* 51:43.

Johns, J.S., P. Barreto, and C. Uhl. 1996. Logging damage during planned and unplanned logging operations in the eastern Amazon. *Forest Ecology and Management.* 89:59-77.

Jung, M. 2005. *The role of forestry sinks in the CDM: Analysing the effects of policy decisions on the carbon market.* HWWA Discussion Paper 21. Hamburg, Germany: Hamburg Institute of International Economics (HWWA).

Kauppi, P. 2001. Technological and economic potential of options to enhance, maintain, and manage biological carbon reservoirs and geo-engineering. *Climate change 2001: Mitigation.* Contribution of Working Group III to the Third Assessment Report of the Intergovernmental Panel on Climate Change (IPCC). Cambridge, U.K.: Cambridge University.

Killeen, T.J. 2007. *A perfect storm in the Amazon wilderness: Development and conservation in the context of the initiative for the integration of the regional infrastructure of South America (IIRSA).* Advances in Applied Biodiversity Science, No. 7. Arlington, VA: Center for Applied Biodiversity Science, Conservation International.

Killeen, T.J., V. Calderon, L. Soria, B. Quezada, M.K. Steininger, G. Harper, L.A. Solórzano, and C.J. Tucker. 2007. Thirty years of land-cover change in Bolivia. *AMBIO: A Journal of the Human Environment.* 36: 600-606.

Lenton, T.M., H. Held, E. Kriegler, J.W. Hall, W. Lucht, S. Rahmstorf, and H.J. Schellnhuber. 2008. Tipping elements in the Earth's climate system. *Proceedings of the National Academy of Sciences.* 105(6):1786-1793. www.pnas.org

Levine, Joel S. 1996. *Biomass burning and global change, Vol. 2: Biomass burning in the tropical and temperate ecosystems.* MIT Press.

Mahli, Y., D. Wood, T.R. Baker, J. Wright, O.L. Phillips, T. Cochrane, P. Meir, J. Chave, S. Almeida, L. Arroyo, N. Higuchi, T.J. Killeen, S.G. Laurance, W.F. Laurance, S.L. Lewis, A. Monteagudo, D.A. Neill, P. Nunez-Vargas, N.C.A. Pittman, C.A. Quesada, R. Salomao, J.N.M. Silva, A.Torres-Lezama, J. Terborgh, R.Vasquez-Martinez, and B. Vincenti. 2006. The regional variation of aboveground live biomass in old-growth Amazonian forests. *Global Change Biology.* 12:1107-1138.

Margulis, S. 2004. *Causes of deforestation in the Brazilian Amazon.* Brasilia: The World Bank.

MIT. 2007. *MIT future of coal study,* http://webmit.edu/coal

Mittermeier, R.A., C.G. Mittermeier, T.M. Brooks, J. Pilgrim, W. Konstant. G.A.B. da Fonseca, and C. Kormos. 2003. Wilderness and biodiversity conservation. *Proceedings of the National Academy of Sciences of the U.S.A.* 100:10309-10313.

Mittermeier, R.A., N. Myers, P. Robles Gil, and C.G. Mittermeier. 1999. *Hotspots.* Mexico City, Mexico: CEMEX.

Mittermeier, R.A., P. Robles Gil, M. Hoffman, J. Pilgrim, T.M. Brooks, C.G. Mittermeier, J. Lamoreaux, and G.A.B. da Fonseca. 2004. *Hotspots revisited.* Mexico City, Mexico: CEMEX.

Myers, N., R.A. Mittermeier, C.G. Mittermeier, G.A.B da Fonseca, and J. Kent. 2000. Biodiversity hotspots for conservation priorities. *Nature.* 403:853-858.

Nabuurs, G.J., O. Masera, K. Andrasko, P. Benitez-Ponce, R. Boer, M. Dutschke, E. Elsiddig, J. Ford-Robertson, P. Frumhoff, T. Karjalainen, O. Kankina, W.A. Kurz, M. Mastumoto, W. Oyhantcabal, N.H. Ravindranath, M.J. Sanze Sanchez, and X. Zhang. 2007. Forestry. In: *Climate change 2007: Mitigation.* Working Group III contribution to the Fourth Assessment Report of the Intergovernmental Panel on Climate Change. Metz, B., O.R. Davidson, P.R. Bosch, R. Dave, L.A. Meyer, eds. Cambridge, U.K. and New York: Cambridge University Press.

Naughton-Treves, L., M. Buck, and K. Brandon. 2005. The role of protected areas in conserving biodiversity and sustaining local livelihoods. *Annual Review of Environment and Resources.* 30:219-252.

Nepstad, D., A. Verissimo, A. Alencar, C. Nobre, E. Lima, P. Lefebvre, P. Schlesinger, C. Potter, P. Moutinho, E. Mendoza, M. Cochrane, and V. Brooks. 1999. Large scale impoverishment of Amazonian forests by logging and fire. *Nature.* 398:505-508.

Nepstad, D., S. Schwartzman, B. Bamberger, M. Santilli, D. Ray, P. Schlesinger, P. Lefebvre, A. Alencar, E. Prinz, G. Fiske, and A. Rolla. 2006. Inhibition of Amazon deforestation and fire by parks and indigenous lands. *Conservation Biology.* 20(1):65-73.

Ong, J.E. 2002. *The hidden costs of mangrove services: Use of mangroves for shrimp aquaculture.* International Science Roundtable for the Media – June 4, 2002, Bali, Indonesia. Joint event of ICSU, IGBP, IHDP, WCRP, DIVERSITAS, START.

Pinard, M.A. and F.E. Putz. 1996. Retaining forest biomass by reducing logging damage. *Biotropica,* 28(3):278-295.

Pinard, M.A., F.E. Putz, and J. Tay. 2000. Lessons learned from the implementation of reduced impact logging in hilly terrain in Sabah, Malaysia. *International Forestry Review.* 2:33-39.

Prior, S., R. O'Sullivan, and C. Streck. 2007. *A carbon stock approach to creating a positive incentive to reduce emissions from deforestation and forest degradation.* Joint Submission to the UNFCCC Secretariat on reducing emissions from deforestation in developing countries. Centre for International Sustainable Development Law and Global Public Policy Institute.

Sánchez-Azofeifa, A., G.C. Daily, A.S.P. Pfaff, and C. Busch. 2003. Integrity and isolation of Costa Rica's national parks and biological reserves: Examining the dynamics of land-cover change. *Biological Conservation.* 109:123–35.

Santilli, M., P. Moutinho, S.Schwartzman, D. Nepstad, L. Curran, and C. Nobre. 2005. Tropical deforestation and the Kyoto Protocol: An editorial essay. *Climatic Change.* 71:267-276.

Sathaye, J. A. C. Najam, T. Cocklin, F. Heller, J. Lecocq, J. Llanes-Regueiro, J. Pan, G. Peschel-Held, S. Rayner, J. Robinson, R. Schaeffer, Y. Sokona, R. Swart, and H. Winkler. 2007. Sustainable development and mitigation. In *Climate Change 2007: Mitigation.* Working Group III contribution to the Fourth Assessment Report of the Intergovernmental Panel on Climate Change. B. Metz, O.R. Davidson, P.R. Bosch, R. Dave, L.A. Meyer, eds. Cambridge, U.K. and New York: Cambridge University Press.

Schwartzman, S. and B. Zimmerman. 2005. Conservation alliances with indigenous people of the Amazon. *Conservation Biology.* 19(3): 721-727.

Sohngen, B. and R. Sedjo. 2006. Carbon sequestration in global forests under different carbon price regimes. *The Energy Journal.* Multi-Greenhouse Gas Mitigation and Climate Policy special issue. 109-126.

Stern, Nicholas. 2006. *The economics of climate change: The Stern report.* Cambridge University Press. Available online at http://www.hm-treasury.gov.uk/independent_reviews/stern_review_economics_climate_change/stern_review_report.cfm.

Tavoni, M., B. Sohngen, and V. Bosetti. 2007. Forestry and the carbon market response to climate change. *Energy Policy.* 35: 5346-5353.

Terborgh, J., C. van Schaik, L. Davenport, M. Rao, eds. 2002. *Making parks work.* Washington, DC: Island Press.

van Schaik, C., J. Terborgh, and B. Dugelby. 1997. The silent crisis: The state of rainforest nature preserves. Pp. 64-89 in *Last stand: Protected areas and the defense of tropical biodiversity.* R. Kramer, C. van Schaik, and J. Johnson, eds. New York: Oxford University Press.

Reforestation and Agroforestry

Albrecht, A. and S.T. Kandji. 2003. Carbon sequestration in tropical agroforestry systems. *Agriculture, Ecosystems and Environment.* 99:15-27.

Atkinson, A.D., J. Beniest, and S. Rao. 2006. Can e-learning support agricultural development in developing countries? Pp. 155-162 in *World agroforestry into the future.* D.P. Garrity, A. Okono, M. Grayson, and S. Parrott, eds. Nairobi, Kenya: World Agroforestry Centre.

Barlow, J., L.A.M. Mestre, T.A. Gardner, C.A. Peres. 2007. The value of primary, secondary and plantation forests for Amazonian birds. *Biological Conservation.* 136:212-231.

Brown, C. 2000. The global outlook for future wood supply from forest plantations. Working paper GFPOS/WP/03. Food and Agriculture Organization, Rome.

Brown, S., M. Burnham, M. Delaney, M. Powell, R. Vaca, and A. Moreno. 2000. Issues and challenges for forest-based carbon-offset projects: A case study of the Noel Kempff climate action project in Bolivia. *Mitigation and adaptation strategies for global change.* 5:99-121.

Brown, S., E. Palola, and M. Lorenzo. 2006. *The possibility of plantations: Integrating ecological forestry into plantation systems.* Reston, VA.: National Wildlife Federation.

Cannell, M. 1999. Environmental impacts of forest monocultures: Water use, acidification, wildlife conservation, and carbon storage. *New Forest.* 17:239-262.

CCBA (Climate, Community and Biodiversity Alliance). 2005. Climate, Community and Biodiversity Project Design Standards (first edition). CCBA, Washington, DC. www.climate-standards.org (accessed Nov. 15, 2007)

Conant, R., K. Paustian, and E.T. Elliott. 2001. Grassland management and conversion into grassland: Effects on soil carbon. *Ecological Applications.* 11:343-355.

Conway, G. 1999. *The doubly green revolution: Food for all in the twenty-first century.* Ithaca, New York: Cornell University Press.

De Jong, B.H.J., L. Soto, G. Montoya, K. Nelson, J. Taylor, and R. Tipper, eds. 1997. Forestry and agroforestry land-use systems for carbon mitigation: An analysis in Chiapas, Mexico. CAB International, Wallingford, United Kingdom.

De Jong, B.H.J., S. Ochoa Gaona, L. Soto-Pinto, M.A. Castillo-Santiago, G. Montoya-Gómez, R. Tipper, and I. March-Mifsut. 1998. Modelling forestry and agroforestry opportunities for carbon mitigation at a landscape level. Pp. 221-237 in *Forest scenario modeling for ecosystem management at landscape level.* G.J. Nabuurs, T. Nuutinen, H. Bartelink, and M. Korhonen, eds. EFI Proceedings, Finland.

Dixon, R.K. 1995. Agroforestry systems: Sources or sinks of greenhouse gases? *Agroforestry Systems.* 31:99-116.

Dixon, R.K., S. Brown, R.A. Houghton, A.M. Solomon, M.C. Trexler, and J. Wisniewski. 1994. Carbon pools and flux of global forest ecosystems. *Science.* 263:185-190.

Donald, P.F. 2004. Biodiversity impacts of some agricultural commodity production systems. *Conservation Biology.* 18:17-37.

Dutschke, M., B. Schlamadinger, J.L.P. Wong, and M. Rumberg. 2005. Value and risks of expiring carbon credits from afforestation and reforestation projects under the CDM. *Climate Policy.* 5:109-125.

Ellis, J. and S. Kamel. 2007. Overcoming barriers to clean development mechanism projects. COM/ENV/EPOC/IEA/SLT. 3. IEA and UNEP. Risø Centre, Paris.

Evans, J. and J.W. Turnbull. 2004. *Plantation forestry in the tropics: The role, silviculture and use of planted forests for industrial, social, environmental and agroforestry purposes.* New York: Oxford University Press.

Farley, K.A., E.G. Jobbágy, and R.B. Jackson. 2005. Effects of afforestation on water yield: A global synthesis with implications for policy. *Global Change Biology.* 11:1565–1576.

FAO (Food and Agriculture Organization). 2001. Forest genetic resources No. 29. FAO, Rome.

FAO (Food and Agriculture Organization). 2006. *Global forest resources assessment 2005,* main report, Progress towards sustainable forest management. Forestry Paper No. 147. FAO, Rome.

Garrity, D.P. 2004. Agroforestry and the achievement of the millennium development goals. *Agroforestry Systems.* 61:5-17.

Garrity, D.P., A. Okono, M. Grayson, and S. Parrott, eds. 2006. *World agroforestry into the future.* Nairobi, Kenya:World Agroforestry Centre.

Gullison, R.E., P.E. Frumhoff, J.G. Canadell, C.B. Field, D.C. Nepstad, K. Hayhoe, L.M. Curran, P. Friedlingstein, C.D. Jones, and C. Nobre. 2007. Tropical forests and climate policy. *Science.* 316:985-986.

Hamilton, K., R. Bayon, G. Turner, and D. Higgins. 2007. State of the voluntary carbon market 2007: Picking up steam. New Carbon Finance, London, England and The Ecosystem Marketplace, Washington, DC.

Hannah, L., G.F. Midgley, and D. Millar. 2002. Climate change-integrated conservation strategies. *Global Ecology and Biogeography.* 11:486-495.

Harvey, C.A. 2007. Designing agricultural landscapes for biodiversity conservation. Pp. 146-165 in *Farming with nature: The science and practice of ecoagriculture.* S.J. Scherr and J.A. McNeely, eds. Washington, DC: Island Press.

Harvey, C.A. and J. Sáenz. 2008. *Evaluación y conservación de biodiversidad en paisajes fragmentados de Mesóamérica.* Heredia, Costa Rica: InBio Press.

Harvey, C.A. and J. González Villalobos. 2007. Agroforestry systems conserve species-rich but modified assemblages of tropical birds and bats. *Biodiversity and Conservation.* 16:2257-2292.

Harvey, C.A., G. Schroth, and O. Zerbock. 2007. Designing agroforestry systems to mitigate climate change, conserve biodiversity and alleviate poverty. Second International Symposium. Multi-strata agroforestry systems with perennial crops: Making ecosystem services count for farmers, consumers and the environment. Turrialba, Costa Rica. September 17-21, 2007.

Jackson, R.B., J.L. Banner, E.G. Jobbagy, W.T. Pockman, and D.H. Wall. 2002. Ecosystem carbon loss with woody plant invasion of grasslands. *Nature.* 418:623-626.

Johns, N.D. 1999. Conservation in Brazil's chocolate forest: The unlikely persistence of the traditional cocoa agroecosystem. *Environmental Management.* 23:31–47.

Kandji, S.T., L.V. Verchot, J. Mackensen, A. Boye, M. van Noordwijk, T.P. Tomich, C. Ong, A. Albrecht, and C. Palm. 2006. Opportunities for linking climate change adaptation and mitigation through agroforestry systems. Pp. 113-121 in *World agroforestry into the future.* D.P. Garrity, A. Okono, M. Grayson and S. Parrott, eds. Nairobi, Kenya: World Agroforestry Centre.

Laird, S.A., G.L. Awung, and R.J. Lysinge. 2007. Cocoa farms in the Mount Cameroon region: Biological and cultural diversity in local livelihoods. *Biodiversity and Conservation.* 16:2401-2427.

Laurence, W.F. 2007. A new initiative to use carbon trading for tropical forest conservation. *Biotropica.* 39:20-24.

Lugo, A.E. 1992. Comparison of tropical tree plantations with secondary forests of similar age. *Ecological Monographs.* 62:1-41.

Makundi, W.R. and J.A. Sathaye. 2004. GHG mitigation potential and cost in tropical forestry-relative role for agroforestry. *Environment, Development and Sustainability* 6:235-260.

Masripatin, N. 2005. Preparing the ground: Indonesia's arrangements for forestry projects under the clean development mechanism. *Unasylva.* 56:12-18.

Michon, G. 2005. Domesticating forests: How farmers manage forest resources. Center for International Forestry Research. Bogor, Indonesia.

Millennium Ecosystem Assessment. 2005. *Ecosystems and human well-being: Synthesis.* Washington, DC: Island Press.

Montagnini, F. and P.K.R. Nair. 2004. Carbon sequestration: An underexploited environmental benefit of agroforestry systems. *Agroforestry Systems.* 61:281-295.

Montagnini, F. and C. Porras. 1998. Evaluating the role of plantations as carbon sinks: An example of an integrative approach from the humid tropics. *Environmental Management.* 22:459-470.

Mosier, A.R. 1998. Soil processes and global change. *Biology and Fertility of Soils.* 27:221-229.

Mutuo, P.K., G. Cadisch, A. Albrecht, C.A. Palm, and L. Verchot. 2005. Potential of agroforestry for carbon sequestration and mitigation of greenhouse gas emissions from soils in the tropics. *Nutrient Cycling in Agroecosystems* 71:43-54.

Nabuurs, G.J., O. Masera, K. Andrasko, P. Benitez-Ponce, R. Boer, M. Dutschke, E. Elsiddig, J. Ford-Robertson, P. Frumhoff, T. Karjalainen, O. Krankina, W.A. Kurz, M. Matsumoto, W. Oyhantcabal, N.H. Ravindranath, M.J. Sanz Sanchez, and X. Zhang. 2007. Forestry. Pp. 541-584 in *Climate Change 2007: Mitigation.* B. Metz, O.R. Davidson, P.R. Bosch, R. Dave, and L.A. Meyer, eds. Cambridge, U.K. and New York: Cambridge University Press.

Nair, P.K.R. 1993. *An introduction to agroforestry.* Dordrecht, The Netherlands: Kluwer Academic Publishers.

Noss, R.F. 2001. Beyond Kyoto: Forest management in a time of rapid climate change. *Conservation Biology.* 15:578.

Pearson, T., S. Walker, and S. Brown. 2005. *Sourcebook for land use, land-use change and forestry projects.* BioCarbon Fund of the World Bank, Winrock International.

Perfecto, I., J. Vandermeer, A. Mas, and L. Soto-Pinto. 2005. Biodiversity, yield and coffee certification. *Ecological Economics.* 37:435-446.

Perfecto, I., R.A. Rice, R. Greenberg, and M.E. van der Voort. 1996. Shade coffee: a disappearing refuge for biodiversity. *BioScience.* 46:598-608.

Piottoa, D., E. Víquez, F. Montagnini, and M. Kanninen. 2004. Pure and mixed forest plantations with native species of the dry tropics of Costa Rica: A comparison of growth and productivity. *Forest Ecology and Management.* 190:359-372.

Redondo-Brenes, A. 2007. Growth, carbon sequestration, and management of native tree plantations in humid regions of Costa Rica. *New Forests.* 34:253-268.

Richards, K.R. and C. Stokes. 2004. A review of forest carbon sequestration cost studies: A dozen years of research. *Climate Change.* 63:1-48.

Sánchez, P.A. 2000. Linking climate change research with food security and poverty reduction in the tropics. *Agriculture, Ecosystem and Environment.* 82:371-383.

SCBD (Secretariat of the Convention on Biological Diversity). 2003. Interlinkages between biological diversity and climate change. Advice on the integration of biodiversity considerations into the implementation of the United Nations Framework Convention on Climate Change and its Kyoto Protocol. CDB Technical Series No. 10. Secretariat of the Convention on Biological Diversity. Montreal, Canada.

Schroeder, P. 1993. Agroforestry systems: Integrated land use to store and conserve carbon. *Climate Research.* 3:53-60.

Schroth, G., G.A.B. da Fonseca, C.A. Harvey, C. Gascon, H.L. Vasconcelos, and A.M.N. Isaac, eds. 2004. *Agroforestry and biodiversity conservation in tropical landscapes.* Washington, DC: Island Press.

Silver, W.L., R. Ostertag, and A.E. Lugo. 2000. The potential for carbon sequestration through reforestation of abandoned tropical agricultural and pasture lands. *Restoration Ecology* 8:339-407.

Soto-Pinto, L., V. Villalvazo, G. Jimenez-Ferrer, N. Ramírez-Marcial, G. Montoya, and F. Sinclair. 2007. The role of coffee knowledge in determining shade composition of multistrata coffee systems in Chiapas, Mexico. *Biodiversity and Conservation.* 16:419-436.

UNFCCC (United Nations Framework Convention on Climate Change). 2007. Distribution of registered project activities by scope. Chart available from http://cdm.unfccc.int/Statistics/Registration/RegisteredProjByScopePieChart.html (accessed Jan. 2008)

van Noordwijk, M., T.P. Tomich, H. de Foresta, and G. Michon. 1997. To segregate or to integrate? The question of balance between production and biodiversity conservation in complex agroforestry systems. *Agroforestry Today.* 9:6–9.

Verchot, L.V., M. van Noordwijk, S. Kandji, T. Tomich, C. Ong, A. Albrecht, J. Mackensen, C. Bantilan, K.V. Anupama, and C. Palm. 2007. Climate change: Linking adaptation and mitigation through agroforestry. *Mitigation and Adaptation Strategies for Global Change.* 12:901-918.

Wagner, R.G., K.M. Little, B. Richardson, and K. Mcnabb. 2006. The role of vegetation management for enhancing productivity of the world's forests. *Forestry.* 79:57-79.

Waterloo, M.J., P.H. Spiertz, H. Diemont, I. Emmer, E. Aalders, R. Wichink-Kruit, and P. Kabat. 2003. Criteria potentials and costs of forestry activities to sequester carbon within the framework of the Clean Development Mechanism. Alterra Rapport 777. Wageningen, The Netherlands.

Watson, J.W. and P.B. Eyzaguirre, eds. 2002. *Proceedings of the second international Home Gardens Workshop,* 17–19 July 2001, Witzenhausen, Germany. Contribution of home gardens to *in situ* conservation of plant genetic resources in farming systems. Rome: International Plant Genetic Resources Institute.

Adaptation

Battarbee, R., P. Cox, C. Freeman, J. Lawton, G. Mace, A. MacKay, D. Read, and J. Shepherd, eds. 2007. *Biodiversity-Climate interactions: Adaptation, mitigation and human livelihoods*. Report of an international meeting held at the Royal Society, 12-13 June 2007. London: The Royal Society.

Cline, W. 2007. *Global warming and agriculture: Impact estimates by country*. Peterson Institute for International Economics.

Gadgil, A., D. Greene, A. Drescher, P. Miller, and Nd. Kibata. 1998. Low cost UV disinfection system for developing countries: Field tests in South Africa. Presented at the first international Symposium on Safe Drinking Water in Small Systems. May 10-13, 1998, Washington, DC. Available online at http://www.osti.gov/accomplishments/documents/fullText/ACC0030.pdf

Gleick, P.H. 2000. *The world's water 2000-2001: The biennial report on freshwater resources*. Washington, DC: Island Press.

IPCC. 2001. *Climate change 2001: Third assessment report*. Intergovernmental Panel on Climate Change (IPCC). Geneva, Switzerland.

IPCC. 2007. *Climate change 2007*. Working Group II contribution to the Fourth Assessment Report of the Intergovernmental panel on Climate Change (IPCC). Geneva, Switzerland.

Kiparsky, M., and P.H. Gleick. 2003. *Climate change and California water resources: A survey and summary of the literature*. Department of Water Resources, Sacramento, CA.

Leary, N., J. Adejuwon, V. Barros, I. Burton, J. Kulkarni, and R. Lasco, eds. 2008. *Climate change and adaptation*. The International START Secretariat, Earthscan, London.

Lorenz, S.J., D. Kasang, and G. Lohmann. 2007. Global water cycle and climate change – Interactions. In *Global change: Enough water for all?* J. Lózan, H. Grassl, P. Hupfer, L. Menzel, and C. Schönwiese, eds. Pp. 157-161. Wissenschaftliche Auswertungen, in cooperation with GEO, Hamburg, Germany.

Millennium Ecosystem Assessment. 2005. *Ecosystems and human well-being*. Washington, DC: Island Press.

Mittermeier, R.A., P. Robles Gil, M. Hoffman, J. Pilgrim, T. Brooks, C.G. Mittermeier, J. Lamoreux, and G.A.B. da Fonseca. 2004. *Hotspots revisited*. Mexico City: CEMEX.

Parmesan, C. and G. Yohe. 2003. A globally coherent fingerprint of climate change impacts across natural systems. *Nature*. 421: 37-42.

Pounds, J.A., M.P.L. Fogden, and J.H. Campbell. 1999. Biological response to climate change on a tropical mountain. *Nature*. 398: 611-615.

Pounds, J.A., M.R. Bustamante, L.A. Coloma, J.A. Consuegra, M.P.L. Fogden, P.N. Foster, E. La Marca, K.L. Masters, A. Merino-Viteri, R. Puschendorf, S.R. Ron, G.A. Sánchez-Azofeita, C.J. Stilland, and B.E. Young. 2006. Ecuador: Overview and first report of chytridiomycosis from South America. *Frog Log*. 42:2-3.

Reddy, A. 1993. Poverty-oriented energy strategies for sustainable development. Paper presented to the International Workshop on Environment and Poverty, July 22-24, 1993, Dhaka (Bangladesh). Organized by the Bangladesh Centre for Advanced Studies for the Global Forum on Environment and Poverty. Available at http://amulya-reddy.org.in/Publication/1993_07_BCAS0722.pdf

Reusch, T.B., A. Ehlers, A. Hammerli, and B. Worm. 2005. Ecosystem recovery after climatic extremes enhanced by genotypic diversity. *Proceedings of the National Academy of Sciences*. 101(27): 10101-10106.

Root, T., J.T. Price, K.R. Hall, S.H. Schneider, C. Rosenzweig, and J.A. Pounds. 2003. Fingerprints of global warming on wild animals and plants. *Nature*. 421: 57-60.

Totten, M. 2007. China's bold initiative. *Solar Today*. March/April 2007. Pp. 38-41. American Solar Energy Society, http://www.solartoday.org/2007/mar_apr07/china.htm

WaterHealth International. 2007. WaterHealth International announces the launch of the blue revolution, February 4, 2007. Available at http://www.waterhealth.com/press/09-Feb-07.php

Terrestrial Biodiversity

Allan, J.D., M. Palmer, and N.L. Poff. 2005. Climate change and freshwater ecosystems. Pp. 272-288 in *Climate change and biodiversity*. T.E. Lovejoy and L. Hannah, eds. New Haven: Yale University Press.

Alroy, J. 2001. A multispecies overkill simulation of the end-Pleistocene megafaunal mass extinction. *Science* 292:1893-1896.

Alvarez, L.W., W. Alvarez, F. Asaro, and H.V. Michel. 1980. Extraterrestrial cause for the Cretaceous-tertiary extinction. *Science* 208:1095-1108.

Anderson, J.J. 1998. Decadal climate cycles and declining Columbia River salmon. Pp. 467-484 in *Sustainable Fisheries Management: Pacific Salmon*, E.E. Knudsen, ed. New York: CRC Press.

Araújo, M.B., M. Cabeza, W. Thuiller, L. Hannah, and P.H. Williams. 2004. Would climate change drive species out of reserves? An assessment of existing reserve-selection methods. *Global Change Biology* 10: 1618-1626.

Araújo, M.B., W. Thuiller, and R.G. Pearson. 2006. Climate warming and the decline of amphibians and reptiles in Europe. *Journal of Biogeography*. 33: 1712-1728.

Barnosky, A.D., P.L. Koch, R.S. Feranec, S.L. Wing, and A.B. Shabel. 2004. Assessing the causes of Late Pleistocene extinctions on the continents. *Science* 306: 70-75.

Bartlein, P.J. and I.C. Prentice.1989. Orbital variations, climate and paleoecology. *Trends in Ecology and Evolution* 4: 195-199.

Bennett, K.D. 1990. Milankovitch cycles and their effects on species in ecological and evolutionary time. *Paleobiology* 16: 11-21.

Broecker, W.S. 1999. What if the conveyor were to shut down? Reflections on a possible outcome of the great global experiment. *GSA Today* 9: 1-5.

Broecker, W.S. 2001. Paleoclimate. Was the medieval warm period global? *Science* 291: 1497-1499.

Coope, G.R. 1995. Insect faunas in ice age environments: Why so little extinction? Pp. 55-74 in *Extinction Rates*. J.H. Lawton and R.M. May, eds. Oxford: Oxford University Press.

Davis, A.J., J.H. Lawton, B. Shorrocks, and L.S. Jenkinson. 1998. Individualistic species responses invalidate simple physiological models of community dynamics under global environmental change. *Journal of Animal Ecology* 67: 600-612.

Davis, M.B. and R.G. Shaw. 2001. Range shifts and adaptive responses to Quaternary climate change. *Science* 292: 673-679.

Foden, W., G.F. Midgley, G. Hughes, W.J. Bond, W. Thuiller, M.T. Hoffman, P. Kaleme, L.G. Underhill, A. Rebelo, and L. Hannah. 2007. A changing climate is eroding the geographical range of the Namib Desert tree aloe through population declines and dispersal lags. *Diversity and Distributions* 13: 645-653.

Francis, R.C. 1990. Climate change and marine fisheries. *Fisheries* 15: 7-9.

Gingerich, P.D. 2006. Environment and evolution through the Paleocene-Eocene thermal maximum. *Trends in Ecology & Evolution* 21: 246-253.

Glen, F. and N. Mrosovsky. 2004. Antigua revisited: The impact of climate change on sand and nest temperatures at a hawksbill turtle (*Eretmochelys imbricata*) nesting beach. *Global Change Biology* 10: 2036-2045.

Hannah, L., T.E. Lovejoy, and S.H. Schneider. 2005. Biodiversity and climate change in context. In *Climate change and biodiversity*. T.E. Lovejoy and L. Hannah, eds. New Haven: Yale University Press.

Hannah, L., G.F. Midgley, T.E. Lovejoy, W.J. Bond, M.L. Bush, J.C. Lovett, D. Scott, and F.I. Woodward. 2002. Conservation of biodiversity in a changing climate. *Conservation Biology* 16: 11-15.

Hannah, L., G.F. Midgley, S. Andelman, M. Araújo, G. Hughes, E. Martinez-Meyer, R. Pearson, and P. Williams. 2007. Protected area needs in a changing climate. *Frontiers in Ecology and the Environment* 5: 131-138.

Hoegh-Guldberg, O. 1999. Climate change, coral bleaching and the future of the world's coral reefs. *Mar.Freshwater Res*. 50: 839-866.

Kennett, J.P. and L.D. Stott. 1991. Abrupt deep-sea warming paleoceanographic changes and benthic extinctions at the end of the paleocene. *Nature* 353: 225-229.

Logan, J.A., J. Regniere, and J.A. Powell. 2003. Assessing the impacts of global warming on forest pest dynamics. *Frontiers in Ecology and the Environment* 1: 130-137.

Markgraf, V., R. Kenny. 1995. Character of rapid vegetation and climate change during the late-glacial in southernmost South America. Pp. 81-102 in *Past and future rapid environmental changes: The spatial and evolutionary responses of terrestrial biota*. B. Huntley, W. Cramer, A.V. Morgan, H.C. Prentice, and J.R.M. Allen, eds. Berlin: Springer-Verlag.

Mayhew, P.J., G.B. Jenkins, and T.G. Benton. 2008. A long-term association between global temperature and biodiversity, origination and extinction in the fossil record. *Proceedings of the Royal Society B-Biological Sciences* 275: 47-53.

Midgley, G.F., L. Hannah, D. Millar, M.C. Rutherford, and L.W. Powrie. 2002. Assessing the vulnerability of species richness to anthropogenic climate change in a biodiversity hotspot. *Global Ecology & Biogeography* 11: 445-451.

Moline, M.A., H. Claustre, T.K. Frazer, O. Schofield, and M. Vernet. 2004. Alteration of the food web along the Antarctic Peninsula in response to a regional warming trend. *Global Change Biology* 10: 1973-1980.

Overpeck, J., C. Whitlock, and B. Huntley. 2003. Terrestrial Biosphere Dynamics in the Climate System: Past and future. Pp. 81-109 in *Paleoclimate, global change, and the future*. K.D. Alverson, R.S. Bradley, and T.F. Pederson, eds. Berlin: Springer-Verlag.

Parmesan, C. and G. Yohe. 2003. A globally coherent fingerprint of climate change impacts across natural systems. *Nature* 421: 37-42.

Pockley, P. 1999. Global warming could kill most coral reefs by 2100. *Nature* 400: 98.

Pounds, J.A., M.P.L. Fogden, and J.H. Campbell. 1999. Biological response to climate change on a tropical mountain. *Nature* 398: 611-615.

Pounds, J.A., M.R. Bustamante, L.A. Coloma, J. A. Consuegra, M.P.L. Fogden, P.N. Foster, E. La Marca, K.L. Masters, A. Merino-Viteri, R. Puschendorf, S.R. Ron, G.A. Sánchez-Azofeifa, C.J. Still, and B.E. Young. 2006. Widespread amphibian extinctions from epidemic disease driven by global warming. *Nature* 439: 161-167.

Rebelo, A.G. 2001. *Proteas: A field guide to the proteas of southern Africa*. Cape Town (South Africa). Cape Town: Fernwood Press.

Root, T., J.T. Price, K.R. Hall, S.H. Schneider, C. Rosenzweig, and J.A. Pounds. 2003. Fingerprints of global warming on wild animals and plants. *Nature* 421: 57-60.

Roy, K., D. Jablonski, and J.W. Valentine. 2001. Climate change, species range limits and body size in marine bivalves. *Ecology Letters* 4: 366-370.

Schneider, C. and C. Moritz. 1999. Rainforest refugia and evolution in Australia's wet tropics. *Proceedings of the Royal Society of London Series B-Biological Sciences* 266: 191-196.

Seimon, T.A., A. Seimon, P. Daszak, S.R.P. Halloy, L.M. Schloegel, C.A. Aguilar, P. Sowell, A.D. Hyatt, B. Konecky, and J.E. Simmons. 2007. Upward range extension of Andean anurans and chytridiomycosis to extreme elevations in response to tropical deglaciation. *Global Change Biology* 13: 288-299.

Stirling, I. and C.L. Parkinson. 2006. Possible effects of climate warming on selected populations of polar bears (*Ursus maritimus*) in the Canadian Arctic. *Arctic* 59: 261-275.

Thuiller, W., S. Lavorel, M.B. Araújo, M.T. Sykes, and I.C. Prentice. 2005. Climate change threats to plant diversity in Europe. *Proceedings of the National Academy of Sciences of the United States of America (PNAS)* 102: 8245-8250.

Walther, G., E. Post, P. Convey, A. Menzel, C. Parmesan, T.J.C. Beebee, J. Fromentin, O. Hoegh-Guldberg, and F. Bairlein. 2002. Ecological responses to recent climate change. *Nature* 416: 389-395.

Ward, P. D. 2006. Impact from the deep, *Scientific American*, October, 65-71, www.sciam.com/

Webb, T.I. 1995. Spatial response of plant taxa to climate change: A palaeoecological perspective. Pp. 55-72 in *Past and future rapid environmental changes: The spatial and evolutionary responses of terrestrial biota*. B. Huntley, W. Cramer, A.V. Morgan, H.C. Prentice, J.R.M. Allen, eds. Berlin: Springer-Verlag.

Williams, P., L. Hannah, S. Andelman, G.F. Midgely, M.B. Araújo, G. Hughes, L. Manne, E. Martinez-Meyer, and R.G. Pearson. 2005. Planning for climate change: Identifying minimum-dispersal corridors for the cape proteaceae. *Conservation Biology* 19, no.4 (August 2005):1063-1074.

Williams, S.E., E.E. Bolitho, and S. Fox. 2004. Climate change in Australian tropical rainforests: An impending environmental catastrophe. *Proceedings of the Royal Society of London, Series B* 270: 1887-1892.

Wilson, R.J., D. Gutiérrez, J. Gutiérrez, D. Martínez, R. Agudo, and V.J. Monserrat. 2005. Changes to the elevational limits and extent of species ranges associated with climate change. *Ecology Letters* 8: 1138-1146.

Zachos, J., M. Pagani, L. Sloan, E. Thomas, and K. Billups. 2001. Trends, rhythms, and aberrations in global climate 65 ma to present. *Science* 292: 686-693.

Freshwater Biodiversity

Abramovitz, Janet. 1996. Imperiled waters, impoverished future: The decline of freshwater ecosystems. Worldwatch Paper No. 128. Washington, DC: Worldwatch Institute.

Allan, J.D. and A.S. Flecker. 1993. Biodiversity conservation in running waters. *Bioscience*. 43(1):32-43.

Alliance for Zero Extinction. 2007. Search the AZE database, accessible at http://www.zeroextinction.org/search.cfm

Bachhuber, F.W. 1982. Quaternary history of the Estancia Valley, central New Mexico. New Mexico Geol. Soc. Guidebook, 33rd Field Conference, Albuquerque Co., II:343-346.

Barbour, C.D. and J.H. Brown. 1972. Fish species diversity in lakes. *American Naturalist*. 108:473-489.

Bronstert, A., and H. Engel. 2007. Changing river discharges. In *Global change: Enough water for all?* J. Lózan, H. Grassl, P. Hupfer, L. Menzel, and C. Schönwiese, eds. Pp. 178-184. Hamburg, Germany: Wissenschaftliche Auswertungen (in cooperation with GEO).

Chase, M.W., D.E. Soltis, R.G. Olmstead, D. Morgan, D.H. Les, B.D. Mishler, M.R. Duvall, R.A. Price, H.G. Hills, Y.-L. Qiu, K.A. Kron, J.H. Rettig, E. Conti, J.D. Palmer, J.R. Manhart, K.J. Sytsma, H.J. Michaels, W.J. Kress, K.G. Karol, W.D. Clark, M. Hedren, B.S. Gaut, R.K. Jansen, K.-J. Kim, C.F. Wimpee, J.F. Smith, G.R. Furnier, S.H. Strauss, Q.-Y. Xiang, G.M. Plunkett, P.S. Soltis, S.M. Swensen, S.E. Williams, P.A. Gadek, C.J. Quinn, L.E. Eguiarte, E. Golenberg, G.H. Learn, Jr., S.W. Graham, S.C.H. Barrett, S. Dayanandan, and V.A. Albert. 1993. Phylogenetics of seed plants: An analysis of nucleotide sequences from the plastid gene rbcL. *Annals of the Missouri Botanical Garden.* 80: 528-580.

Dilcher, D.L. 1990. The occurrence of fruits with affinities to Ceratophyllaceae in lower and mid-Cretaceous sediments. [Abstract.] *Amer. J. Bot..* 76: 162.

Döll, P. and M. Flörke. 2005. Global-scale estimation of diffuse groundwater recharge. Frankfurt Hydrology Paper 03. Frankfurt, Germany: Institute of Physical Geography.

Gleick, P.H. 2000. The world's water 2000-2001. *The biennial report on freshwater resources.* Washington, DC: Island Press.

Gleick, P.H. 1996. Water resources. In *Encyclopedia of climate and weather.* S.H. Schneider, ed. Vol. 2, pp. 817-23. New York: Oxford University Press.

Griffiths, Mark. 2006. [no title] *The Linnean.* 22(3):14-15.

Horn, M.H. 1972. The amount of space available for marine and freshwater fishes. *Fish. Bull.* U.S. 70:1295-1297.

Intergovernmental Panel on Climate Change (IPCC). 2001. *Climate change 2001: Impacts, adaptation, and vulnerability.* Cambridge, UK: Cambridge University Press.

Intergovernmental Panel on Climate Change (IPCC). 2007. *Climate change 2007,* three vols. Cambridge, UK: Cambridge University Press.

Kiparsky, M. and P.H. Gleick. 2003. *Climate change and California water resources: A survey and summary of the literature.* Sacramento, CA: Department of Water Resources.

Les, D.H. 1988. The origin and affinities of the Ceratophyllaceae. *Taxon.* 37: 326-345.

Lorenz, S.J., D. Kasang, and G. Lohmann. 2007. Global water cycle and climate change – Interactions. In *Global change: Enough water for all?* J. Lózan, H. Grassl, P. Hupfer, L. Menzel, and C. Schönwiese, eds. Pp. 157-161. Hamburg, Germany: Wissenschaftliche Auswertungen (in cooperation with GEO).

Mackay, A.W., R.J. Flower, and L.Z. Granina. 2002. Lake Baikal. Pp. 403-421 in *The physical geography of northern Eurasia: Russia and neighbouring states.* M. Shahgedanova and A. Goudie, eds. Oxford, U.K.: OUP.

McCallister, D., A. Hamilton, and B. Harvey. 1997. Global freshwater biodiversity: Striving for the integrity of freshwater ecosystems. *Sea Wind.* 11, 1-139.

McCloskey, M. 1995. Wild rivers of the North: A reconnaissance-level inventory. Pp. 130-138. in *Arctic Wilderness.* V.G. Martin and N. Tyler, eds. Golden, CO: Fulcrum Publishing.

Millennium Ecosystem Assessment. 2005. *Ecosystems and Human Well-being.* Washington, DC: Island Press.

Miller, R.R. 1981. Co-evolution of deserts and pupfishes (Genus *Cyprinodon*) in the American Southwest. Pp. 39-94 in *Fishes in North American Deserts.* R.J. Naiman and D.L. Soltz, eds. New York: John Wiley & Sons.

Mittermeier, R.A., P. Robles Gil, M. Hoffman, J. Pilgrim, T. Brooks, C.G. Mittermeier, J. Lamoreux, and G.A.B. da Fonseca . 2004. *Hotspots revisited.* Mexico City: CEMEX.

Postel, S. and B. Richter. 2003. *Rivers for life. Managing water for people and nature.* Washington, DC: Island Press.

Qiu, Y.-L., J. Lee, F. Bernasconi-Quadroni, D.E. Soltis, P.S. Soltis, M. Zanis, Z. Chen, V. Savolainen, and M.W. Chase. 1999. The earliest angiosperms: Evidence from mitochondrial, plastid and nuclear genomes. *Nature.* 402: 404-407.

Qiu, Y.-L., J.-Y. Lee, F. Bernasconi-Quadroni, D.E. Soltis, P.S. Soltis, M. Zanis, E. Zimmer, Z. Chen, V. Savolainen, and M. Chase. 2000. Phylogeny of basal angiosperms: Analyses of five genes from three genomes. *International Journal of Plant Sciences.* 161 (Supplement): S3-S27.

Ravenga, C., J. Brunner, N. Henninger, K. Kassem, and R. Payne. 2000. Pilot analysis of freshwater ecosystems: Freshwater systems. 83 pp. Washington, DC: World Resources Institute.

Reeves, C.C., Jr. 1969. Pluvial Lake Palomas, northwestern Chihuahua, Mexico. Pp. 143-154 in *Guidebook of the border region.* D.A. Cordoba, S.A. Wengerd, and J. Shomaker, eds. New Mexico Geol. Soc. Field Conf. 20.

Rosenburg, D.M, R. McCully, and C.M. Pringle. 2000. Global-scale environmental effects of hydrological alterations: Introduction. *BioScience.* 50: 746-751.

Schuchardt, B., M. Schirmer, and H. Sterr, 2007. Sea level rise and hydrological problems of coastal zones. In *Global change: Enough water for all?* J. Lózan, H. Grassl, P. Hupfer, L. Menzel, and C. Schönwiese, eds. Pp. 211-215. Hamburg, Germany: Wissenschaftliche Auswertungen (in cooperation with GEO).

Smith, M.L. 2007. The last wild waters: A snapshot of the remaining freshwater wilderness. In *The wild planet project.* C.F. Kormos and V.G. Martin, eds. Pp. 41-42. Boulder, CO: The WILD Foundation.

Smith, M.L. and B. Chernoff. 1981. Breeding populations of cyprinodontoid fishes in a thermal stream. *Copeia.* 1981(3):701-702.

Smith, M.L. and R.R. Miller. 1986. The evolution of the Rio Grande Basin as inferred from its fish fauna. Pp. 457-485. In *The zoogeography of North American freshwater fishes.* C.H. Hocutt and E.O. Wiley, eds. New York: Wiley Interscience.

Strayer, D.L. 2006. Challenges for freshwater invertebrate conservation. *Journal of the North American Benthological Society.* 25(2):271–287.

Thomas, C.D., A. Cameron, R.E. Green, M. Bakkenes, L.J. Beaumont, Y.C. Collingham, B.F.N. Erasmus, M.F. de Siqueira, A. Grainger, L. Hannah, L. Hughes, B. Huntley, A.S. van Jaarsveld, G.F. Midgley, L. Miles, M.A. Ortega-Huerta, A.T. Peterson, O.L. Phillips, S.E. Williams. 2004. Extinction risk from climate change. *Nature.* 427:145-148.

Tilman, D., J. Fargione, B. Wolff, C. D'Antonio, A. Dobson, R. Howarth, D. Schindler, W.H. Schlesinger, D. Simberloff, D. Swackhamer. 2001. Forecasting agriculturally driven global environmental change. *Science.* 292: 281-284.

United Nations Population Division. 2007. *World population prospects: The 2004 revision population database.* Available online at http://esa.un.org/unpp

United Nations Task Force on Water and Sanitation. 2005. *Health, dignity and development: What will it take?* New York: Stockholm International Water Institute and UN Millennium Project.

U.S. Bureau of the Census. 2007. Population clock. Available online at www.census.gov.

Wescoat, J.L., and G.F. White. 2003. *Water for life: Water management and environmental policy.* New York: Cambridge University Press.

World Business Council for Sustainable Development. 2007. Home page. www.wbcsd.org

World Health Organization. 2006. *World water development report.* Geneva: WHO Geneva.

World Health Organization and UNICEF. 2006. *Meeting the MGD drinking water and sanitation target: The urban and rural challenge of the decade.* Geneva: WHO.

The Role of Oceans

Ainley, D.G., E.D. Clarke, K. Arrigo, W.R. Fraser, A. Kato, K.J. Barton, and P.R. Wilson. 2005. Decadal-scale changes in the climate and biota of the Pacific sector of the Southern Ocean, 1950s to the 1990s. *Antarctic Science* 17(2):171-182, http://www.penguinscience.com/reprints/Ainley_et_al_Regime_shift.pdf

Barth, J.A., B.A. Menge, J. Lubchenco, F. Chan, J.M. Bane, A.R. Kirincich, M.A. McManus, K.J. Nielsen, S.D. Pierce, and L. Washburn. 2007. Delayed upwelling alters nearshore coastal ocean ecosystems in the northern California current. *Proceedings of the National Academy of Sciences* 104(10): 3719-3724.

Boer, G.J., B. Yu, S.-J. Kim, and G.M. Flato. 2004. Is there observational support for an El Niño-like pattern of future global warming? *Geophysical Research Letters* 31(L06201).

Boyd, P.W., T. Jickells, C.S. Law, S. Blain, E.A. Boyle, K.O. Buesseler, K.H. Coale, J.J. Cullen, H.J.W. de Baar, M. Follows, M. Harvey, C. Lancelot, M. Levasseur, N.P.J. Owens, R. Pollard, R.B. Rivkin, J. Sarmiento, V. Schoemann, V. Smetacek, S. Takeda, A. Tsuda, S. Turner, and A.J. Watson. 2007. Mesoscale iron enrichment experiments 1993-2005: Synthesis and future directions. *Science* 315(5812):612-617.

Bryan, F.O., G. Danabasoglu, N. Nakashiki, Y. Yoshida, D.-H. Kim, J. Tsutsui, and S.C. Doney. 2006. Response of the North Atlantic thermohaline circulation and ventilation to increasing carbon dioxide in CCSM3. *Journal of Climate* 19(11): 2382-2397, http://www.whoi.edu/science/MCG/doneylab/papers/i1520-0442-19-11-2382.pdf

Buesseler, K.O., S.C. Doney, D.M. Karl, P.W. Boyd, K. Caldeira, F. Chai, K.H. Coale, H.J.W. de Baar, P.G. Falkowski, K.S. Johnson, R.S. Lampitt, A.F. Michaels, S.W.A. Naqvi, V. Smetacek, S. Takeda, and A.J. Watson. 2008. Ocean iron fertilization–Moving forward in a sea of uncertainty. *Science* 319(5860):162.

Clarke, A. and C.M. Harris. 2003. Polar marine ecosystems: Major threats and future change. *Environmental Conservation* 30(1):1-25.

Clarke, A., E.J. Murphy, M.P. Meredith, J.C. King, L.S. Peck, D.K.A. Barnes, and R.C. Smith. 2007. Climate change and the marine ecosystem of the western Antarctic Peninsula. *Philosophical Transactions of the Royal Society B* 362(1477):149-166.

Colosi, J.A. and W. Munk. 2006. Tales of the venerable Honolulu tide gauge. *Journal of Physical Oceanography* 36(6):967-996.

Doney, S.C. 2006. The dangers of ocean acidification. *Scientific American* 294(3): 58-65, http://www.planktos.com/pdf/TheDangersOfOceanAcidification.pdf

Ducklow, H.W., K. Baker, D.G. Martinson, L.B. Quetin, R.M. Ross, R.C. Smith, S.E. Stammerjohn, M. Vernet, and W. Fraser. 2007. Marine pelagic ecosystems: The West Antarctic Peninsula. *Philosophical Transactions of the Royal Society B* 362(1477):67-94, http://pubmedcentral.nih.gov/articlerender.fcgi?artid=1764834

Eakin, C.M., J.A. Morgan, and the Caribbean Bleaching Collaboration. Record-setting coral bleaching: The result of thermal stress (in preparation).

Edgar, G.J., S. Banks, R.H. Bustamante, A. Chiriboga, S.A. Earle, L. Garske, P.W. Glynn, S. Henderson, C.P. Hickman, K.A. Miller, F. Rivera, and G. Wellington. El Niño, sea urchins, and fisheries: Interactive threats to marine species in Galapagos (in press).

Feely, R.A., C.L. Sabine, K. Lee, W. Berelson, J. Kleypas, V.J. Fabry, and F.J. Millero. 2004. Impact of anthropogenic CO_2 on the $CaCO_3$ system in the oceans. *Science* 305(5682):362-366, http://www.pmel.noaa.gov/pubs/outstand/feel2633/feel2633.shtml

Ferguson, S.H., I. Stirling, and P. McLoughlin. 2005. Climate change and ringed seal (*Phoca hispida*) recruitment in western Hudson Bay. *Marine Mammal Science* 21 (1): 121-135.

Guinotte, J.M., J. Orr, S. Cairns, A. Freiwald, L. Morgan, and R. George. 2006. Will human-induced changes in seawater chemistry alter the distribution of deep-sea scleractinian corals? *Frontiers in Ecology and the Environment* 4(3):141-146, http://www.mcbi.org/publications/pub_pdfs/Guinotte_at_al_2006.pdf

Hawkes, L.A., A.C. Broderick, M.H. Godfrey, and B.J. Godley. 2007. Investigating the potential impacts of climate change on a marine turtle population. *Global Change Biology* 13(5):923-932.

IIED (International Institute for Environment and Development). 2007. Climate, carbon, conservation, and communities. IIED/WWF briefing, www.iied.org/pubs/pdfs/17011IIED.pdf

IPCC (International Panel on Climate Change). 2007. *The physical science basis: Summary for policymakers.* Contribution of Working Group I to the Fourth Assessment Report of the Intergovernmental Panel on Climate Change. Cambridge, U.K. and New York: Cambridge University Press, http://www.ipcc.ch

Kleypas, J.A., R.A. Feely, V.J. Fabry, C. Langdon, C.L. Sabine, and L.L. Robbins. 2006. *Impacts of ocean acidification on coral reefs and other marine calcifiers: A guide for future research.* Report from workshop held April 18-20, 2005, St. Petersburg, FL. Sponsored by NSF, NOAA, and the U.S. Geological Survey.

Levitus, S., J. Antonov, and T. Boyer. 2005. Warming of the world ocean, 1955-2003. *Geophysical Research Letters* 32(L02604).

Manabe, S. and R.J. Stouffer. 1994. Multiple-century response of a coupled ocean-atmosphere model to an increase of atmospheric carbon dioxide. *Journal of Climate* 7(1):5-23, http://ams.allenpress.com/archive/1520-0442/7/1/pdf/i1520-0442-7-1-5.pdf

Mast, R.B., ed. 2006. *The state of the world's sea turtles.* Vol. 1, www.seaturtlestatus.org

Mast, R.B., ed. 2007. *The state of the world's sea turtles.* Vol. 2, www.seaturtlestatus.org

McGranahan, G., D. Balk, and B. Anderson. 2007. The rising tide: Assessing the risks of climate change and human settlements in low elevation coastal zones. *Environment and Urbanization* 19(1):17-37, http://sedac.ciesin.columbia.edu/gpw/docs/McGranahan2007.pdf

McMahon, C.R. and G.C. Hays. 2006. Thermal niche, large-scale movements and implications of climate change for a critically endangered marine vertebrate. *Global Change Biology* 12 (7):1330-1338, http://www.swan.ac.uk/bs/turtle/reprints/McMahon&Hays_GCB_2006.pdf

Nerem, R.S., E. Leuliette, and A. Cazenave. 2006. Present-day sea-level change: A review. *C.R. Geosciences* 338(14-15):1077-1083.

OECD (Organisation for Economic Co-operation and Development). 2003. Development and climate change in Fiji: Focus on coastal mangroves, www.oecd.org/dataoecd/46/58/21056315.pdf

Orr, J.C., V.J. Fabry, O. Aumont, L. Bopp, S.C. Doney, R.A. Feely, A. Gnanadesikan, N. Gruber, A. Ishida, F. Joos, R.M. Key, K. Lindsay, E.M. Maier-Reimer, R. Matear, P. Monfray, A. Mouchet, R.G. Najjar, G-K. Plattner, K.B. Rodgers, C.L. Sabine, J. L. Sarmiento, R. Schlitzer, R.D. Slater, I.J. Totterdell, M-F. Weirig, Y. Yamanaka, and A. Yool. 2005. Anthropogenic ocean acidification over the twenty-first century and its impact on calcifying organisms. *Nature* 437:681-686, http://www.ipsl.jussieu.fr/~jomce/acidification/paper/Orr_OnlineNature04095.pdf

Overland, J.E. and M. Wang. 2007. Future regional Arctic sea ice declines. *Geophysical Research Letters* 34(L17705).

Perry, A.L., P.J. Low, J.R. Ellis, and J.D. Reynolds. 2005. Climate change and distribution shifts in marine fishes. *Science* 308(5730):1912-1915.

Rahmstorf, S. 2007. A semi-empirical approach to projecting future sea-level rise. *Science* 315(5810):368-370.

Riebesell, U., I. Zondervan, B. Rost, P.D. Tortell, R.E. Zeebe, and F.M.M. Morel. 2000. Reduced calcification of marine plankton in response to increased atmospheric CO_2. *Nature* 407:364-367.

Robinson et al. 2006. Climate change and migratory species extended summary from Defra. In *Migratory species and climate change: Impacts of a changing environment on wild animals.* Pp. 46-57. Heidrun Frisch, ed. Bonn, Germany: UNEP/CMS.

Sabine, C.L., R.A. Feely, N. Gruber, R.M. Key, K. Lee, J.L. Bullister, R. Wanninkhof, C.S. Wong, D.W.R. Wallace, B. Tilbrook, F.J. Millero, T-H. Peng, A. Kozyr, T. Ono, and A.F. Rios. 2004. The oceanic sink for anthropogenic CO_2. *Science* 305(5682):367-371, http://www.gfdl.noaa.gov/reference/bibliography/2004/cls0401.pdf

Seager, R., D.S. Battisti, J. Yin, N. Gordon, N. Naik, A.C. Clement, and M.A. Cane. 2002. Is the Gulf Stream responsible for Europe's mild winters? *Quarterly Journal of the Royal Meteorological Society* 128(586):2563-2586, http://www.ldeo.columbia.edu/res/div/ocp/gs/pubs/Seager_etal_QJ_2002.pdf

Serreze, M.C., M.M. Holland, and J. Stroeve. 2007. Perspectives on the Arctic's shrinking sea-ice cover. *Science* 315(5818):1533-1536.

Sheppard, C.R.C. 2003. Predicted recurrences of mass coral mortality in the Indian Ocean. *Nature* 425:294-297.

Siedler, G., J. Church, and J. Gould, eds. 2001. *Ocean circulation and climate: Observing and modeling the global ocean.* International Geophysics Series 77. London: Academic Press.

Stirling, I. and C.L. Parkinson. 2006. Possible effects of climate warming on selected populations of polar bears (*Ursus maritimus*) in the Canadian Arctic. *Arctic* 59(3):261-275.

Trenberth, K.E. and J.M. Caron. 2001. Estimates of meridional atmosphere and ocean heat transports. *Journal of Climate* 14:3433-3443, http://www.cgd.ucar.edu/cas/papers/jclim2001a/transpts.html

Willis, J.K., D. Roemmich, and B. Cornuelle. 2004. Interannual variability in upper-ocean heat content, temperature, and thermosteric expansion on global scales. *Journal of Geophysical Research* 109(C12036), http://www-argo.ucsd.edu/globalhc_final.pdf

Wormworth, J. and K. Mallon. 2006. Bird species and climate change: The global status report version 1.0. A report to World Wide Fund for Nature.

Human Dimensions

Ackerman, Frank. 2007. *Debating climate economics: The Stern review vs. its critics.* Global Development and Environment Institute, Tufts University, www.ase.tufts.edu/gdae/Pubs/rp/SternDebateReport.pdf

Association of British Insurers. 2005. *Financial risks of climate change.* London, England. http://www.abi.org.uk/Display/File/Child/552/Financial_Risks_of_Climate_Change.pdf

Bindoff, N.L., J. Willebrand, V. Artale, A, Cazenave, J. Gregory, S. Gulev, K. Hanawa, C. Le Quéré, S. Levitus, Y. Nojiri, C.K. Shum, L.D. Talley, and A. Unnikrishnan. 2007. Observations: Oceanic climate change and sea level. In *Climate change 2007: The physical science basis.* Contribution of Working Group I to the Fourth Assessment Report of the Intergovernmental Panel on Climate Change. S. Solomon, D. Qin, M. Manning, Z. Chen, M. Marquis, K.B. Averyt, M. Tignor, and H.L. Miller, eds. Cambridge, United Kingdom and New York: Cambridge University Press. http://www.ipcc.ch/pdf/assessment-report/ar4/wg1/ar4-wg1-chapter5.pdf

Brahmbhatt, Heena, G. Kigozi, F. Wabwire-Mangen, D. Serwadda, N. Sewankambo, T. Lutalo, M. Wawer, C. Abramowsky, D. Sullivan, R. Gray. 2003. The effects of placental malaria on mother-to-child HIV transmission in Rakai, Uganda. *AIDS.* 17: 21 November, Pp. 2539-41.

Cline, W.R. 2007. *Global warming and agriculture: New country estimates show developing countries face declines in agricultural productivity.* Washington, DC: Center for Global Development, http://www.cgdev.org/content/publications/detail/14425

Cline, W.R. 1992. *The Economics of global warming.* Washington, DC: Institute for International Economics.

CNA Corporation. 2007. *National security and climate change.* http://securityandclimate.cna.org/

Combes, S. 2005. *Are we putting our fish in hot water?* Gland, Switzerland: World Wildlife Fund.

Confalonieri, U., B. Menne, R. Akhtar, K.L. Ebi, M. Hauengue, R.S. Kovats, B. Revich, and A. Woodward. 2007. *Human health. Climate change 2007: Impacts, adaptation and vulnerability.* Contribution of Working Group II to the Fourth Assessment Report of the Intergovernmental Panel on Climate Change. M.L. Parry, O.F. Canziani, J.P. Palutikof, P.J. van der Linden, and C.E. Hanson, eds. Pp. 391-431. Cambridge, UK: Cambridge University Press.

Daily, G.C. and K. Ellison. 2002. *The New Economy of Nature: The Quest to Make Conservation Profitable.* Washington, DC: Island Press.

Danielsen, F., M.K. Sorensen, M.F. Owling, V. Selvam, F. Parish, N.D. Burgess, T. Hiraishi, V.M. Karunagaran, M.S. Rasmussen, L.B. Hansen, A. Quarto, and N. Suryadiputra. 2005. The Asian tsunami: A protective role for coastal vegetation. *Science.* 310 (28): 643.

Dasgupta, S., B. Laplante, C. Meisner, D. Wheeler, D. Jianping Yan. 2007. *The impact of sea level rise on developing countries: A comparative analysis.* World Bank Policy Research Working Paper No. 4136. Washington, DC.

Emanuel, K., R. Sundararajan, and J. Williams. 2008. Hurricanes and global warming: Results from downscaling IPCC AR4 simulations. *Bull. Amer. Meteor. Soc.* 89: 347-367.

Epstein, P.R. and E. Mills. 2005. *Climate change futures: Health, ecological and economic dimensions.* Boston: The Center for Health and the Global Environment, Harvard Medical School. Available online at: www.climatechangefutures.org/pdf/CCF_Report_Final_10.27.pdf

Giorgi, F. and X. Bi. 2005. Updated regional precipitation and temperature changes for the 21st century from ensemples of recent AOGCM simulations. *Geophysical Research Letters*, L21715

Gleditsch, Nils, T. Petter, K.F. Owen, and B. Lacina. 2004. *Conflicts over shared rivers: Resource wars or fuzzy boundaries?* Paper presented to the 45th annual convention of the International Studies Association, 17 March, Montreal, http://www.prio.no/files/file45233_isa_proceeding_14244.pdf

Hansen, James. 2007. Scientific reticence and sea level rise, *Environmental Research Letters* 2, 024002, May 24, 2007, http://stacks.iop.org/ERL/2/024002

Harvey, Fiona and Jim Pickard. 2008. Stern takes bleaker view on warming. *Financial Times.* Published April 16, 2008. Accessed from: http://www.ft.com/cms/s/0/d3e78456-0bde-11dd-9840-0000779fd2ac,dwp_uuid=728a07a0-53bc-11db-8a2a-0000779e2340.html?nclick_check=1

Höppe, Peter and Roger Pielke Jr. 2006. *Climate change and disaster losses workshop: Understanding and attributing trends and projections.* Sponsored by Munich Re, U.S. National Science Foundation, Tyndall Center for Climate Change Research, and GKSS Research Center, May 25-26, 2006, http://sciencepolicy.colorado.edu/sparc/research/projects/extreme_events/munich_workshop/workshop_report.html

Intergovernmental Panel on Climate Change (IPCC). 2007. Summary for policymakers. Pp 7-22. in *Climate change 2007: Impacts, adaptation and vulnerability.* Contribution of Working Group II to the Fourth Assessment Report of the Intergovernmental Panel on Climate Change. M.L. Parry, O.F. Canziani, J.P. Palutikof, P.J. van der Linden, and C.E. Hanson, eds. Cambridge UK: Cambridge University Press. Available online at: http://www.ipcc.ch/pdf/assessment-report/ar4/wg2/ar4-wg2-spm.pdf

International Federation of Red Cross and Red Crescent Societies (IFRC). 2003. *World disasters report 2002.* IFRC: Geneva, Switzerland.

Kahn, M.E. 2005. The death toll from natural disasters: The role of income, geography, and institutions. *Atmospheric Environment.* 39:509–520.

Klare, Michael. 2002. *Resource wars: The new landscape of global conflict.* New York, NY: Holt Paperbacks.

Mcgranahan, G., D. Balk, and B. Anderson. 2007. The rising tide: Assessing the risks of climate change and human settlements in low elevation coastal zones. *Environment and Urbanization.* 19(1): 17–37.

Nicholls, R.J., P.P. Wong, V.R. Burkett, J.O. Codignotto, J.E. Hay, R.F. McLean, S. Ragoonaden, and C.D. Woodroffe. 2007. Coastal systems and low-lying areas. Pp 315-356. In *Climate change 2007: Impacts, adaptation and vulnerability.* Contribution of Working Group II to the Fourth assessment report of the Intergovernmental Panel on Climate Change. M.L. Parry, O.F. Canziani, J.P. Palutikof, P.J. van der Linden, and C.E. Hanson, eds. Cambridge UK: Cambridge University Press. Available online at: http://www.ipcc.ch/pdf/assessment-report/ar4/wg2/ar4-wg2-chapter6.pdf

Oppenheimer M., B. O'Neill, M. Webster, and S. Agrawala. 2007. Climate change: The limits of consensus. *Science.* 317: 1505-1506.

Pascual, M., J. A. Ahumada, L.F. Chaves, X. Rodó, and M. Bouma. 2006. Malaria resurgence in the East African highlands: Temperature trends revisited. *Proceedings of the National Academy of Sciences.* 103:5829–5834. www.pnas.org/cgi/content/short/103/15/5829

Pattanayak, S.K., C.G. Corey, Y.F. Lau, and R. Kramer. 2005. *Conservation and health: A microeconomic study of forest protection and child malaria in Flores, Indonesia.* RTI Working Paper. Research Triangle Institute, North Carolina.

Poverty-Environment Partnership. 2003. *Poverty and climate change: Reducing the vulnerability of the poor through adaptation.* A joint publication prepared by African Development Bank; Asian Development Bank; Department for International Development, UK; Directorate General for Development, European Commission; Federal Ministry for Economic Cooperation and Development, Germany; Ministry of Foreign Affairs—Development Cooperation, The Netherlands; Organisation for Economic Cooperation and Development; United Nations Development Programme; United Nations Environment Programme, The World Bank. http://www.energyandenvironment.undp.org/undp/index.cfm?module=Library&page=Document&DocumentID=5050

Rahmstorf, Stefan. 2007. A semi-empirical approach to projecting future sea-level rise, *Science.* 315: 5810, 368-70.

Repetto, R., W. Magrath, M. Wells, C. Beer, F. Rossini. 1989. *Wasting assets: Natural resources in the national income accounts.* World Resources Institute.

Simms, Andrew. 2006. *Up in smoke? Latin America and the Caribbean: the threat from climate change to the environment and human development.* Third report from the Working Group on Climate Change and Development. London: New Economics Foundation.

Stern, N. 2006. *The economics of climate change: The Stern review.* Cambridge, UK: Cambridge University Press. Available online at: http://www.hm-treasury.gov.uk/ independent_reviews/stern_review_economics_climate_change/sternreview_index.cfm

Sterner, T., and U.M. Persson. 2007. *An even Sterner review: Introducing relative prices into the discounting debate.* Resources for the Future discussion paper RFF DP 07-37, July. Available online at: www.rff.org/Documents/RFF-DP-07-37.pdf

Struck, D. 2006. On the roof of Peru, omens in the ice retreat of once-mighty glacier signals water crisis, mirroring worldwide trend. *Washington Post* Foreign Service. Saturday, July 29, 2006. Pg. A01.

Teagasc. 2007. Declining bee numbers raise concerns over plant pollination. *ScienceDaily.* Retrieved October 30, 2007, from http://www.sciencedaily.com/releases/2007/05/070510114621.htm

Telford, John, Margaret Arnold, and Alberto Harth, with ASONOG. 2004. *Learning lessons from disaster recovery: The case of Honduras.* Disaster risk management working paper series, no. 8. Washington, DC: The World Bank.

United Nations Development Programme (UNDP). 2007. *Human development report 2007: Climate change and human development—Rising to the challenge.* Palgrave Macmillan. Available online at: http://hdr.undp.org/en/reports/global/hdr2007-2008/

United Nations Development Programme (UNDP). 2004. *Reducing disaster risk: A challenge for development.* New York, www.undp.org/bcpr

Vittor, Amy, R.H. Gilman, J. Tielsch, G. Glass, T. Shields, W.S. Lozano, V. Pinedo-Cancino, and J.A. Patz. 2006. The effect of deforestation on the human-biting rate of *Anopheles darlingi,* the primary vector of *Falciparum* malaria in the Peruvian Amazon. *American Journal of Tropical Medicine and Hygiene.* 74(1): 3–11, www.ajtmh.org/

Watson, Robert T., Ian R. Noble, Bert Bolin, N.H. Ravindranath, David J. Verardo, and David J. Dokken. *IPCC special report on land use, land-use change and forestry.* 2000. Cambridge UK: Cambridge University Press. Available online at: http://www.grida.no/climate/ipcc/land_use/index.htm

WBGU. 2008. *World in transition: Climate change as a security risk,* Wissenschaftliche Beirat der Bundesregierung Globale Umweltveränderungen (German Advisory Council on Global Change), Earthscan. Available online at: http://www.wbgu.de

Weitzman, Martin. 2007. The Stern review of economics of climate change. Book review for the *Journal of Economic Literature*, April 31, 2007. American Economics Association.

World Bank. 2004. *Environment matters.* Washington, DC: The World Bank.

World Bank. 1997. *Clean water, blue skies – China's environment in the new century.* Washington, DC: The World Bank. Available online at: www.worldbank.org/

Tipping Points

ACIA. 2005. *Arctic climate impact assessment.* Cambridge University Press, 1042 pp, http://www.acia.uaf.edu/pages/scientific.html

Aldhous, P. 2004. Borneo is burning. *Nature.* 432: 144-146.

Archer, D. 2007. Methane hydrate stability and anthropogenic climate change. *Biogeosciences.* 4:521–544. July 25, 2007, http://geosci.uchicago.edu/~archer/reprints/archer.2007.hydrate_rev.pdf

Archer, D. 2006. *Destabilization of methane hydrates: A risk analysis.* Report prepared for the German Advisory Council on Global Change. October, www.wbgu.de/wbgu_sn2006_ex01.pdf

Archer, D. 2005. The fate of fossil fuel CO_2 in geologic time. *Journal of Geophysical Research.* doi:10.1029/2004JC002625, http://geosci.uchicago.edu/~archer/reprints/archer.ms.fate_co2.pdf

Archer, D. and B. Buffett. 2005. Time-dependent response of the global ocean clathrate reservoir to climatic and anthropogenic forcing. *Geochemistry, Geophysics, Geosystems.* 6, Q03002, doi:10.1029/2004GC000854.

Buffett, B. and D. Archer. 2004. Global inventory of methane clathrate: Sensitivity to changes in the deep ocean. *Earth and Planetary Science Letters.* 227: 185–199, http://geosci.uchicago.edu/~archer/reprints/buffett.2004.clathrates.pdf

Canadell, J.G., D. Pataki, R. Gifford, R. Houghton, Y. Luo, M. Raupach, P. Smith, and W. Steffen. 2007. Saturation of the terrestrial carbon sink. Chap. 6 in: *Terrestrial ecosystems in a changing world.* J.G. Canadell, D. Pataki, L. Pitelka, eds. The IGBP Series. Berlin: Springer-Verlag. www.globalcarbonproject.org/global/pdf/Canadell.2007.SinkSaturation.Springer.pdf

Canadell, J.G., C. Field, C. Lequere, N. Nakicenovic, and M. Raupach. 2006. Vulnerabilities of the global carbon cycle in the 21st century, global carbon project activity overview and progress. August 23, 2006, www.globalcarbonproject.org/global/doc/VulnerabilityActivityReport2006-07.doc

Cox, P., R. Betts, C.D. Jones, S.A. Spall, and I.J. Totterdell. 2000. Acceleration of global warming due to carbon-cycle feedbacks in a coupled climate model. *Nature.* 408: 184–187.

Davidson, E.A. and I.A. Janssens. 2006. Temperature sensitivity of soil carbon decomposition and feedbacks to climate change. *Nature.* 440: 165-173, March 9, 2006.

Dyurgerov, M.B. and M.F. Meier. 2005. Glaciers and the changing earth system: A 2004 snapshot.

Occasional Paper 58. Boulder, CO: Institute of Arctic and Alpine Research, University of Colorado, http://instaar.colorado.edu/other/occ_papers.html

Forster, P., V. Ramaswamy, P. Artaxo, T. Berntsen, R. Betts, D.W. Fahey, J. Haywood, J. Lean, D.C. Lowe, G. Myhre, J. Nganga, R. Prinn, G. Raga, M. Schulz, and R. Van Dorland. 2007: Changes in atmospheric constituents and in radiative forcing. In *Climate change 2007: The physical science basis.* Contribution of Working Group I to the Fourth Assessment Report of the Intergovernmental Panel on Climate Change. S. Solomon, D. Qin, M. Manning, Z. Chen, M. Marquis, K.B. Averyt, M.Tignor, and H.L. Miller, eds. Cambridge, UK and New York: Cambridge University Press, http://www.ipcc.ch/pdf/assessment-report/ar4/wg1/ar4-wg1-chapter2.pdf

Gregory, J.M., P. Huybrechts, and S.C.B. Raper. 2004. Climatology: Threatened loss of the Greenland ice-sheet, *Nature.* 428: 616.

Gruber, N., P. Friedlingstein, C.B. Field, R. Valentini, M. Heimann, J.F. Richey, P. Romero, E.-D. Schulze, and A. Chen. 2004. The vulnerability of the carbon cycle in the 21st Century: An assessment of carbon–climate–human interactions. In *Global carbon cycle: Integrating human, climate, and the natural world.* C.B. Field and M. Raupach, eds. Pp. 45–76. Washington, DC: Island Press.

Hansen, J., Mki. Sato, R. Ruedy, K. Lo, D.W. Lea, and M. Medina-Elizade. 2006. Global temperature change. *Proceedings of the National Academy of Sciences.* 103, 14288-14293, doi:10.1073/pnas.0606291103, http://pubs.giss.nasa.gov/abstracts/2006/Hansen_etal_1.html

Intergovernmental Panel on Climate Change (IPCC). 2000. Special report on emission scenarios. Nebojsa Nakicenovic and Rob Swart, eds. Intergovernmental Panel on Climate Change, www.ipcc.ch/pdf/special-reports/spm/sres-en.pdf

Jorgenson, M.T., C.H. Racine, J.C. Walters, and T.E. Osterkamp. 2001. Permafrost degradation and ecological changes associated with a warming climate in central Alaska. *Climatic Change.* 48(4):551-579.

Jorgenson, M.T., and T.E. Osterkamp. 2005. Response of boreal ecosystems to varying modes of permafrost degradation. *Canadian Journal of Forest Research.* 35:2100-2111.

Jorgenson, M.T., Y.L. Shur, and E R. Pullman. 2006. Abrupt increase in permafrost degradation in Arctic Alaska, *Geophysical Research Letters*, 33, L02503, doi:10.1029/2005GL024960

Knorr, W., I.C. Prentice, J.I. House, and E.A. Holland. 2005. Long-term sensitivity of soil carbon turnover to warming. *Nature.* 433: 299-301.

Krabill, W., E. Hanna, P. Huybrechts, W. Abdalati, J. Cappelen, B. Csatho, E. Frederick, S. Manizade, C. Martin, J. Sonntag, R. Swift, R. Thomas, and J. Yungel. 2004. Greenland ice sheet: Increased coastal thinning. *Geophysical Research Letters.* 31: L24402, doi:10.1029/2004GL021533.

Lawrence, D.M. and A.G. Slater. 2005. A projection of severe near-surface permafrost degradation during the 21st century. *Geophysical Research Letters.* 32: L24401.

Lenton, T.M., H. Held, E. Kriegler, J. Hall, W. Lucht, S. Rahmstorf, and H. Schellnhuber. 2008. Tipping elements in the Earth's climate system. *Proceedings of the National Academy of Sciences.* 105: no. 6, pp. 1786-1793, Feb. 14, 2008, www.pnas.org/

Li, Wenhong, R. Dickinson, R. Fu, G. Niu, Z. Yang, and J. Canadell. 2007. Future precipitation changes and their implications for tropical peatlands, *Geophysical Research Letters.* 34: L01403. www.globalcarbonproject.org/global/pdf/Wenhong.2007.FuturePreciptTropicalPeatlands.GRL.pdf

McGuire, A.D., F.S. Chapin III, J.E. Walsh, and C. Wirth. 2006. Integrated regional changes in arctic climate feedbacks: Implications for the global climate system. *Annual Review of Environment and Resources.* 31:61-91.

McGuire, A.D., L.G. Anderson, T.R. Christiansen, S. Dallimore, L. Guou, D. Hayes, M. Heimann, T. Lorenson, R.W. Macdonald, and N. Roulet. 2008. Sensitivity of the carbon cycle in the Arctic to climate change. Arctic Carbon Cycle Synthesis Project, National Science Foundation review Paper.

Meinshausen, M. 2007. Emission pathways and concentration levels under a 2°C climate target. Presentation at thematic session on "Climate impact of different levels of warming," Temporary Committee on Climate Change, European Parliament. September 10, 2007, www.europarl.europa.eu/comparl/tempcom/clim/sessions/20070910/meinshausen_en.pdf

Meinshausen, M. 2005. On the risk of overshooting 2 degrees C, Avoiding dangerous climate change. International Symposium on the Stabilisation of greenhouse gas concentrations. Hadley Centre, Met Office. Exeter, UK. February 1-3, 2005, www.stabilisation2005.com/programme.html.

Murdiyarso, D. and L. Lebel. 2007. Local to global perspectives on forest and land fires in Southeast Asia. *Mitigation and Adaption Strategies for Global Change.* 12(1): 3-11.

Oppenheimer, M. and R.B. Alley. 2004. The West Antarctic ice sheet and long term climate policy. *Climatic Change.* 64: 1-10.

Osterkamp, T.E. 2007. Characteristics of the recent warming of permafrost in Alaska. *Journal of Geophysical Research.* 112, F02S02, doi:10.1029/2006JF000578

Page, S.E., R.A.J. Wüst, D. Weiss, J.O. Rieley, W. Shotyk, and S. Limin. 2004. A record of Late Pleistocene and Holocene carbon accumulation and climate change from an equatorial peat bog (Kalimantan, Indonesia): Implications for past, present and future carbon dynamics. *Journal of Quaternary Science.* 19: 625-635.

Peterson, B.J., J. McClelland, R. Curry, R.M. Holmes, J.E. Walsh, and K. Aagaard. 2006. Trajectory shifts in the arctic and subarctic freshwater cycle. *Science.* 313:5790, 1061–1066.

Population Reference Bureau (PRB). 2001. Understanding and using population projections. December 2001, www.prb.org/Publications/PolicyBriefs/UnderstandingandUsingPopulationProjections.aspx

Rahmstorf, S. 2006. Thermohaline ocean circulation. In *Encyclopedia of Quaternary Sciences.*, S.A. Elias, ed. Elsevier, Amsterdam, www.pik-potsdam.de/~stefan/thc_fact_sheet.html

Raupach, M.R. and J.G. Canadell. 2006. Observing a vulnerable carbon cycle. In *Observing the continental scale greenhouse gas balance of Europe.* Chap. 3. Ecological Studies. H. Dolman, A. Freibauer, and R. Valentini, eds. 2007. New York: Springer-Verlag.

Sabine C.L., M. Heimann, P. Artaxo, D.C.E. Bakker, C-T.A. Chen, C.B. Field, N. Gruber, C. Le Quéré, R.G. Prinn, J.D. Richey, P.R. Lankao, J. Sathaye, and R. Valentini. 2004. Current status and past trend in the global carbon cycle. In *The global carbon cycle: Integrating humans, climate, and the natural world.* C.B.Field and M.R. Raupach, eds. Pp. 17–44. Washington, DC: Island Press.

Schmidt, G. 2004. Methane: A scientific journey from obscurity to climate super-stardom. NASA Goddard Institute for Space Studies, September 2004, http://www.giss.nasa.gov/research/features/methane/

Shur, Y.L. and M.T. Jorgenson. 2007. Patterns of permafrost formation and degradation in relation to climate and ecosystems. *Permafrost and Periglacial Processes.* 18:1, 7–19, February 22, 2007.

Stroeve, J., M. Holland, M. Serreze, and T. Scambos. 2007. Arctic sea ice decline: Faster than forecast? *Journal of Geophysical Research.* 34: L09501, doi: 10.1029/2007GL029703, European Geosciences Union.

Sturm, M., D.K. Perovich, and M.C. Serreze. 2003. Meltdown in the north. *Scientific American.* 289(4):42-48.

UNESCO-SCOPE. 2006. The global carbon cycle. UNESCO-SCOPE Policy Briefs. October 2006 – No. 2. Paris: UNESCO-Scientific Committee on Problems of the Environment, http://www.icsu-scope.org/Unesco_scope.htm

Walker, G. 2007. A world melting from the top down. *Nature.* 446: 718-721.

Walter, K.M., S.A. Zimov, J.P. Chanton, D. Verbyla, and F.S. Chapin III. 2006. Methane bubbling from Siberian thaw lakes as a positive feedback to climate warming. *Nature.* 443: 71-75.

Ward, P.D. 2007. *Under a green sky: Global warming, the mass extinctions of the past, and what they can tell us about our future.* New York: Harper Collins.

Ward, P.D. 2006. Impact from the deep. *Scientific American.* October. Pp. 65-71, www.sciam.com/

Watson, R. 2007. The impacts of global warming. Presentation at thematic session on Climate impact of different levels of warming. Temporary Committee on Climate Change, European Parliament. September 10, 2007, http://www.europarl.europa.eu/comparl/tempcom/clim/sessions/default_en.htm

WGBU. 2006. *The future oceans – Warming up, rising High, turning sour.* Special report. German Advisory Council on Global Change (Wissenschaftlicher Beirat der Bundesregierung Globale Umweltveränderungen), http://www.wbgu.de

Zimov, S.A., E.A.G. Schuur, and F.S. Chapin III. 2006. Permafrost and the global carbon budget. *Science.* 312:612-613.

A Call to Action

Bordetsky, A., S. Casey-Lefkowitz, D. Lovaas, E. Martin-Perera, M. Nakagawa, B. Randall, D. Woynillowicz. 2007. *Driving it home: Choosing the right path for fueling North America's transportation future.* A joint report by the Natural Resources Defense Council, Western Resource Advocates and Pembina Institute, www.nrdc.org/energy/drivingithome/drivingithome.pdf

Canadell, Joséph G., D.E. Pataki, R. Gifford, R.A. Houghton, Y. Luo, M.R. Raupach, P. Smith, W. Steffen. 2007. Saturation of the terrestrial carbon sink. Chap. 6 in *Terrestrial ecosystems in a changing world.* J.G. Canadell, D. Pataki, L. Pitelka, eds. The IGBP Series. Berlin: Springer-Verlag, www.globalcarbonproject.org/global/pdf/Canadell.2007.SinkSaturation.Springer.pdf

Capoor, K. and P. Ambrosi. 2007. State and trends of the carbon market 2007. Washington, DC: International Emissions Trading Association and The World Bank, http://carbonfinance.org/docs/Carbon_Trends_2007-_FINAL_-_May_2.pdf

CCBA. 2008. The climate, community & biodiversity project design standards. Climate, Community & Biodiversity Alliance, www.climate-standards.org/

Conference Board. 2008. Use green taxes and market instruments to reduce greenhouse gas emissions. The Conference Board of Canada. http://sso.conferenceboard.ca/e-Library/LayoutAbstract.asp?DID=2426

Cowart, R. 2007. Resource choices in a carbon-constrained world. National Association of Regulatory Utility Commissioners (NARUC) annual meeting, November 12, 2007, www.raponline.org/

Danielsen, F., M.K. Sørensen, M.F. Olwig, V. Selvam, F. Parish, N.D. Burgess, T.Hiraishi, V.M. Karunagaran, M.S. Rasmussen, L.B. Hansen, A. Quarto, N. Suryadiputra. 2005. The Asian Tsunami: A Protective Role for Coastal Vegetation. *Science* 310:643.

EIA, International Energy Outlook. 2007. Energy Information Administration. http://www.eia.doe.gov/oiaf/ieo/pdf/0484(2007).pdf

FAO, Global Forest Resources Assessment. 2005. Progress towards sustainable forest management FAO Forestry. Paper (FAO). 0258-6150, no. 147, UN Food and Agriculture Organization.

Fargione, Joséph, J. Hill, D. Tilman, S. Polasky, P. Hawthorne. 2008. Land clearing and the biofuel carbon debt, *Science Express.* 10.1126/science.1152747. www.sciencexpress.org/

Farrell, A.E. and A.R. Brandt. 2006. Risks of the oil transition. *Environmental Research Letters,* October 30, http://www.iop.org/EJ/abstract/1748-9326/1/1/014004/

da Fonseca, Gustavo A.B., C.M. Rodríguez, G. Midgley, J. Busch, L. Hannah, R.A. Mittermeier. 2007. No Forest Left Behind. *PLoS Biology.* 5, issue 8: 1645-1646. http://biology.plosjournals.org/archive/1545-7885/5/8/pdf/10.1371_journal.pbio.0050216-S.pdf

Gitay, Habiba, A. Suárez, R.T. Watson. D. Dokken. 2002. Climate Change and Biodiversity. IPCC Technical Paper V, April 2002, Intergovernmental Panel on Climate Change, www.ipcc.ch/pdf/technical-papers/climate-changes-biodiversity-en.pdf

Hamilton, Katherine, R. Bayon, G. Turner, D. Higgins. 2007. State of the voluntary carbon markets 2007: *Picking up steam.* July 18, 2007. Joint report by New Carbon Finance and The Ecosystem Marketplace, http://www.carbon.sref.info/an-example/market-news

Hansen, J., M. Sato, P. Kharecha, D. Beerling, V. Masson-Delmotte, M. Pagani, M. Raymo, D. Royer, J. Zachos. 2008. Target atmospheric CO_2: Where should humanity aim? Goddard Institute of Space Studies, NASA. Main paper can be found at http://arxiv.org/abs/0804.1126 and the supporting material at http://arxiv.org/abs/0804.1135

Houghton, R.A. 2005. Tropical deforestation as a source of greenhouse gas emissions. In *Tropical deforestation and climate change.* Paolo Moutinho and Stephen Schwartzman, eds. Instituto de Pesquisa Ambiental da Amazônia, http://ibcperu.nuxit.net/doc/isis/5748.pdf

IFAD. 2001. *Rural poverty report 2001—The challenge of ending rural poverty.* International Fund for Agriculture Development, Oxford University Press, http://www.ifad.org/poverty/

IPCC. 2007. *Climate Change 2007.* Fourth Assessment on Climate Change of the Intergovernmental Panel on Climate Change. Multi-volumes, Cambridge University Press, available online at http://www.ipcc.ch/

IPCC. 2001. *Climate Change 2001.* Third Assessment on Climate Change of the Intergovernmental Panel on Climate Change. Multi-volumes, Cambridge University Press, available online at http://www.ipcc.ch/

Jagdeo. 2007. His Excellency Bharrat Jagdeo of Guyana, President of the Cooperative Republic of Guyana, Commonwealth Finance Ministers Meeting (CFMM) opening address, October 15, 2007.

Meinshausen, Malte. 2005. On the risk of overshooting 2 degrees C: Avoiding Dangerous Climate Change, International Symposium on the Stabilisation of greenhouse gas concentrations, Hadley Centre, Met Office, Exeter, UK, February 1-3, 2005. www.stabilisation2005.com/programme.html

MGI. *Curbing global energy demand growth: The energy productivity opportunity.* McKinsey Global Initiative, May 2007, www.fypower.org/pdf/Curbing_Global_Energy_FR.pdf

Ramsar Convention. 2001. Wetland Values and Functions, Ramsar Convention on Wetlands of International Importance. www.ramsar.org/info/values_intro_e.htm

Resilience Alliance. 2007a. Assessing and managing resilience in social-ecological systems: A practitioner's workbook, http://www.resalliance.org/3871.php

Resilience Alliance. 2007b. Assessing resilience in social-ecological systems - A workbook for scientists. http://www.resalliance.org/3871.php

Santilli, Marcio, P. Moutinho, S. Schwartzman, D. Nepstad, L. Curran, C. Nobre. 2005. Tropical deforestation and the Kyoto protocol, an editorial essay. *Climatic Change* 71: 267–276, DOI: 10.1007/s10584-005-8074-6.

Searchinger, T., R. Heimlich, R.A. Houghton, F. Dong, A. Elobeid, J. Fabiosa, S. Tokgoz, D. Hayes, T. Yu. 2008. Use of U.S. croplands for biofuels increases greenhouse gases through emissions from land use change, *ScienceExpress.* February 7, www.sciencexpress.org

Glossary

Stern, Nicholas. 2006. *The Stern Review Report on the Economics of Climate Change*, Cambridge University Press. http://www.hm-treasury.gov.uk/independent_reviews/stern_review_economics_climate_change/stern_review_report.cfm

Tomkins, Emma and Neil Adger. 2003. Building resilience to climate change through adaptive management of natural resources. Tyndall Centre Working Paper No. 27, January 2003, Tyndall Centre for Climate Change Research, www.tyndall.ac.uk/publications/working_papers/wp27.pdf

UNFCCC. 2008a. Nairobi work programme on impacts, vulnerability and adaptation to climate change. Accessed April 2, 2008. http://unfccc.int/adaptation/sbsta_agenda_item_adaptation/items/3633.php

UNFCCC. 2008b. National adaptation action plans (NAPAs). Accessed April 2, 2008, http://unfccc.int/adaptation/napas/items/2679.php

UNFCCC. 2007. National greenhouse gas inventory data for the period 1990–2005, FCCC/SBI/2007/30, October 24, 2007.

UNFCCC. 2002. Text of the convention. http://unfccc.int/resource/docs/convkp/conveng.pdf

UNFCCC. 1992. United Nations Framework Convention on Climate Change. unfccc.int/resource/docs/convkp/conveng.pdf

Wang, Tao and Jim Watson. 2007. Who owns China's carbon emissions? Tyndall Briefing Note No. 23, October 2007. Tyndall Centre for Climate Change Research. http://tyndall.webapp1.uea.ac.uk/publications/briefing_notes/bn23.pdf

Wilson, E.O. 2006. *The creation, An appeal to save life on Earth.* New York: W.W. Norton.

World Bank. 2006. Clean energy & development: Towards an investment framework, April 5, 2006, http://siteresources.worldbank.org/DEVCOMMINT/Documentation/20890696/DC2006-0002(E)-CleanEnergy.pdf

WRI. 2008. Climate Analysis Indicators Tool (CAIT) Version 5.0. World Resources Institute, http://cait.wri.org

Abrupt climate change The nonlinearity of the climate system may lead to abrupt climate change, sometimes called "rapid climate change," "abrupt events," or even "surprises." The term "abrupt" often refers to time scales faster than the typical time scale of the responsible forcing. However, not all abrupt climate changes need be externally forced. Some possible abrupt events that have been proposed include a dramatic reorganization of the thermohaline circulation, rapid deglaciation, and massive melting of permafrost or increases in soil respiration leading to fast changes in the carbon cycle. Others may be truly unexpected, resulting from a strong, rapidly changing forcing of a nonlinear system.

Acclimatization The physiological adaptation to climatic variations.

Adaptation Adjustment in natural or human systems in response to actual or expected climatic stimuli or their effects, which moderates harm or exploits beneficial opportunities. Various types of adaptation can be distinguished, including anticipatory, autonomous, and planned adaptation.

Additionality Reductions in emissions by sources or enhancement of removals by sinks that are additional to any that would occur in the absence of a Joint Implementation (JI) or a Clean Development Mechanism (CDM) project activity as defined in the Kyoto Protocol Articles on JI and CDM. This definition may be further broadened to include financial, investment, technology, and environmental additionality. Under financial additionality, the project activity funding is additional to existing Global Environmental Facility (GEF) support, other financial commitments of parties included in Annex I, official development assistance (ODA), and other systems of cooperation. Under investment additionality, the value of the emissions reduction unit (ERU)/certified emission reduction (CER) unit shall significantly improve the financial or commercial viability of the project activity. Under technology additionality, the technology used for the project activity shall be the best available for the circumstances of the host party. Environmental additionality refers to the environmental integrity of the claimed amount by which greenhouse-gas emissions are reduced due to a project relative to its baseline. A project activity has further additionality if the incentive from the sale of emission allowances helps to overcome barriers to its implementation.

Afforestation Planting of new forests on lands that historically have not contained forests. For a discussion of the term forest and related terms such as afforestation, reforestation, and deforestation, see the IPCC *Special Report on Land Use, Land-Use Change, and Forestry* (IPCC, 2000). See also the report on *Definitions and Methodological Options to Inventory Emissions from Direct Human-Induced Degradation of Forests and Devegetation of Other Vegetation Types* (IPCC, 2003).

Albedo The fraction of solar radiation reflected by a surface or object, often expressed as a percentage. Snow-covered surfaces have a high albedo, the surface albedo of soils ranges from high to low, and vegetation-covered surfaces and oceans have a low albedo. The Earth's planetary albedo varies mainly through varying cloudiness, snow, ice, leaf area, and land-cover changes.

Ancillary benefits Policies aimed at some target (e.g. climate-change mitigation) may be paired with positive side effects, such as increased resource-use efficiency, reduced emissions of air pollutants associated with fossil-fuel use and improved transportation, agriculture, land-use practices, employment, and fuel security. Ancillary *impacts* may be used when the effects may be negative. Policies directed at abating air pollution may consider greenhouse gas (GHG) mitigation an ancillary benefit, but this perspective is not considered in this assessment. See Co-benefits.

Anthropogenic emissions Emissions of greenhouse gases, greenhouse-gas precursors, and aerosols associated with human activities. These include the burning of fossil fuels, deforestation, land-use changes, livestock, fertilizers, etc., that result in a net increase in emissions.

Assemblage Multiple species of plants and animals living in the same place and time.

Baseline/reference The baseline (or reference) is the state against which change is measured. It might be a "current baseline," in which case it represents observable, present-day conditions, or it might be a "future baseline," which is a projected future set of conditions excluding the driving factor of interest. Alternative interpretations of the reference conditions can give rise to multiple baselines.

Biodiversity The variability among living organisms from all sources, including inter alia, terrestrial, marine, and other aquatic ecosystems and the ecological complexes of which they are part. This includes diversity within species, between species, and of ecosystems.

Biofuel Any liquid, gaseous, or solid fuel produced from plant or animal organic matter (e.g., soybean oil, alcohol from fermented sugar, black liquor from the paper manufacturing process, wood as fuel, etc.). Second-generation biofuels are products such as ethanol and biodiesel derived from ligno-cellulosic biomass by chemical or biological processes.

Biosphere (terrestrial and marine) The part of the Earth system comprising all ecosystems and living organisms, in the atmosphere, on land (terrestrial biosphere), or in the oceans (marine biosphere), including derived dead organic matter, such as litter, soil organic matter, and oceanic detritus.

Boreal forest Forests of pine, spruce, fir, and larch stretching from the east coast of Canada westward to Alaska and continuing from Siberia westward across the entire extent of Russia to the European plain. The climate is continental, with long, very cold winters (up to six months with mean temperatures below freezing), and short, cool summers (50 to 100 frost-free days). Precipitation increases during summer months, although annual precipitation is still small. Low evaporation rates can make this a humid climate. See Taiga.

Cap Mandated restraint as an upper limit on emissions. The Kyoto Protocol mandates emissions caps in a scheduled time frame on the anthropogenic greenhouse-gas emissions released by Annex B countries. By 2008 to 2012, for example, the European Union must reduce its CO_2-equivalent emissions of six greenhouse gases (GHGs) to a level 8% lower than the 1990 level.

Carbon Capture and Storage (CCS) A process consisting of the separation of CO_2 from industrial and energy-related sources, transport to a storage location, and long-term isolation from the atmosphere.

Carbon dioxide (CO_2) Roughly 3.7 units of CO_2 equal 1 unit of carbon (C), or, alternatively, 1 unit of CO_2 equals 0.27 units of C. CO_2 plays a critical role in creating and regulating the Earth's climate. It is the reference gas against which other greenhouse gases are measured and, therefore, has a Global Warming Potential (GWP) of 1.

Carbon sequestration The incremental addition to a carbon stock. Sequestration and stocks are often confused. For example, a 450-year old *Pseudotsuga-Tsuga* (Douglas fir/hemlock) forest in Canada has a very large accumulated stock (600 tons of carbon per hectare, tC/ha) with a low annual sequestration rate of about 3 tC/ha. In contrast, a pasture of *Panicum* and *Brachiaria* grasses in Brazil might have up to 70 tC/ha, but when converted through an afforestation effort with fast-growing tree species may experience a sequestration rate of 8 tC/ha per year.

Carbon stocks, sinks, and sources A stock that is absorbing carbon is called a "sink," and a stock that is releasing carbon is known as a "source." The global carbon cycle continually experiences fluxes, or flows, between the carbon stocks stored in oceans, land, and the atmosphere.

Certified Emission Reduction Unit (CER) Equal to one metric ton of CO_2-equivalent emissions reduced or sequestered through a Clean Development Mechanism (CDM) project, calculated using Global Warming Potentials (GWPs). In order to reflect potential non-permanence of afforestation and reforestation project activities, the use of temporary certificates for Net Anthropogenic Greenhouse Gas Removal was decided by COP 9 (Conference of the Parties). Temporary CERs are often referred to as tCERs.

Cholera A waterborne intestinal infection caused by a bacterium (*Vibrio cholerae*) that results in frequent watery stools, cramping abdominal pain, and eventual collapse from dehydration and shock.

Clathrate (methane) A partly frozen slushy mix of methane gas and ice, usually found in sediments.

Clean Development Mechanism (CDM) A mechanism established by Article 12 of the Kyoto Protocol for project-based emission reduction activities in developing countries. The CDM is designed to meet two main objectives: to address the sustainable development needs of the host country and to increase the opportunities available to parties to meet their reduction commitments.

Climate Climate, in a narrow sense, is usually defined as the average weather or, more rigorously, as the statistical description in terms of the mean and variability of relevant quantities over a period of time ranging from months to thousands or millions of years. The classical period for averaging these variables is thirty years, as defined by the World Meteorological Organization. The relevant quantities are most often surface variables such as temperature, precipitation, and wind. Climate in a wider sense is the state, including a statistical description, of the climate system. In various chapters in this report, different averaging periods, such as a period of twenty years, are also used.

Climate change Climate change refers to a change in the state of the climate that can be identified (e.g., by using statistical tests) by changes in the mean and/or the variability of its properties and that persists for an extended period, typically decades or longer. Climate change may be due to natural internal processes or external forcings, or to persistent anthropogenic changes in the composition of the atmosphere or in land use. Note that the Framework Convention on Climate Change (UNFCCC), in Article 1, defines climate change as "a change of climate which is attributed directly or indirectly to human activity that alters the composition of the global atmosphere and which is in addition to natural climate variability observed over comparable time periods." The UNFCCC thus makes a distinction between climate change attributable to human activities altering the atmospheric composition and climate variability attributable to natural causes.

Climate feedback An interaction mechanism between processes in the climate system is a climate feedback when the result of an initial process triggers changes in secondary processes that in turn influence the initial one. A positive feedback intensifies the initial process; a negative feedback reduces the initial process. An example of a positive climate feedback is when higher temperatures as an initial process cause melting of the Arctic ice, leading to less reflection of solar radiation, which leads to higher temperatures. An example of a negative feedback is when higher temperatures increase the amount of cloud cover (thickness or extent) that could reduce incoming solar radiation and so limit the increase in temperature.

Climate system The climate system is the highly complex system consisting of five major components: the atmosphere, the hydrosphere, the cryosphere, the land surface, and the biosphere, and the interactions between them. The climate system evolves in time under the influence of its own internal dynamics and because of external forcings, such as volcanic eruptions and solar variations, and anthropogenic forcings, such as the changing composition of the atmosphere and changing patterns of land use.

Climate threshold The point at which external forcing of the climate system, such as the increasing atmospheric concentration of greenhouse gases (GHGs), triggers a significant climatic or environmental event that is considered unalterable, or recoverable only on very long time scales, such as widespread bleaching of corals or a collapse of oceanic circulation systems.

Cloud feedback A climate feedback involving changes in any of the properties of clouds as a response to other atmospheric changes. Understanding cloud feedbacks and determining their magnitude and sign require an understanding of how a change in climate may affect the spectrum of cloud types, the cloud fraction and height, the radiative properties of clouds, and estimates of the impact of these changes on the Earth's radiation budget. At present, cloud feedbacks remain the largest source of uncertainty in climate-sensitivity estimates. See Radiative forcing.

CO_2-equivalent concentration The concentration of CO_2 that would cause the same amount of radiative forcing as a given mixture of CO_2 and other greenhouse gases (GHGs).

CO_2-equivalent emission The amount of CO_2 emission that would cause the same integrated radiative forcing, over a given time horizon, as an emitted amount of a well-mixed greenhouse gas (GHG) or a mixture of well-mixed GHGs. The equivalent CO_2 emission is obtained by multiplying the emission of a well-mixed GHG by its Global Warming Potential (GWP) for the given time horizon. For a mix of GHGs, it is obtained by summing the equivalent CO_2 emissions of each gas. Equivalent CO_2 emission is a standard and useful metric for comparing emissions of different GHGs but does not imply exact equivalence of the corresponding climate-change responses.

Co-generation The use of waste heat from thermal electricity-generation plants (e.g., condensing heat from steam turbines or hot flue gases exhausted from gas turbines) for industrial use, buildings, or district heating. Synonym for combined heat and power (CHP) generation.

Coccolithophores Single-celled microscopic phytoplankton algae that construct shell-like structures from calcite (a form of calcium carbonate). See also Ocean acidification.

Connectivity Natural links among reefs and neighboring habitats, especially seagrass beds, mangroves, and back-reef lagoons that provide dispersal and genetic replenishment. Also refers to linkages among coastal lands and adjacent catchments, which are sources of freshwater, sediments, and pollutants. The mechanisms include ocean currents, terrestrial runoff and watercourses, larval dispersal, spawning patterns, and movements of adult fishes and other animals. Connectivity is an important process to ensure the productive function of the plant and animal species that contribute to the overall health of an ecosystem.

Coral The term "coral" has several meanings, but is usually the common name for the Order *Scleractinia*, all members of which have hard limestone skeletons and which are divided into reef-building and non-reef-building, or cold- and warm-water corals.

Coral bleaching The paling of corals and other animals with *zooxanthellae* resulting from a loss of these symbiotic algae. Bleaching occurs in response to physiological shock due primarily to periods of increased water temperature coincident with high levels of light. Bleaching can also be caused by changes in salinity or turbidity.

Coral reefs Rock-like limestone (calcium carbonate) structures built by corals along ocean coasts (fringing reefs) or on top of shallow, submerged banks or shelves (barrier reefs, atolls), most conspicuous in tropical and subtropical oceans.

Deforestation Conversion of forest to non-forest. For a discussion of the term forest and related terms such as afforestation, reforestation, and deforestation, see the IPCC *Special Report on Land Use, Land-Use Change, and Forestry* (IPCC, 2000). See also the report on *Definitions and Methodological Options to Inventory Emissions from Direct Human-Induced Degradation of Forests and Devegetation of Other Vegetation Types* (IPCC, 2003).

Degradation Reduction in the condition of a forest or other land area and the capacity of that forest to provide goods and services.

Desertification The United Nations Convention to Combat Desertification defines land degradation as a reduction or loss in arid, semi-arid, and dry sub-humid areas, of the biological or economic productivity and complexity of rain-fed cropland, irrigated cropland, or range, pasture, forest, and woodlands resulting from land uses or from a process or combination of processes, including processes arising from human activities and habitation patterns, such as (i) soil erosion caused by wind and/or water; (ii) deterioration of the physical, chemical, and biological or economic properties of soil; and (iii) long-term loss of natural vegetation.

Ecological community A community of plants and animals characterized by a typical assemblage of species and their abundances. See also Ecosystem.

Ecological corridor A thin strip of vegetation used by wildlife, potentially allowing movement of biotic factors between two areas.

Ecosystem A system of living organisms interacting with each other and their physical environment. The boundaries of what could be called an ecosystem are somewhat arbitrary, depending on the focus of interest or study. Thus, the extent of an ecosystem may range from very small spatial scales to, ultimately, the entire Earth.

Ecosystem approach The ecosystem approach is a strategy for the integrated management of land, water, and living resources that promotes conservation and sustainable use in an equitable way. An ecosystem approach is based on the application of appropriate scientific methodologies focused on levels of biological organization, that encompass the essential structure, processes, functions, and interactions among organisms and their environment. It recognizes that humans, with their cultural diversity, are an integral component of many ecosystems. The ecosystem approach requires adaptive management to deal with the complex and dynamic nature of ecosystems and the absence of complete knowledge or understanding of their functioning. Priority targets are conservation of biodiversity and of the ecosystem structure and functioning in order to maintain ecosystem services.

Ecosystem functions Include ecosystem physicochemical integrity, regeneration, and succession; genetic, species, and ecosystem diversity; and natural cycles that affect the productivity of the ecosystem.

Ecosystem services Ecological processes or functions having monetary or non-monetary value to individuals or society at large. These include (i) supporting services such as productivity or biodiversity maintenance; (ii) provisioning services such as food, fiber, or fish; (iii) regulating services such as climate regulation or carbon sequestration; and (iv) cultural services such as tourism or spiritual and aesthetic appreciation.

El Niño-Southern Oscillation (ENSO) The term El Niño was initially used to describe a warm-water current that periodically flows along the coast of Ecuador and Peru, disrupting the local fishery. It has since become identified with a basin-wide warming of the tropical Pacific Ocean east of the dateline. This oceanic event is associated with a fluctuation of a global-scale tropical and subtropical surface pressure pattern called the Southern Oscillation. This coupled atmosphere-ocean phenomenon, with preferred time scales of roughly two to seven years, is collectively known as the El Niño-Southern Oscillation (ENSO). It is often measured by the surface pressure anomaly difference between Darwin and Tahiti and the sea-surface temperatures in the central and eastern equatorial Pacific. During an ENSO event, the prevailing trade winds weaken, reducing upwelling and altering ocean currents such that the sea surface temperatures warm, further weakening the trade winds. This event has a great impact on the wind, sea-surface temperature, and precipitation patterns in the tropical Pacific. It has climatic effects throughout the Pacific region and in many other parts of the world, through global teleconnections. The cold phase of ENSO is called La Niña.

Emission scenario A plausible representation of the future development of emissions of substances that are potentially radiatively active (e.g., greenhouse gases [GHGs], aerosols), based on a coherent and internally consistent set of assumptions about driving forces (e.g., demographic and socioeconomic development, technological change) and their key relationships. Concentration scenarios, derived from emission scenarios, are used as inputs to a climate model to compute climate projections. In IPCC (1992) a set of emission scenarios was presented that were used as a basis for the climate projections in IPCC (1996). These emission scenarios are referred to as the IS92 scenarios. In the IPCC Special Report on Emission Scenarios (Nakićenović and Swart, 2000) new emission scenarios, the so-called SRES scenarios, were published, some of which were used, among others, as a basis for the climate projections presented in Chapters 9 to 11 of IPCC (2001) and Chapters 10 and 11 of IPCC (2007). For the meaning of some terms related to these scenarios, see SRES.

Emissions trading A market-based approach to achieving environmental objectives. It allows those reducing GHG emissions below their emissions cap to use or trade the excess reductions to offset emissions at another source inside or outside the country. In general, trading can occur at the intra-company, domestic, and international levels. The Second Assessment Report by the IPCC adopted the convention of using permits for domestic trading systems and quotas for international trading systems. Emissions trading under Article 17 of the Kyoto Protocol is a tradable quota system based on the assigned amounts calculated from the emission-reduction and limitation commitments listed in Annex B of the Protocol.

Endemic Restricted or peculiar to a locality or region. With regard to human health, endemic can refer to a disease or agent present or usually prevalent in a population or geographical area at all times.

Ethanol A colorless, volatile, flammable liquid (C_2H_5OH) that can be produced from petroleum refineries via the chemical hydration of ethylene or via the biological fermentation of simple molecules, such as glucose and fructose (monosaccharide). Anhydrous ethanol (ethanol with less than 1% water) can be blended with gasoline in varying quantities up to pure ethanol (E100), and most spark-ignited gasoline style engines will operate well with mixtures of 10% ethanol (E10).

Eutrophication The process by which a body of water (often shallow) becomes (either naturally or by pollution) rich in dissolved nutrients, with a seasonal deficiency in dissolved oxygen.

Exajoule (EJ) Metric unit equaling one quintillion Joules of energy (10^{18}), or one million trillion Joules. It is equivalent to 160 million barrels of oil, or 6.6 billion gallons of gasoline, or 34 million metric tons of coal.

Externality/External cost/External benefit Externalities arise from a human activity, when agents responsible for the activity do not take full account of the activity's impact on others' production and consumption possibilities, while there exists no compensation for such impact. When the impact is negative, so are external costs. When positive, they are referred to as external benefits. The impacts of pollution on ecosystems, water courses, or air quality represent classic cases of negative externality.

Extirpation The disappearance of a species from part of its range; local extinction.

Feedback An interaction mechanism between processes is called a feedback. When the result of an initial process triggers changes in a second process and that, in turn, influences the initial one. A positive feedback intensifies the original process, and a negative feedback reduces it. See Climate feedback.

Framework Convention on Climate Change See United Nations Framework Convention on Climate Change (UNFCCC).

General circulation The large-scale motions of the atmosphere and the ocean as a consequence of differential heating on a rotating Earth, which tend to restore the energy balance of the system through transport of heat and momentum.

Generalist A species that can tolerate a wide range of environmental conditions.

Global dimming Global dimming refers to perceived widespread reduction of solar radiation received at the surface of the Earth from about the year 1961 to around 1990.

Global warming potential (GWP) An index, based upon radiative properties of well-mixed greenhouse gases (GHGs), measuring the radiative forcing of a unit mass of a given well-mixed GHG in the present-day atmosphere integrated over a chosen time horizon, relative to that of CO_2. The GWP represents the combined effect of the differing times these gases remain in the atmosphere and their relative effectiveness in absorbing outgoing thermal infrared radiation. The Kyoto Protocol is based on GWPs from pulse emissions over a 100-year time frame.

Greenhouse effect Greenhouse gases (GHGs) effectively absorb thermal infrared radiation, emitted by the Earth's surface, by the atmosphere itself due to the same gases, and by clouds. Atmospheric radiation is emitted to all sides, including downward to the Earth's surface. Thus, GHGs trap heat within the surface-troposphere system. This is called the greenhouse effect. Thermal infrared radiation in the troposphere is strongly coupled to the temperature of the atmosphere at the altitude at which it is emitted. In the troposphere, the temperature generally decreases with height. Effectively, infrared radiation emitted to space originates from an altitude with a temperature of, on average, −19°C, in balance with the net incoming solar radiation, whereas the Earth's surface is kept at a much higher temperature of, on average, +14°C. An increase in the concentration of GHGs leads to an increased infrared opacity of the atmosphere and, therefore, to an effective radiation into space from a higher altitude at a lower temperature. This causes a radiative forcing that leads to an enhancement of the greenhouse effect, the so-called enhanced greenhouse effect.

Greenhouse gas (GHG) GHGs are those gaseous constituents of the atmosphere, both natural and anthropogenic, that absorb and emit radiation at specific wavelengths within the spectrum of thermal infrared radiation emitted by the Earth's surface, the atmosphere itself, and by clouds. This property causes the greenhouse effect. Water vapor (H_2O), carbon dioxide (CO_2), nitrous oxide (N_2O), methane (CH_4) and ozone (O_3) are the primary GHGs in the Earth's atmosphere. Moreover, there are a number of entirely human-made GHGs in the atmosphere, such as the halocarbons and other chlorine- and bromine-containing substances, dealt with under the Montreal Protocol. Beside CO_2, N_2O, and CH_4, the Kyoto Protocol deals with the GHGs sulphur hexafluoride (SF_6), hydrofluorocarbons (HFCs), and perfluorocarbons (PFCs).

Gross Domestic Product (GDP) GDP is the monetary value of all goods and services produced within a nation.

Gross National Product (GNP) GNP is the monetary value of all goods and services produced in a nation's economy, including income generated abroad by domestic residents, but without income generated by foreigners.

Habitat The locality or natural home in which a particular plant, animal, or group of closely associated organisms lives.

Herbaceous Flowering, non-woody.

Hydrofluorocarbons (HFCs) One of the six gases or groups of gases to be curbed under the Kyoto Protocol. They are produced commercially as a substitute for chlorofluorocarbons (CFCs). HFCs are largely used in refrigeration and semiconductor manufacturing. Their Global Warming Potentials (GWPs) range from 1,300 to 11,700.

Hypoxic events Events that lead to a deficiency of oxygen.

Indigenous peoples No internationally accepted definition of indigenous peoples exists. Common characteristics often applied under international law, and by United Nations agencies to distinguish indigenous peoples, include residence within or attachment to geographically distinct traditional habitats, ancestral territories, and their natural resources; maintenance of cultural and social identities and social, economic, cultural, and political institutions separate from mainstream or dominant societies and cultures; descent from population groups present in a given area, most frequently before modern states or territories were created and current borders defined; and self-identification as being part of a distinct indigenous cultural group and the desire to preserve that cultural identity.

Kyoto Protocol The Kyoto Protocol to the United Nations Framework Convention on Climate Change (UNFCCC) was adopted in 1997 in Kyoto, Japan, at the Third Session of the Conference of the Parties (COP) to the UNFCCC. It contains legally binding commitments, in addition to those included in the UNFCCC. Countries included in Annex B of the Protocol (most Organization for Economic Cooperation and Development countries and countries with economies in transition) agreed to reduce their anthropogenic greenhouse gas (GHG) emissions (carbon dioxide [CO_2,] methane [CH_4], nitrous oxide [N_2O], hydrofluorocarbons, perfluorocarbons, and sulphur hexafluoride) by at least 5% below 1990 levels in the commitment period 2008 to 2012. The Kyoto Protocol entered into force on February 16, 2005.

Land use and Land-use change (LULUCF) Land use refers to the total of arrangements, activities, and inputs undertaken in a certain land-cover type (a set of human actions). The term land use is also used in the sense of the social and economic purposes for which land is managed (e.g., grazing, timber extraction, and conservation). Land-use change refers to a change in the use or management of land by humans, which may lead to a change in land cover. Land cover and land-use change may have an impact on the surface albedo, evapotranspiration, sources and sinks of greenhouse gases (GHGs), or other properties of the climate system and may thus have a radiative forcing and/or other impacts on climate, locally or globally. See also the IPCC Report on *Land Use, Land-Use Change, and Forestry* (IPCC, 2000).

La Niña See El Niño-Southern Oscillation.

Leakage Refers to unexpected carbon losses related to a particular carbon-offset project.

The leakage may be due to unforeseen circumstances that were beyond the control of a forest conservation or sequestration project. Unforeseen events include extreme weather, political instability, climate change, pests, disease, fire, or cancellation of contracts that lead to logging. Research on leakage suggests that it can be anticipated and avoided through good project design. Where leakage is unavoidable, net carbon estimates can be revised, incorporating leakage effects.

Market-based regulation Regulatory approaches using price mechanisms (e.g., taxes and auctioned tradable permits), among other instruments, to reduce GHG emissions.

Market distortions and imperfections In practice, markets will always exhibit distortions and imperfections, such as lack of information, distorted price signals, lack of competition, and/or institutional failures related to regulation, inadequate delineation of property rights, distortion-inducing fiscal systems, and limited financial markets.

Methane (CH_4) Methane is one of the six greenhouse gases (GHGs) to be mitigated under the Kyoto Protocol. It is the major component of natural gas and associated with all hydrocarbon fuels, animal husbandry, and agriculture. Coal-bed methane is the gas found in coal seams.

Millennium Development Goals (MDGs) A list of ten goals, including eradicating extreme poverty and hunger, improving maternal health, and ensuring environmental sustainability, adopted in 2000 by the UN General Assembly (i.e., 191 States) to be reached by 2015. The MDGs commit the international community to an expanded vision of development and have been commonly accepted as a framework for measuring development progress.

Mitigation An anthropogenic (human) intervention to reduce the anthropogenic forcing of the climate system. It includes strategies to reduce greenhouse gas (GHG) sources and emissions and enhance greenhouse gas sinks.

Nonlinearity A process is called nonlinear when there is no simple proportional relation between cause and effect. The climate system contains many such nonlinear processes, resulting in a system with a potentially very complex behavior. Such complexity may lead to abrupt climate change. See also Predictability.

Ocean acidification Increased concentrations of CO_2 in seawater causing a measurable increase in acidity (i.e., a reduction in ocean pH). This may lead to reduced calcification rates of calcifying organisms such as corals, mollusks, algae, and crustacea.

Opportunity costs The cost of an economic activity forgone through the choice of another activity.

Ozone The triatomic form of oxygen (O_3), a gaseous atmospheric constituent.

In the troposphere, it is created both naturally and by photochemical reactions involving gases resulting from human activities (photochemical smog). In high concentrations, tropospheric ozone can be harmful to many living organisms. Tropospheric ozone acts as a greenhouse gas (GHG). In the stratosphere, ozone is created by the interaction between solar ultraviolet radiation and molecular oxygen (O_2). Depletion of stratospheric ozone, due to chemical reactions that may be enhanced by climate change, results in an increased ground-level flux of ultraviolet (UV) B radiation.

Ozone layer The stratosphere contains a layer in which the concentration of ozone is greatest, the so-called ozone layer. The layer extends from about 12 to 40 km above the Earth's surface. The ozone concentration reaches a maximum between about 20 and 25 km. This layer is being depleted by human emissions of chlorine and bromine compounds. Every year, during the Southern Hemisphere spring, a very strong depletion of the ozone layer takes place over the Antarctic region, caused by anthropogenic chlorine and bromine compounds in combination with the specific meteorological conditions of that region. This phenomenon is called the ozone hole.

Palaeoclimate Climate during periods prior to the development of measuring instruments, including historic and geologic time, for which only proxy climate records are available.

Peat Peat is formed from dead plants, typically sphagnum mosses, which are only partially decomposed due to the permanent submergence in water and the presence of conserving substances such as humic acids.

Peatland Typically a wetland, such as a mire, slowly accumulating peat.

Pelagic community The community of organisms living in the open waters of a river, a lake, or an ocean (in contrast to benthic communities living on or near the bottom of a water body).

Permafrost Ground (soil or rock and included ice and organic material) that remains at or below 0°C for at least two consecutive years.

pH A dimensionless measure of the acidity of water (or any solution) given by its concentration of hydrogen ions (H+). pH is measured on a logarithmic scale where pH = $-\log10(H^+)$. Thus, a pH decrease of 1 unit corresponds to a 10-fold increase in the concentration of H+, or acidity.

Phytoplankton The plant forms of plankton. Phytoplankton are the dominant plants in the sea and are the basis of the entire marine food web. These single-celled organisms are the principal agents of photosynthetic carbon fixation in the ocean. See Zooplankton.

Plankton Microorganisms living in the upper layers of aquatic systems. A distinction is made between phytoplankton, which

depend on photosynthesis for their energy supply, and zooplankton, which feed on phytoplankton.

PPM Refers to the atmospheric concentration of greenhouse gases (GHG) expressed as carbon dioxide (CO_2) equivalents in parts per million volume (ppmv). Confusion has arisen in the climate literature, media coverage, and public understanding because of two different ppm figures being reported. The IPCC formula for CO_2 forcing: Total Forcing = 5.35 log(CO_2 equivalent/ CO_2 original), where CO_2orig is the 1750 concentration (278 ppmv). There are two main ways it is used: 1) to group together all the forcings from the Kyoto greenhouse gases (CO_2, CH_4, N_2O and CFCs); and 2) to group together all forcings (including ozone, sulphate aerosols, black carbon, etc.). The first is simply a convenience, but the second is what matters to the planet. CO_2e (Kyoto) = 460 ppmv. However, including all the forcings (some of which are negative), you get a net forcing of around 1.6 Watts per square meter (Wm^2) and a CO_2e (total) of 375 ppmv with quite a wide error bar. The important number is CO_2e (total), which was about 386 ppm at the end of 2007.

Predictability The extent to which future states of a system may be predicted based on knowledge of current and past states of the system. Since knowledge of the climate system's past and current states is generally imperfect, as are the models that utilize this knowledge to produce a climate prediction, and since the climate system is inherently non-linear and chaotic, predictability of the climate system is inherently limited. Even with arbitrarily accurate models and observations, there may still be limits to the predictability of such a non-linear system.

Projection A potential future evolution of a quantity or set of quantities, often computed with the aid of a model. Projections are distinguished from predictions in order to emphasize that projections involve assumptions concerning, for example, future socioeconomic and technological developments that may or may not be realized and are, therefore, subject to substantial uncertainty.

Pteropods Planktonic, small marine snails with swimming organs resembling wings.

Radiative forcing Radiative forcing is the change in the net, downward minus upward, irradiance (expressed in Watts per square meter, Wm^2) at the tropopause due to a change in an external driver of climate change (e.g., a change in the concentration of CO_2 or the output of the sun. Radiative forcing is computed with all tropospheric properties held fixed at their unperturbed values and, after allowing for stratospheric temperatures, if perturbed, to readjust to radiative-dynamical equilibrium. Radiative forcing is called instantaneous if no change in stratospheric temperature is accounted for. For the purposes of this report, radiative forcing is further defined as the change relative to the year 1750 and, unless otherwise noted, refers to a global

and annual average value. Radiative forcing is not to be confused with cloud radiative forcing, a similar terminology for describing an unrelated measure of the impact of clouds on the irradiance at the top of the atmosphere.

REDD (Reducing Emissions from Deforestation and Forest Degradation) Often refers to the policy approaches and positive incentives on issues relating to Reducing Emissions from Deforestation and Forest Degradation in developing countries and the role of conservation, sustainable management of forests, and enhancement of forest carbon stocks in developing countries (see the UNFCCC Decision -/CP.13, http://unfccc.int/files/meetings/cop_13/ application/pdf/cp_redd.pdf).

Reforestation Planting of forests on lands that have previously contained forests but that have been converted to some other use. For a discussion of the term forest and related terms such as afforestation, reforestation, and deforestation, see the IPCC report on *Land Use, Land-Use Change, and Forestry* (IPCC, 2000). See also *Definitions and Methodological Options to Inventory Emissions from Direct Human-Induced Degradation of Forests and Devegetation of Other Vegetation Types* (IPCC, 2003).

Refuge Place where species and/or communities survive environmental changes. Species may remain restricted to the vicinity of a refuge or disperse from a refuge, thus decolonizing wider areas following further environmental changes. Past refuges might include places where species have survived glacial periods.

Reservoir A component of the climate system, other than the atmosphere, which has the capacity to store, accumulate, or release a substance of concern, for example, carbon, a greenhouse gas (GHG), or a precursor. Oceans, soils, and forests are examples of reservoirs of carbon. Pool is an equivalent term (note that the definition of pool often includes the atmosphere). The absolute quantity of the substance of concern held within a reservoir at a specified time is called the stock.

Resilience The ability of a social or ecological system to absorb disturbances while retaining the same basic structure and ways of functioning, the capacity for self-organization, and the capacity to adapt to stress and change.

Riparian Relating to or living or located on the bank of a natural watercourse (such as a river) or sometimes of a lake or a tidewater.

Risk Probability that a situation will produce harm under specified conditions. It is a combination of two factors: the probability that an adverse event will occur and the consequences of the adverse event. Risk encompasses impacts on human and natural systems and arises from exposure and hazard. Hazard is determined by whether a particular situation or event has the potential to cause harmful effects.

Salinization The accumulation of salts in soils.

Savanna Tropical or subtropical grassland or woodland biomes with scattered shrubs, individual trees, or a very open canopy of trees, all characterized by a dry (arid, semi-arid, or semi-humid) climate.

Scenario A plausible and often simplified description of how the future may develop, based on a coherent and internally consistent set of assumptions about driving forces and key relationships. Scenarios may be derived from projections, but are often based on additional information from other sources, sometimes combined with a narrative storyline. See also SRES; Emission scenario.

Sea-level change Sea level can change, both globally and locally, due to changes in the shape of the ocean basins, changes in the total mass of water, and changes in water density. Sea-level changes induced by changes in water density are called steric. Density changes induced by temperature changes only are called thermosteric, while density changes induced by salinity changes are called halosteric.

Sequestration See Carbon sequestration.

Silviculture Cultivation, development, and care of forests.

Silvopastoral systems Farm systems where trees are integrated with livestock production.

Sink Any process, activity, or mechanism that removes a greenhouse gas (GHG), an aerosol, or a precursor of a GHG or aerosol from the atmosphere.

Social cost of carbon The value of the climate change impacts from 1 ton of carbon emitted today as CO_2, aggregated over time and discounted back to the present day; sometimes also expressed as value per ton of CO_2.

Source Any process, activity, or mechanism that releases a greenhouse gas (GHG), an aerosol, or a precursor of a GHG or aerosol into the atmosphere.

SRES The storylines and associated population, GDP, and emissions scenarios associated with the Special Report on Emissions Scenarios (SRES), and the resulting climate-change and sea-level rise scenarios. Four families of socio-economic scenarios (A1, A2, B1, and B2) represent different world futures in two distinct dimensions: a focus on economic versus environmental concerns and global versus regional development patterns.

Stabilization Keeping constant the atmospheric concentrations of one or more greenhouse gases (GHGs) (e.g., CO_2) or of a CO_2-equivalent basket of GHG. Stabilization analyses or scenarios address the stabilization of the concentration of GHG in the atmosphere.

Stock See Reservoir.

Stratosphere The highly stratified region of the atmosphere above the troposphere extending from about 10 km (ranging from 9 km at high latitudes to 16 km in the tropics on average) to about 50 km altitude.

Succulent Succulent plants (e.g., cacti) possessing organs that store water, thus facilitating survival during drought conditions.

Taiga The northernmost belt of boreal forest adjacent to the Arctic tundra.

Teleconnection A connection between climate variations over widely separated parts of the world. In physical terms, teleconnections are often a consequence of large-scale wave motions, whereby energy is transferred from source regions along preferred paths in the atmosphere.

TeraWatt-year (TWy) A TWy is an amount of energy corresponding to a use rate of one trillion Watts over the duration of one year. It is equal to 31.5 exajoules. The world consumes about 15 TWy per year.

Thermocline The layer of maximum vertical temperature gradient in the ocean, lying between the surface ocean and the abyssal ocean. In subtropical regions, its source waters are typically surface waters at higher latitudes that have subducted and moved Equator-ward. At high latitudes, it is sometimes absent, replaced by a halocline, which is a layer of maximum vertical salinity gradient.

Thermohaline circulation (THC) Large-scale circulation in the ocean that transforms low-density upper-ocean waters to higher-density intermediate and deep waters and returns those waters back to the upper ocean. The circulation is asymmetric, with conversion to dense waters in restricted regions at high latitudes and the return to the surface involving slow upwelling and diffusive processes over much larger geographic regions. The THC is driven by high densities at or near the surface, caused by cold temperatures and/or high salinities. However, despite its suggestive though common name, it is also driven by mechanical forces such as wind and tides. Frequently, the name THC has been used synonymously with Meridional Overturning Circulation.

Thermokarst A ragged landscape full of shallow pits, hummocks, and depressions often filled with water (ponds) that results from the thawing of ground ice or permafrost. Thermokarst processes are the processes driven by warming that lead to the formation of thermokarst.

Threshold The level of magnitude of a system process at which sudden or rapid change occurs. A point or level at which new properties emerge in an ecological, economic, or other system, invalidating predictions based on mathematical relationships that apply at lower levels.

Transesterification The chemical process of exchanging the alkoxy group of an ester compound by combining it with an alcohol, producing a different ester compound and a different alcohol through a process that is often catalyzed by the addition of an acid or base. Transesterification is the process of catalytically reacting vegetable oils or animal fats with a short chain aliphatic alcohol, methanol, or ethanol to produce biodiesel fuel.

Tundra A treeless, level, or gently undulating plain characteristic of the Arctic and sub-Arctic regions characterized by low temperatures and short growing seasons.

Uncertainty An expression of the degree to which a value (e.g., the future state of the climate system) is unknown. Uncertainty can result from lack of information or from disagreement about what is known or even knowable. It may have many types of sources, from quantifiable errors in the data to ambiguously defined concepts or terminology, or uncertain projections of human behavior. Uncertainty can therefore be represented by quantitative measures (e.g., a range of values calculated by various models) or by qualitative statements (e.g., reflecting the judgment of a team of experts).

United Nations Framework Convention on Climate Change (UNFCCC) The Convention was adopted on May 9, 1992, in New York and signed at the 1992 Earth Summit in Rio de Janeiro by more than 150 countries and the European community. Its ultimate objective is the "stabilization of greenhouse gas (GHG) concentrations in the atmosphere at a level that would prevent dangerous anthropogenic interference with the climate system." It contains commitments for all parties. Under the Convention, parties included in Annex I (all OECD countries and countries with economies in transition) aim to return GHG emissions not controlled by the Montreal Protocol to 1990 levels by the year 2000. The convention entered in force in March 1994. See Kyoto Protocol.

Urban heat island (UHI) The relative warmth of a city compared with surrounding rural areas, associated with changes in runoff, the concrete-jungle effects on heat retention, changes in surface albedo, changes in pollution and aerosols, and so on.

Vulnerability Vulnerability is the degree to which a system is susceptible to, and unable to cope with, adverse effects of climate change, including climate variability and extremes. Vulnerability is a function of the character, magnitude, and rate of climate change and variation to which a system is exposed, its sensitivity, and its adaptive capacity.

Wetland A transitional, regularly waterlogged area of poorly drained soils, often between an aquatic and a terrestrial ecosystem, fed from rain, surface water, or groundwater.

Wetlands are characterized by a prevalence of vegetation adapted for life in saturated soil conditions.

Yedoma Ancient organic material trapped in permafrost that is hardly decomposed; windblown dust. Called yedoma in Siberia.

Zooplankton The animal forms of plankton. They consume phytoplankton or other zooplankton.

Sources

Glossary, IPCC 2007. Fourth Assessment Report, Working Group I, http://www.ipcc.ch/pdf/assessment-report/ar4/wg1/ar4-wg1-annexes.pdf

Glossary, IPCC 2007. Fourth Assessment Report, Working Group II, http://www.ipcc.ch/pdf/assessment-report/ar4/wg2/ar4-wg2-app.pdf

Glossary, IPCC 2007. Fourth Assessment Report, Working Group III, http://www.ipcc.ch/pdf/assessment-report/ar4/wg3/ar4-wg3-annex1.pdf

List of Contributors

Full credentials listed on contributor's first mention

Introduction

Russell A. Mittermeier
President
Conservation International
r.mittermeier@conservation.org

Michael Totten
*Chief Advisor, Climate, Water
and Ecosystem Services*
The Center for Environmental
Leadership in Business
Conservation International
m.totten@celb.org

Laura Ledwith Pennypacker
Director, International Policy
Program, The Center for
Conservation and Government
Conservation International
l.ledwith@conservation.org

Glenn T. Prickett
*Senior Vice President &
Executive Director,*
The Center for Environmental
Leadership in Business, Conservation
International
g.prickett@celb.org

Guy Midgley
Chief Specialist Scientist
Global Change Research Group
Kirstenbosch Research Center
South African National Biodiversity
Institute
midgley@sanbi.org

Frederick Boltz
*Vice-President,
Conservation Strategies,*
Programs & Science Division
Conservation International
f.boltz@conservation.org

Cristina G. Mittermeier
Executive Director
International League of
Conservation Photographers
c.mittermeier@conservation.org

Alistair Graham
Global Programs Advisor
The Humane Society International
alistair@hsi.org.au

Carlos Manuel Rodríguez
*Regional Vice President,
Mexico and Central America*
Conservation International
cmRodríguez@conservation.org

Thomas Brooks
Senior Director
The Center for Applied
Biodiversity Science
Conservation International
t.brooks@conservation.org

Lee Hannah
Senior Researcher
The Center for Applied
Biodiversity Science
Conservation International
l.hannah@conservation.org

Benjamin Vitale
Managing Director
Conservation &
Community Carbon Fund
Conservation International
b.vitale@conservation.org

Katrina Brandon
Senior Technical Advisor
The Center for Applied
Biodiversity Science
Conservation International
k.brandon@conservation.org

Toby Janson-Smith
Senior Director
Ecosystems Service Investments
The Center for Environmental
Leadership in Business
Conservation International
t.janson@celb.org

Lisa Handy
*Senior Director,
U.S. Government Affairs*
The Center for Conservation
and Government
Conservation International
l.handy@conservation.org

Michael Kennedy
Director
The Humane Society International
michael@hsi.org.au

José Maria Cardoso da Silva
Vice President, South America
South American Division
Conservation International
j.silva@conservation.org

Peter A. Seligmann
Chairman and CEO
Conservation International
p.seligmann@conservation.org

Claude Gascon
*Executive Vice-President for
Programs and Science*
Conservation International
c.gascon@conservation.org

Olivier Langrand
Senior Vice President,
The Center for Conservation
and Government
Conservation International
o.langrand@conservation.org

Niels Crone
Chief Operations Officer
Conservation International
n.crone@conservation.org

Lisa Famolare
*Vice President,
Guianas Regional Program*
Conservation International
l.famolare@conservation.org

David Singh
Executive Director, CI-Guyana
Conservation International
d.singh@conservation.org

Jorgen Thomsen
*Senior Vice President
and Executive Director*
Conservation Funding Division
Conservation International
j.thomsen@conservation.org

Roberto Cavalcanti
*Senior Vice President,
Knowledge and Learning*
Conservation International
r.cavalcanti@conservation.org

Frank Hawkins
*Vice President, Africa and
Madagascar Division*
Conservation International
f.hawkins@conservation.org

Leon Rajaobelina
*Regional Vice President, Madagascar
and Indian Ocean Islands*
Conservation International
l.rajaobelina@conservation.org

James Mackinnon
*Senior Technical Director, Mada-
gascar and Indian Ocean Islands*
Conservation International
j.mackinnon@conservation.org

Luis Suárez
Executive Director, Peru Program
Conservation International
l.Suárez@conservation.org

Jatna Supriatna
Regional Director, Indonesia
Conservation International
j.supriatna@conservation.org

Alexander Peal
Country Director, Liberia Program
Conservation International
a.peal@conservation.org

Luis Espinel
*Acting Executive Director,
Peru Program*
Conservation International
l.espinel@conservation.org

Vance Martin
President, The WILD Foundation
vance@wild.org

Energy Efficiency

Michael Totten
Conservation International
m.totten@celb.org

Renewable Energy

Michael Totten
Conservation International
m.totten@celb.org

Biofuels

John Buchanan
Senior Director, Business Practices
The Center for Environmental
Leadership in Business
Conservation International
j.buchanan@celb.org

Christine Dragisic
Business Practices Manager
The Center for Environmental
Leadership in Business
Conservation International
c.dragisic@celb.org

Forest Conservation

Frederick Boltz
Conservation International
f.boltz@conservation.org

Aaron Bruner
*Director, Conservation Incentives and
Protected Area Financing*
Conservation International
a.bruner@conservation.org

Claude Gascon
Conservation International
c.gascon@conservation.org

Russell A. Mittermeier
Conservation International
r.mittermeier@conservation.org

Reforestation
and Agroforestry

Celia A. Harvey
Advisor, Climate Change Initiatives
Conservation Strategies
Conservation International
c.harvey@conservation.org

Goetz Schroth
*Senior Advisor,
Land Use Strategies Program*
Conservation International
g.schroth@conservation.org

Lorena Soto-Pinto
Researcher
Department of Agroecology
El Colegio de la Frontera Sur,
Chiapas, México
lsoto@ecosur.mx

Olaf Zerbock
*Manager,
Climate Change Initiatives*
Conservation Strategies Department
Conservation International
o.zerbock@conservation.org

Jonathan Philipsborn
*Program Coordinator,
Climate Change Initiatives &
Conservation Strategies*
Conservation International
j.philipsborn@conservation.org

Terrestrial Biodiversity

Lee Hannah
Senior Researcher
The Center for Applied
Biodiversity Science
Conservation International
l.hannah@conservation.org

Miguel B. Araújo
Associate Professor of Research
Biodiversity and Global Change
Lab, National Museum of Natural
Sciences, Madrid, Spain
maraujo@mncn.csic.es

Guy Midgley
South African National
Biodiversity Institute
midgley@sanbi.org

Sandy Andelman
*Vice President,
Tropical Ecology, Assessment and
Monitoring Initiative*
The Center for Applied
Biodiversity Science
Conservation International
s.andelman@conservation.org

Enrique Martínez-Meyer
Researcher
Instituto de Biologia
Universidad Nacional
Autónoma de México
emm@ibiologia.unam.mx

Richard Pearson
Research Scientist
Center for Biodiversity and
Conservation, Department of
Herpetology
American Museum of
Natural History
pearson@amnh.org

Paul Williams
Researcher Entomologist
Head of Hymenoptera Division
Entomology
Natural History Museum,
London UK
paw@nhm.ac.uk

Gustavo A.B. da Fonseca
Team Leader, Natural Resources
Global Environment Facility
Professor of Zoology
Federal University of Minas Gerais,
Brazil
gfonseca1@thegef.org

Timothy J. Killeen
Senior Research Scientist
The Center for Applied
Biodiversity Science
Conservation International
t.killeen@conservation.org

Andrea Kutter
Senior Natural Resources Specialist
Global Environment Facility
akutter@thegef.org

Laura Ledwith Pennypacker
Conservation International
l.ledwith@conservation.org

Russell A. Mittermeier
Conservation International
r.mittermeier@conservation.org

Paulo Gustavo do Prado Pereira
*Environmental Policy Director,
Brazil Program*
Conservation International
p.prado@conservation.org

José Maria Cardoso da Silva
Vice President, South America
South American Division
Conservation International
j.silva@conservation.org

Michael Totten
Conservation International
m.totten@celb.org

Will R. Turner
Ecologist
The Center for Applied
Biodiversity Science
Conservation International
w.turner@conservation.org

Freshwater Biodiversity

Michael Leonard Smith
Senior Research Scientist

The Center for Applied
Biodiversity Science
Conservation International
m.smith@conservation.org

Tracy A. Farrell
*Senior Director,
Conservation Initiatives*
Programs and Science
Conservation International
t.farrell@conservation.org

L.J. Gorenflo
Associate Professor
Department of
Landscape Architecture
Pennsylvania State University
lgorenflo@psu.edu

The Role of Oceans

Emily Pidgeon
*Senior Technical Advisor
Regional Marine Strategies*
Conservation International
e.pidgeon@conservation.org

Scott C. Doney
Senior Scientist
Marine Chemistry and Geochemistry
Woods Hole Oceanographic
Institution
sdoney@whoi.edu

Human Dimensions

Katrina Brandon
Senior Technical Advisor
The Center for Applied
Biodiversity Science
Conservation International
k.brandon@conservation.org

Tipping Points

M. Torre Jorgenson
Senior Scientist, ABR, Inc.
Environmental Research
and Services
tjorgenson@abrinc.com

Michael Totten
Conservation International
m.totten@celb.org

A Call to Action

Laura Ledwith Pennypacker
Conservation International
l.ledwith@conservation.org

Michael Totten
Conservation International
m.totten@celb.org

Russell A. Mittermeier
Conservation International
r.mittermeier@conservation.org

Carlos Manuel Rodríguez
Conservation International
cmRodríguez@conservation.org

Guy Midgley
South African National
Biodiversity Institute
midgley@sanbi.org

Benjamin Vitale
Conservation International
b.vitale@conservation.org

Glenn T. Prickett
Conservation International
g.prickett@celb.org

Frederick Boltz
Conservation International
f.boltz@conservation.org

Joanna Durbin
*Director of the Climate, Community
& Biodiversity Alliance*
The Center for Leadership in Business
Conservation International
j.durbin@conservation.org

Lead Authors

Russell A. Mittermeier, President of Conservation International since 1989, is the only active field biologist to head an international conservation organization. Named a "hero for the planet" and a "new eco hero" by two international magazines, Mittermeier is regarded as a world leader in the field of tropical forest conservation. Trained as a primatologist and herpetologist, he has traveled widely in more than 120 countries, and conducted field work in more than 20—with much of his field work having focused on Amazonia (particularly Brazil and Suriname), the Atlantic forest region of Brazil, and Madagascar. Since 1977, he has also served as chairman of the IUCN/SSC Primate Specialist Group. He has been an Adjunct Professor at the State University of New York at Stony Brook since 1978 and President of the Margot Marsh Biodiversity Foundation since 1996. In 2004 he was elected an IUCN Regional Councilor for North America and the Caribbean. He graduated Summa Cum Laude and Phi Beta Kappa from Dartmouth in 1971 and went on to Harvard University for a Doctorate in Biological Anthropology (1977). In addition to English, Mittermeier is fluent in German, Portuguese, Spanish, French and Sranan Tongo, the Creole language of Suriname. He has published more than 500 scientific and popular articles and 17 books, including the trilogy *Megadiversity, Hotspots,* and *Wilderness,* and, most recently, *Wildlife Spectacles, Hotspots Revisited, Transboundary Conservation, Lemurs of Madagascar,* and *Pantanal: South America's Wetland Jewel.*

Michael Totten is chief advisor on climate, water, and biodiversity at Conservation International. He has been promoting a portfolio strategy for simultaneously addressing climate stabilization, biodiversity protection, and human well-being since 1989, when he drafted the 250-page Global Warming Prevention Act (HR1078), sponsored by one-third of the House of Representatives. Totten was recipient of the Lewis Mumford Award for the Environment in 1999 for pioneering Internet applications promoting ecologically sustainable practices, and green design tools, technologies, and policies.

Laura Ledwith Pennypacker is Director for International Policy & Science at Conservation International. She provides leadership and coordination for CI's international policy engagement, with a particular emphasis on securing the protection and sustainable management of the world's biodiversity hotspots and high-biodiversity wilderness areas, and promoting innovative solutions to address large-scale threats to biodiversity, such as climate change. She received her Masters in Public Policy from Harvard University and a BA in Economics and History from Emory University. Prior to joining CI, she was an economic consultant specializing in market competitiveness in the energy and transport sectors, and provided socio-economic development guidance to American Indian tribes.

Frederick Boltz is Vice-President for Conservation Strategies at Conservation International. In this role, he oversees CI's headquarters-based experts in conservation planning, practice, and monitoring, who provide direct technical guidance to and build the capacity of CI's field staff and partners in over 30 countries. Fred is a natural resource economist, with a PhD from the University of Florida. He has 19 years of experience in economic, social, and ecological aspects of biodiversity conservation and tropical forest management. He has worked throughout the tropics, with most intensive field experience in China, Madagascar, Brazil, Bolivia, and Rwanda. A native English speaker, Fred has learned French, Spanish, Portuguese, Malagasy, and Chinese. He has published scientific articles in *Ecological Economics, Journal of Forest Economics,* and *Forest Policy and Economics,* and co-authored a chapter of Goodman and Benstead's *The Natural History of Madagascar* (2004).

Cristina Goettsch Mittermeier is Executive Director of the International League of Conservation Photographers. She has co-edited 9 books, including a series published with Conservation International and Cemex. *Megadiversity: Earth's Wealthiest Countries for Biodiversity* (1996); *Hotspots: Earth's Biologically Richest and Most Endangered Ecoregions* (1998); *Wilderness Areas: Earth's Last Wild Places* (2002); *Wildlife Spectacles* (2003); *Hotspots Revisited* (2005); *Transboundary Conservation: A New Vision for Protected Areas* (2005); and *Pantanal: South America's Wetland Jewel* (2005) are all part of that series. Her latest book project, *The Human Footprint,* was produced with the Wildlife Conservation Society in New York in conjunction with her own organization, the International League of Conservation Photographers (ILCP). She founded ILCP, a prestigious group of photographers, in 2005 (www.ilcp.com).

Guy Midgley trained as a plant physiologist and ecologist at the Universities of Stellenbosch (BS), UCT (MS), and Natal (PhD), and has been employed as a research scientist by the South African National Biodiversity Institute (SANBI) or its predecessor Institutes since 1983. He has been engaged in research on climate change impacts on ecosystems and biodiversity and development of adaptation strategies since the early 1990s. He now leads SANBI's Climate Change research thrust and contributes to the work of South Africa's National Climate Change Committee (NCCC) and the South African Scientific Committee on Global Change (SASCGC). He is the author of roughly 80 publications and book chapters, co-lead author of the Ecosystems chapter of the Fourth Assessment Report of the IPCC, and lead author of several key policy-related reports to regional and national government. He has worked in several countries around the world, including Chile, Australia, USA, Germany, France, Botswana and Namibia, and continues to collaborate with a range of scientists around the world engaged in global change research. He is a research fellow with Conservation International.

Carlos Manuel Rodríguez is the Vice-President and Director of the Mexico and Central America Center for Biodiversity Conservation (CBC) at Conservation International. Rodríguez was the Minister of Environment and Energy for the Republic of Costa Rica until 2006. Identifying, valuing and capturing Payment for Environmental Services (PES) for standing forest within protected areas, private forests, and Indian reserves is one of his internationally recognized achievements. He has held various political positions over the past 12 years, including Director of the National Parks Service. He is also founder and Board member of many environmental NGOs in Costa Rica and tropical research Institutes. During his tenure in the Ministry of the Environment, he built on Costa Rica's strong conservation history by bolstering the country's mechanisms for terrestrial conservation and expanding into the realm of marine conservation. In recognition of his contributions to marine conservation, where he pushed to protect up to 25%, or 12.5 million hectares, of Costa Rica's Exclusive Economic Zone, he was honored as the first ever recipient of the Global Ocean Conservation Award in 2005. Rodríguez had tremendous success in strengthening Costa Rica's internationally recognized system of protected areas both by securing future funding and through the introduction of a system of payments for ecosystem services. Using PES as a market-oriented mechanism for forest conservation is based on the financial recognition of the environmental services of carbon fixation, biodiversity conservation, and water production being given by owners of forests and three plantations in Costa Rica. Today, as CI's regional director for Mexico and Central America, Rodríguez is leading conservation efforts throughout the region, from the United States-Mexico border through Panama. Among his immediate goals are working with the governments of other Central American countries to ensure that environmental services are recognized as national assets that can spur both conservation and economic development. He is also developing a climate change mitigation and adaptation strategy for CI throughout the region. Rodríguez was the Minister of Environment and Energy for the Republic of Costa Rica until 2006.

Glenn T. Prickett is a Senior Vice President with Conservation International. He founded and continues to serve as Executive Director of CI's *Center for Environmental Leadership in Business* (www.celb.org), a division of CI that engages leading global corporations in creating environmental solutions. Under his leadership, CI has pioneered innovative partnerships with business leaders such as Wal-Mart, Bank of America, Starbucks, McDonald's Alcoa, BP, and many others across a wide range of industries. These partnerships are changing business practices of key industries and generating significant investments in conservation around the globe. Prickett also leads CI's efforts to combat climate change and to ensure that endangered species and vulnerable communities can adapt to its impacts. This is a multi-disciplinary effort involving dozens of CI scientists, economists, policy analysts, natural resource managers, community development specialists, and communicators. Under his leadership, CI has become a powerful voice in international policy debates and an effective partner for businesses, governments, and communities who are taking concrete action to tackle climate change. Prickett is a widely recognized expert on the environment, business, and public policy. He is co-author of *Footprints in the Jungle: Natural Resources Industries, Infrastucture, and Biodiversity Conservation* published by Oxford University Press. Prior to joining CI, Prickett served as Chief Environmental Advisor at the U.S. Agency for International Development (USAID) during the Clinton Administration and prior to that as a Senior Associate with the Natural Resources Defense Council (NRDC) in Washington, DC. He currently serves on the boards of the Keystone Center, the Northern Virginia Conservation Trust, and the Great Falls Citizens Association. Prickett graduated from Yale University in 1988 with a BA in economics and political science.

Claude Gascon is the Executive Vice-President for Programs and Science at Conservation International. Prior to joining CI he was the Project Director and Scientific Coordinator for Biological Dynamics of Forest Fragments Project (BDFFP) in Brazil. He also directed a large-scale research and conservation project investigating the distribution and abundance of vertebrate species in the southwestern Amazon region. This project was the single largest scientific expedition in the Amazon since the 19th century. Gascon also holds a Visiting Professor position with the Department of Ecology at the Instituto de Pesquisas da Amazonia. His research has resulted in over 70 publications and 3 books emphasizing conservation and forest fragmentation in the Amazon, amphibians, and wildlife management. His most recent book, *Lessons From Amazonia: the Ecology and Conservation of a Fragmented Forest*, was published last year by Yale University and is already considered a classic.

Peter A. Seligmann co-founded Conservation International in 1987 and has been a leader in conservation efforts for more than 30 years. During his stewardship, CI has earned a reputation as an organization on the cutting edge of conservation, creating innovative and lasting solutions for biodiversity and sustainable development problems. He has developed strong conservation partnerships between CI and leaders in industry, science, government, and entertainment, both in the United States and abroad. He continues to prove that people can live in harmony with their natural surroundings. Seligmann began his career in 1976 at The Nature Conservancy, serving as the organization's western region land steward. He later became Director of the California Nature Conservancy. He has an MS in Forestry and Environmental Science from Yale University, a BS in Wildlife Ecology from Rutgers University, and honorary Doctorates in Science from Michigan State University and Rutgers University.

Olivier Langrand is head of the Center for Conservation and Government at Conservation International. He is responsible for building high-level political support for international biodiversity conservation, including increased public funding for CI and other international conservation programs and overseeing the Indigenous and Traditional Peoples Initiative. He has twenty-two years of experience in international biodiversity conservation program planning and management. His field of expertise includes ecological research and surveys, forest and wetland management, agronomy, forestry, agro-forestry, ecotourism, and income-generating activities for communities. He holds an MS from the University of Natal in South Africa in zoology with broad basis in ecology, natural habitat, and species management. He is also an expert on the birds of the southwestern Indian Ocean islands and has written two authoritative books on the avifauna of Madagascar, the Comoros, the Mascarenes, and the Seychelles.

Featured Photographers

James Balog has consistently broken new ground in the art of photographing nature over the course of his twenty-five-year career. His images have received international acclaim, including the Leica Medal of Excellence and the premier awards for both nature and science photography at World Press Photo in Amsterdam. His exhibitions have been shown at more than 100 museums and galleries from Greece and Paris to New York and Los Angeles. He was the first photographer ever commissioned to create a full plate of stamps for the U.S. Postal Service. Many major magazines, including *National Geographic, The New Yorker, Life, Vanity Fair, The New York Times Magazine, Audubon,* and *Outside* have published his work. He is a contributing editor to National Geographic *Adventure,* and is a Fellow of the International League of Conservation Photographers.

Daniel Beltrá is a Spanish photographer who has brought the sensibility of a news photographer to the documentation of nature and the environment for more than two decades. In 1990, he began collaboration with Greenpeace International, becoming one of their key assignment photographers and covering some of the world's most pressing ecological issues. Over the past seven years, in several journeys throughout the Amazon, he has documented droughts, floods, and deforestation in clear and telling images. Beltrá spends up to eight months each year in the field. On four separate Arctic expeditions he was a frontline observer of climate change. In the Patagonian ice fields at the tip of South America, he created the iconic image of the disappearing glacier shown in the Oscar-winning documentary *An Inconvenient Truth*—and six more of his images are included in Al Gore's multimedia presentation. His images have appeared in *Time, Business Week, Der Spiegel, Geo, Paris Match,* and *Stern.* They have also been seen in many of the world's leading newspapers, including *The New York Times, The Financial Times, The International Herald Tribune, The Guardian, Le Monde, Le Figaro, El Pais, El Corriere de la Sera,* and *Asahi Shimbun.* Beltrá is an Associate of the International League of Conservation Photographers. A native speaker of Spanish, Beltrá is also fluent in English and French and conversant in Portuguese. He has lived with his wife, Shoshana, in Seattle for the past seven years.

Michael Forsberg grew up in Nebraska and is dedicated to working extensively in the prairies of the Great Plains. Ultimately, he hopes his photographs capture the true spirit of the wide-open spaces of the Great Plains, build appreciation for its often misunderstood wildlife and landscapes, and inspire conservation efforts far into the future. Forsberg is also widely recognized for his extraordinary photographic work on sandhill cranes. In addition to the Platte River in Nebraska, Forsberg has traveled to thirteen locations and four countries on the North American continent to photograph cranes and their habitats, from the Alaskan tundra to the arid high plains, and from Cuban nature preserves to suburban backyards. His work has appeared in many publications, including *National Geographic, Audubon, Natural History, National Wildlife,* and in books published by National Geographic and the Smithsonian, among others. Forsberg is also an Associate with the International League of Conservation Photographers and a charter member of the North American Nature Photographers Association. He lives in Lincoln, Nebraska, with his wife, Patty, daughters Elsa and Emme, and dogs Grace and Charlie.

Tim Laman is a field biologist and wildlife photojournalist. He credits his childhood in Japan, where he had easy access to the mountains and oceans, for his strong interest in exploring nature, both above and below water. Laman first went to the rain forests of Borneo in 1987, and the Asia-Pacific region has been the major focus for both his scientific research and photography ever since. His pioneering research in the rain-forest canopy in Borneo led to a PhD from Harvard and his first *National Geographic* article in 1997. Since then, he has pursued his passion for exploring wild places and documenting little-known and endangered wildlife by becoming a regular contributor to *National Geographic,* with fifteen articles to his credit to date, all of which have had a conservation message. Laman has developed a reputation for being able to come back with shots from the wild of nearly impossible subjects, like gliding animals in Borneo, displaying Birds of Paradise, and some of the most critically endangered birds in the world such as the Nuku Hiva Pigeon and the Visayan Wrinkled Hornbill of the Philippines. He firmly believes that promoting awareness through photography can make a difference for conservation. Laman is a Fellow of the International League of Conservation Photographers.

Frans Lanting has been hailed as one of the great nature photographers of our time. For more than two decades he has documented wildlife and our relationship with nature in environments from the Amazon to Antarctica. He portrays wild creatures as ambassadors for the preservation of complete ecosystems, and his many publications have increased worldwide awareness of endangered ecological treasures in far corners of the Earth. His work has been commissioned frequently by the National Geographic Society, where he served as a Photographer-in-Residence. His assignments have ranged from a first look at the fabled bonobos of the Congo basin to a circumnavigation by sailboat of South Georgia Island in the sub-Antarctic. Lanting's work also includes profiles of ecological hot spots, stories on Hawaii's volcanoes, Zambia's Luangwa Valley, and a series of photo essays on American landscapes. He makes his home in Santa Cruz, California, with his wife, Christine Eckstrom, a producer, videographer, and former staff writer at National Geographic who collaborates with him on fieldwork and publishing projects. Lanting is a Fellow of the International League of Conservation Photographers.

Sarah Leen is a freelance photographer who works primarily for *National Geographic* magazine. In 1979, as a student at the University of Missouri's School of Journalism, she was awarded a National Geographic Society internship after winning the College Photographer of the Year competition. That summer, she received her first *National Geographic* story assignment. After eight years of working for the *Topeka Capital Journal, The Columbia Daily Tribune,* and *The Philadelphia Inquirer,* she began freelancing for a variety of magazines, including fourteen stories for *National Geographic.* She teaches every summer at the Maine Photographic Workshops in Rockport, Maine, as well as for the University of Missouri's School of Journalism's Missouri Photo Workshop, which travels to a different town in Missouri every year and focuses on producing documentary picture stories. She has also begun teaching at the Palm Beach Photographic Centre and attending their annual photo festival—Fotofusion. Sarah lives by the Chesapeake Bay in Edgewater, Maryland, with her husband, Bill Marr, and their three cats.

Cristina Goettsch Mittermeier's work focuses on the delicate relationship between nature's most spectacular and endangered wildlife and Earth's vanishing traditional human cultures. She was trained as a marine biologist and, through the years, became a biodiversity conservation consultant. Her work as a conservationist and photographer has taken her to more than sixty countries, including some of the most remote areas of our planet. In addition to her native language, Spanish, she speaks English and Portuguese Her work has been published in several books, including nine she has coauthored with other scientists and photographers. Her photography has also been featured in several major magazines, including *National Geographic, National Geographic Explorer,* and *Nature's Best Magazine* in the United States, *Rumbos* in Mexico, and *Explorador, Veja* and *Terra* in Brazil. Mittermeier sits on the Advisory Board of Nature's Best Foundation, the Chairman's Council of Conservation International, and the Board of Directors of the WILD Foundation. She currently serves as the Executive Director of the International League of Conservation Photography. Born in Mexico, she now makes her home in Great Falls, Virginia, with her husband Russell Mittermeier, President of Conservation International, and children Michael, Juliana, and John.

Acknowledgments

Paul Nicklen grew up on Baffin Island in Nunavut, Canada, where his was one of the few non-Inuit families in a small settlement of 140 Inuit. As a child, without television, radio, and computer games, he would spend all of his waking hours in the hills watching wildlife, weather, and the light play shadow games across the landscape. At that young age, the seed to become a nature photographer was deeply planted. Late one night in his fourth and final year of a marine biology degree at the University of Victoria, he wrote feverishly on scrap paper, outlining his career as a nature photographer. Nicklen later worked as a wildlife biologist for four years in the Northwest Territories with species such as lynx, grizzly bears, bison, caribou, and polar bears. A three-month solo expedition into the high arctic to live on the open tundra confirmed for him that he could better serve wildlife populations by becoming a nature photojournalist rather than being a biologist or just a wildlife photographer. His work has been published in hundreds of magazines around the world, and he has had seven stories appear in *National Geographic* magazine. Nicklen is a Fellow of the International League of Conservation Photographers. He lives with his wife, Lyn Hartley, and their dog, Bo, in the country outside of Whitehorse, Yukon.

Joel Sartore is a life-long Nebraskan who brings a sense of humor and a Midwestern work ethic to all of his National Geographic magazine assignments. More than twenty years of experience (including more than fifteen with the National Geographic Society) have allowed him to cover everything from the remote Amazon rain forest to beer-drinking, mountain-racing firefighters in the United Kingdom. Besides the work he has done for *National Geographic*, he has completed assignments for *Time, Life, Newsweek, Sports Illustrated*, and numerous book projects. Sartore and his work have been the subject of several national broadcasts, including National Geographic's *Explorer*, the NBC *Nightly News*, NPR's *Weekend Edition*, and CBS *Sunday Morning*, as well as an hour-long PBS documentary. Sartore is a Fellow of the International League of Conservation Photographers.

John Stanmeyer has spent more than ten years focusing on Asian issues. For seven years, he has been working on a book about the AIDS epidemic throughout Asia, as well as continuing his photographic documentation on the radical changes in Indonesia since 1997. Stanmeyer is a co-founding member of VII, a photojournalist-owned agency. He has been a contract photographer with *Time* magazine since 1998 and works regularly on assignment with *National Geographic* magazine. He has been the recipient of numerous honors, including the Robert Capa Magazine Photographer of the Year, as well as World Press and Picture of the Year awards. Stanmeyer was born in the United States and is presently living in Indonesia.

We would like to recognize the following people: Emma Patricia Gómez for coordinating our work with Cemex; Dan Roe and Tony Henshaw for their unwavering support; Jill Lucena, Ella Outlaw and Doan Nguyen for helping us coordinate the launching events and ancillary activities; Gina Martin and the NG Image Collection family for their patience and generosity; and Carolina Hoyos for her generous support. Finally, we would like to thank Patricio Robles Gil for his vision in crafting and building the Cemex Conservation Book Series, and his generosity in allowing the ILCP to become the editorial body for this important series.

—*Cristina Mittermeier, Series Editor*

A Climate for Life

The following organizations contributed to making this book:

Conservation International's mission is to conserve the Earth's living natural heritage, our global biodiversity, and to demonstrate that human societies are able to live harmoniously with nature.

The International League of Conservation Photographer's (ILCP) mission is to further environmental and cultural conservation through ethical photography. We believe that awe-inspiring photography is a powerful force for the environment, especially when paired with the collaboration of committed scientists, politicians, religious leaders and policy makers. We plan to replace environmental indifference with a new culture of stewardship and passion for our beautiful planet.

The WILD Foundation works to protect the planet's last wild places and the wildlife and people who depend upon them, because wilderness areas provide essential social, spiritual, biological and economic benefits. We believe that intact wilderness areas are an essential core element of a healthy modern society.

South African National Biodiversity Institute's (SANBI) purpose of the Biodiversity Programmes, Policy and Planning Directorate is to ensure that it responds appropriately to biodiversity-related global policy and national priorities, makes systematic contributions to the development of national biodiversity priorities, and demonstrates the value of conserving biodiversity and the relevance of biodiversity to the improvement of the quality of life of all South Africans.

Humane Society International (HSI) is the global arm of The Humane Society of the United States (HSUS). Founded in 1991, HSI has expanded HSUS program activities into Central and South America, Africa, and Asia. HSI's Asian, Australian, and European offices, as well as offices in Costa Rica and Canada, help carry out and support field activities and programs in over 35 countries. Its international efforts encompass relationships with the United Nations and work with various treaty and international agreements, including those involving the World Trade Organization and the UN Food and Agriculture Organization, affecting animals and their habitats. HSI works with national and jurisdictional governments, humane organizations, and individual animal protectionists to find practical, culturally sensitive, and long-term solutions to common animal problems.

Staff

Cristina G. Mittermeier, *Series Editor*
Lisa Lytton, *Project Editor/Art Director*
Kathy Moran, *Photography Advisor*
Alex Novak, *Text Editor*
Leah Painter Roberts, *Photography Editor*
Jenna Pirog, *Photography Assistant*
Krista Shyler, *Photography Research*
Jenny Nichols, *ILCP Project Director*
Sean McNaughton, *Graphics Editor*
Noel Grove, *Features Writer*
Rebecca Barns, *Release Editor*
Ilhuixóchitl Langlé, *Spanish Translation*
David Palmer, *Translation Consultant*

Photography Permissions
Listed by page number

Dust Jacket, 122-123: Frans Lanting/Minden Pictures
12-13, 14-15, 107, 197, 206, 207, 208-209, 209, 218-219: Frans Lanting
1: Mattias Klum/National Geographic Image Collection
2-3, 6-7: Christian Ziegler
8: Michio Hoshino/Minden Pictures
10: Tim Fitzharris/Minden Pictures
16-17, 44, 202, 250-251: Tui De Roy/Minden Pictures
18: Garth Lenz
42-43: Tom Sistak
48-49, 59, 60, 62-63, 64, 65, 66, 66-67, 68-69, 74-75, 86-87, 103: Sarah Leen/National Geographic Image Collection
50-51, 135: George Steinmetz
52: Amy Gulick
55: Ashley Cooper/Corbis
56: Jeff Haynes/AFP/Getty Images
57: China Photos/Getty Images
70-71, 216-217, 240-241, 284, 292: Annie Griffiths Belt
72-73: George Steinmetz/Corbis
76: Todd Glaser/Aurora Photos
79, 88, 156-157, 158-159, 230, 242, 263, 278-279: Peter Essick/Aurora Photos
81: Thomas Hoepker/Magnum Photos
83: Chuck Pefley/Aurora Photos
85: Arctic-Images/Corbis
89: Christopher Thomas/Getty Images
90-91: Chris Linder
92-93, 100: Robert Clark
94-95, 96-97, 98, 148, 149, 150, 150-151, 152-153, 154-155, 228: Daniel Beltrá/Greenpeace
104: Amit Bhargava/Corbis
109: Benedicte Kurzen/The New York Times/Redux
110, 114, 115, 116, 116-117, 118-119, 133, 184, 222, 224, 225, 282, 313: Joel Sartore
112-113, 130: Alex Webb/Magnum Photos
120-121, 140-141: Pete Oxford/Minden Pictures
126: Pete Oxford/naturepl.com
124-125, 171, 300-301: Stuart Franklin/Magnum Photos
129, 260: Randy Olson/National Geographic Image Collection
138, 326: Thomas D. Mangelsen
142, 143, 144-145, 182-183, 257, 273: Tim Laman/National Geographic Image Collection
146-147: Rob Haviv/VII
160: Peter Dennen/Aurora Photos
163: Scott Warren/Aurora Photos
164: Jason Lee/X01757/Reuters/Corbis
167: Jurgen Freund/naturepl.com
168: Gary Braasch
173: Christian Ziegler/Minden Pictures
174-175, 176, 177, 178-179, 179, 180-181: Cristina Goettsch Mittermeier
188-189, 210-211, 214-215: Michael Nichols/National Geographic Image Collection
190-191, 244-245, 258, 259, 266, 267, 268, 268-269, 270-271, 304-305, 309: Paul Nicklen/National Geographic Image Collection
192-193, 220-221: Luciano Candisani
194: Gerry Ellis/Minden Pictures
201: Yva Momatiuk & John Eastcott/Minden Pictures
204-205: Robert B. Haas/National Geographic Image Collection
212: Vincent Munier
213: Joel Berger/Wildlife Conservation Society
226: Beverly Joubert/National Geographic Image Collection
229, 288: Karen Kasmauski
232-233, 234, 235, 236, 236-237, 238-239, 239: Michael Forsberg
243: Jurnasyanto Sukarno/epa/Corbis
246-247, 252, 272: Brian Skerry/National Geographic Image Collection
248-249: Michael Aw
255, 264-265: David Doubilet
256: Fred Bavendam/Minden Pictures
274-275: Thomas P. Peschak
276-277: Jaipal Singh/epa/Corbis
280-281: Andrew Gombert/epa/Corbis
286: Smiley N. Pool/Dallas Morning News/Corbis
289: Reuters/STR/Landov Media
290: Khin Maung Win/AFP/Getty Images
294-295: Steve Winter/National Geographic Image Collection
296, 297, 298-299, 299: John Stanmeyer/VII
302-303, 318, 319, 320-321: James Balog
306: Bernhard Edmaier
314: Joel Sartore/National Geographic Image Collection
316-317: Melissa Farlow/National Geographic Image Collection
322-323: Norbert Rosing
324-325: Vincent Munier/Minden Pictures
340-341: Orsolya Haarberg